GW00778043

What to do with Stardust?

A mindful guide to
health, wellbeing and success

Neil Dennehy

This book is intended to supplement, not replace,
the advice of trained health professionals.
If you suspect or know that you have any health condition
or consideration that requires medical attention,
consult a health professional before engaging in
any of the activities suggested within.

The author specifically disclaims any liability, loss, or risk,
personal or otherwise, that is incurred as a consequence,
directly or indirectly, of the use and application
of any of the contents of this book.

Text, cover design and cover art copyright © Neil Dennehy, 2019

Neil Dennehy has asserted his right to be identified
as the Author of the Work in accordance with the
Copyright, Designs and Patents Act 1998

Cover image attribution;
Alex Andrews
David Becker
Marc Shulte

Paperback ISBN   978-1-9162426-0-9
Hardback ISBN   978-1-9162426-1-6
eBook ISBN   978-1-9162426-2-3
Audiobook ISBN   978-1-9162426-3-0

For Roma and Luca, my favourite people in the world

Contents

Introduction

We are made of Stardust and most of us don't even know it! It has taken approximately 14 billion years of cosmic evolution to create you, exactly as you are. The ability of your mind to imagine, and your body to create is already astounding. Still, you hold the potential to become even more. You and your gifts are extremely valuable.

But, have you ever felt that there should be more to life? Do you have dreams and goals waiting to be turned into reality? Have you ever admired others for living their best life? Do you want more confidence in your ability and a plan to follow so you can do the same? Would you like to enjoy improved health, fitness, energy and vitality so that you can wake each morning looking forward to the new experiences each day will bring? Do you want greater control of your mental and emotional states so that you can overcome challenges with more ease? If you have answered yes to any of these questions, this book is for you.

I have been there myself, frustrated and disillusioned, knowing deep down that I had more to give and do. I believed that life should and could be more enjoyable, but struggled with self-doubt. I was unable to see a way to change me or my life in the ways I wanted. At my darkest point, after a prolonged period, devoid of hope that I would find joy once more, I almost took my own life. What a waste that would have been as I would have missed out on all that was to come! I learned more about the potential that we all possess for greater wellbeing, confidence, personal development and to choose the lives we lead. I put these into practice and my life became far more enjoyable, interesting, satisfying and exciting.

How we choose to live our lives is important for our own enjoyment and satisfaction but also for the betterment of our world and everyone in it. When you shine, the world also becomes a little brighter. "What to do with Stardust?" is filled with many practical and simple, life-changing habits that you can make yours. It is structured to help you develop a positive self-image, an attitude of self-love, improved health and wellbeing, more compassion for others, increased confidence in your own ability and a means to create the future you desire. Armed with these, you can set goals, achieve them and enjoy the journeys you take along the way.

1

At 13 years old, I was tired of being overweight, unfit and the butt of fat-jokes and comments. I decided to get fitter and was amazed at the difference my new habits made to my energy levels, fitness and my body-shape within weeks. This inspired a life-long interest in how the body, mind and emotions work in relation to feeling good. I qualified as a health and fitness instructor in 1998, a Neuromuscular physical therapist in 2004, and have worked full-time in healthcare ever since. In that time, I have seen the many benefits of exercise and physical therapy but also their limitations, which encouraged me to explore other forms of healthcare. This led to the development of a wider, more holistic approach to wellness.

I have personally experienced the depths of mental and emotional disharmony in my late teens, and the challenges of trying to balance life in my late twenties. At 28, I was living two lives, running a business and living alone half the time, and a single parent to two young children the rest. When I realised that I was overwhelmed and needed change, I became interested in meditation, mindfulness and self-reflection. As I practiced, I observed the effects of my own thoughts and beliefs on my emotional state and the resulting choices I made in life. This awareness allowed me to understand myself better and see more clearly where I was holding myself back. I noticed similar self-limiting patterns were common in my clinic clients, friends and family. I have included many personal accounts of these patterns or beliefs that you may relate to in the hope that you can also let them go.

I have studied, tried and tested a wide variety of health-improving, life-affirming and effective life-changing habits over the past 28 years. These have transformed my life and I now enjoy more wellbeing, confidence, contentment, positivity, peace of mind and productivity. Along with enjoying closer relationships with family and friends, I run my clinic, workshops, sing, song-write, write poetry and books, illustrate, coach and enjoy health and fitness. My life is now filled with great people, new and interesting experiences, music, creativity and travel. I wrote "What to do with Stardust?" to share the best of what I have learned so far so that you may reap rewards in areas of your life that you would like to improve.

A change of course can sometimes seem so challenging that we don't even take that first step, especially if self-doubt limits us, or we have experienced past failures. I would remind you, however, that turning even slightly off our current course and maintaining that new heading brings us to a completely different place. New, productive and positive habits form and become normal to us very quickly. They become stronger once we feed them. You already have within you all it takes to make life-improving changes. With some understanding, guidance and encouragement, you can get there faster and with more ease. You can become healthier, more balanced, energetic, optimistic, confident, content and productive. It's all here for you, within your grasp, waiting for you to make it yours.

2

what to do with Stardust?

My main motivation for writing this book is that I love to see people shine. It gives me goose-bumps every time I see someone show the world their true spirit through acts of courage, kindness, creativity, humour, determination or passion. These actions make our world more beautiful and inspire others to do the same. Like a candle sharing its flame to light another, they ignite passion and lift spirits and yet the givers flame continues to burn just as brightly. I want this book to help you to see your innate gifts and talents, to make you want to develop them and use them in meaningful ways. My wish is that it encourages you to let your light shine brightly and boldly so that you can give your gifts to the world. I want you to shine like the stars you came from.

All we truly have to work with is the present moment. It is always in the now that we make choices and take action to help create our future moments.

The time is now.
The place is here.
The person is you.

Are you willing to begin using your moments mindfully and with positive intent to create the life you want?

Are you prepared to start exploring all the possibilities that lay in front of you?

Are you ready to ask yourself, "What to do with Stardust?"

How to use this book

- Read it all
- Accept the wonder that is you
- Understand your value and importance
- Embrace your potential to be and do more
- Take care of your valuable body and mind
- Give yourself permission to feel good
- Commit to living the life you want
- Make a plan that serves you and our world
- Build that life
- Shine!

"What to do with Stardust?" encourages health, wellbeing and positive life-choices from a holistic viewpoint. As such, it contains a wide range of information. The sections that you are already interested in will resonate with you, but others may bring more balance to your life. Reading it all ensures that you get the full message of this book and the opportunity to add more options to your routine. I would suggest keeping this book on a bedside locker, coffee table or bathroom shelf, in full view, so that it reminds of your importance, your potential and to become who you were always meant to be.

Let the understanding that our existence is astounding become part of your view of yourself and others.

Appreciate your worth. You will want to take care of that which you believe to be valuable.

Accept that you are here to fulfil a purpose. This world need you and all you have to offer. We all have tremendous potential to develop ourselves further. Use this as encouragement to become the person you want to be.

Develop a healthy body and mind so that you can achieve all that you wish to. It will be the best investment you will ever make.

Let feeling good be part of your intention for all that you do, directly in the moment and as a consequence of your actions.

Make a commitment to living your life, your way, by believing in your right to such a life and acting on your belief.

Plan for how you are going to improve life for you and others. Make time and space for it, then build it.

PART 1

You Matter

You Matter

Chapter 1

We are Stardust!

"You are a miracle, just as you are, fruit of the heavens, gift of a star"

When we were children, most of us believed that we were special in some way. We dreamt that we had magical abilities or superpowers that would be revealed when we reached a certain age, said the magic word or found the key to unlock them. This dream was generally accompanied by an urge to use these abilities to make the world a better place by using our powers to save the world and defeat the bad guys. The success of the Harry Potter and Marvel or DC comic books, cartoons and movies shows the need we still have to entertain those dreams.

This is not a new phenomenon. Tales and legends exist in all cultures about heroes with superhuman abilities that saved their people from monsters and tyrants. We have always wanted to be special and we have always wanted to make the world better. As you read through this book, you will see that you are indeed special, that you possesses many abilities and that you can certainly make the world a better place in practical and important ways.

This section is not intended to be an in-depth science or religious lesson but rather a very simplified and brief look at how our greatest minds currently agree on the origin of the universe and humankind. This understanding will allow you to accept the sheer magnitude of our own existence. Nor is it meant to spark a debate or argument of science versus god or divine influence. I see no good reason why both cannot exist harmoniously, with a little tweaking of the older ideas and an open mind.

There are many theories and beliefs, in every culture on the planet, that strive to explain our beginnings. The few mentioned in this chapter are all equally miraculous. If there is another truth, I'm sure it's just as wondrous.

The BIG BANG THEORY

You've probably heard of this "big-bang" theory? I mean the origin of our universe and not the television show of which I am a fan myself. The generally accepted scientific theory of our origin, albeit very simplified, is that once upon a time, around 14 billion years ago, there was nothing. There was no universe to speak of, no planets, moons, stars or galaxies and certainly no lifeforms. Nothing, that is, except a small ball of incredible energy. Nobody knows how or from where, this ball came to be, but it's the start of our universe as we know it.

This ball of energy exploded, or at least, expanded so rapidly and to such a huge extent that we could imagine it as an explosion. Its tiny energy fragments became the first atoms i.e. hydrogen and helium. Atoms are the little bits that all matter is made of! These simple atoms then roamed around a while, about 300 million years, before some started to react with other atoms. When they came together and started to dance around each other, things got hot. In fact, they reached approximately 15 million degrees Fahrenheit or 8 million degrees Celsius, and the first stars were born. The intense heat and pressure within stars caused the simple atoms to fuse together creating even more complex atoms. These atoms are listed in the periodic table of elements you might remember from school.

Now even stars have a limited lifespan and when they die, the most massive stars explode, sending these universal building blocks we call atoms hurtling through space. Their stardust became the atomic ingredients or raw materials that reformed to create everything in the physical universe, including you! In a sense, your body and everything in it has endured up to 10 billion degrees and unimaginable pressure within a star, in fact, that's what was needed to make you. The stardust in us has already travelled unfathomable distances across this universe to be right here, right now. Our stardust has been formed and reformed as part of many, many other things before it became part of us. That most likely includes other stars, planets, earth, water, air, trees, plants, other creatures, even other people. We are made of the same "stuff" as the most interesting, admirable and amazing people we can think of, just mixed a little differently in our own unique way.

We are the result of 14 billion years of universal evolution, of an eternal cosmic dance of creation and recreation. It's worth repeating that. We are the result of 14 billion years of universal evolution, of an eternal cosmic dance of creation and recreation. We... Are... Stardust!!! Take a few moments to let that sink in.

Not to leave out those of you with a more religious approach to creation, the Book of Genesis in the Bible suggests that the universe and everything in it was created by an infinitely wise and benevolent God in six days. If an infinitely wise God made you and I, exactly as we are – how wrong could it be? Buddhist texts say that the earth and stars spontaneously formed from nothing - a whole universe from nothing – miraculous! Hinduism talks of a giant serpent floating on an ocean of nothingness out of which wakes the sleeping lord Vishnu. Vishnu then created, from himself, his servant Brahma to create the world and all it contains. Mind-blowing stuff!

There are some of us that believe this universe is a totally random accident, the result of trial and error on an almost infinite scale and others that believe it's all an illusion and doesn't really exist. If the former is true, the odds against you being here, now, and reading this, are incalculable, which still makes you a miracle. The latter is mind-boggling because it would mean that we are pure consciousness experiencing an illusion of our own creation. Living the dream perhaps?

There are many more stories of creation and of how we came to be, all of which are different but equally incredible. No matter what way you look at it, the universe and all it contains is awesome. This is not a word I use lightly but I am in awe of it all! Whether we believe in a supreme, divine being that created our universe, an underlying universal intelligence, the scientific theory of the big bang or a random series of events, the greatest miracle we know of has led to you, here and now.

Feeling a little special yet?

WHAT CAN WE DO WITH STARDUST?

We often talk of somebody having "the right stuff". So now that you know you are made of the same "stuff" as the people you admire most, the most interesting creatures and the most stunning sights on the planet, or rather in the universe, you surely understand that you have and always had, the right stuff! Now you can ask yourself "What can I do with my stardust?", "How can I make the most of what I've got?" and "How can I take care of this body I've been given and choose my direction in life?". While you're at it, "What are the possibilities?" and "How can I make a difference?".

We sometimes limit ourselves due to an underlying sense that we are not 'good enough'. We subscribe to a role and then play that role throughout our lives with thoughts such as "I'm just ___ so I could never be ____". The reality is that we are designed to change and adapt according to how we think and act. It helps to think of the body as a machine that must be used and serviced to be at its best. The mind can be viewed as the computer program within that machine that needs to be cleaned and upgraded regularly.

The various aspects of our lives can be compared to a garden that we care for with our body and mind. When we pay a little regular attention to the areas we want to improve, they will flourish. Taking care of your stardust is, like all things, simpler when you know how.

EMBRACE THE CHANGE

"The bad news is nothing lasts forever, the good news is nothing lasts forever" – J. Cole.

If stuck in habits that are not working for us, we should remember that change is not just possible but inevitable. Since the universe is undergoing continuous creation through the reforming of its stardust, the only constant in the universe is change. The only guarantee, no matter how hard we might try to keep things the same, is that all will change.

Everything changes, nothing can remain the same. Our bodies, our minds, our emotions, beliefs and the world around us are constantly developing and evolving. This is the true nature of the universe and everything in it. Even Mount Everest, the highest peak of the Himalayan mountain range was once at the bottom of the ocean. Now it rises to astounding heights.

Accepting our own value, potential and evolving nature removes many of the blocks and chains that hold us back from doing what we want to do and living how we want to live. We can then focus our attention and energy on what we really want to achieve, unhindered. If the earth at your feet can rise from the bottom of the ocean to the spectacular heights of the Himalayan mountain range, what change is possible for us?

REALISING OUR POTENTIAL

One of the most defining traits of humankind is the potential we all possess. We are extremely adaptive creatures and can develop and learn throughout our lives. We have been doing this through our written history and long before. We create clothing to tolerate extreme temperatures, build shelters for protection, modify the land around us to produce food through farming and create all manner of machinery and technology. If you look around you right now, you will see items that were engineered and constructed via human ingenuity and labour. Hence, due to our natural ability to adapt, we find ourselves living all over the planet in many environments that are not suited to us in our original, natural state. Simply put, we can succeed almost anywhere if we just put our minds to it and roll up our sleeves.

GENETIC POTENTIAL

Our potential is not limited to what we can build or create individually or collectively, although that is very impressive. Potential is built into us, hard-wired into our anatomy and physiology. Potentiality is innate in the cells that make up our bodies and is only recently being seen and understood in a process known as 'gene expression'.

Our genetic code or genes are like a blueprint and instruction manual that control the development and function of cells of our bodies. DNA gives the order that tells each cell what type of cell it is to become and what it must do. The information and orders from our genes make us what we are and cause us to operate the way we do. Our DNA code decides if we will be tall or small, soft, muscular or lean, blonde-haired or brown-eyed. Interestingly, the complete manual, for our entire body, is present in almost every cell but only the necessary instructions for that specific cell are switched on. This explains why, under normal circumstances, a hair cell doesn't become a muscle or nerve cell and why we don't grow skin where we need bones or blood. The important part, for us, about this switching on or off of genes, when discussing potentiality, is that while many of our genes are unchangeable within our lifetime, others can be switched on or off by our environment, lifestyle choices and our thought patterns.

The study of Epigenetics tells us that, 'Where we are, what we do and how we think' can effect change in us from the inside out. That's fantastic news because it means that we are not simply genetically determined or born to be a specific way. Certainly, we are genetically predisposed or more likely to have some traits, but we also have some real control over what we become. Where there is choice, there is power and we have lots of choice.

It has also been found that some of the genetic changes, made in a body because of its current needs, will be passed on to offspring. This suggests that if we start teaching our bodies to be healthier at an early age, we can pass on healthier genes to our children. If you have kids already, that isn't an option, but they will see your healthy habits as a normal way-of-life, and hopefully, make healthy living a part of theirs. Your effort to improve your health now can positively affect your future children and grandchildren. Think of it as a long-term investment. Even if you're not ready to take care of yourself for your own sake, do it for your kids.

BRAIN POTENTIAL

Another example of human potentiality comes from the study of Neuroplasticity. This is the brain's ability to change and develop. It was once thought that our brains developed as children and adolescents, only to lose brain cells as we got older. It turns out that our brains can develop and change at any age, again according to our needs. Our regular behaviour is a key trigger for this brain development. How we use our brains most often directs this change. The brain can be trained to improve at different activities just like the body can through exercise i.e. "you can teach an old dog new tricks".

When we use certain specific sections of our brain more, they grow and become stronger and more efficient. If we choose to develop creativity, music-skills, languages, mathematics, positivity etc., the brain will start to change as soon as we do. It's never too late to begin training our brains to do what we want!

What that all means is that, to a large degree, we can write or reprogram ourselves. This, of course, has the knock-on effect of rewriting the story of our lives. Writing our own life story is possible if we want it to be. We're already doing it each day, only our outcome may be less than ideal if we're doing it unconsciously and without positive intent. We might currently be scribbling and doodling aimlessly instead of consciously writing the lines we want to be part of our story. We may even be writing 'bad' scripts because we've assigned ourselves unhealthy roles and believe that's all we can be or do. What could we do if we were more mindful and purposeful in our actions? What if we chose our roles instead?

We may be standing at a ships wheel that's spinning out of control, telling ourselves that we're powerless against the wind and waves that drive us, when all we need to do is grab the wheel and steer. I do agree that there may be an overall destiny or fate that sets the main story of our lives, but I also believe that we get to fill in all the details for ourselves. The seas, currents and winds are there, but we can choose which direction to sail.

PROOF OF THE PUDDING

Masses of information on epigenetics and neuroplasticity can be found online should you want more details on the research that's ongoing in those areas. Nonetheless we all like a personal recommendation that tells us "I have used this and yes it works!". I have indeed used them myself and have seen the results first-hand. I've also shared most of the advice in this book with clients and friends over the years with positive results. I've included the best of what I've learned so far and I can highly recommend them all.

Lifestyle changes have allowed me to transform from being an unhealthy, overweight kid with a fondness for sweets who got easily out of breath. I became a fitter, far more energetic individual, helping me achieve national sporting success. I still have a sweet tooth, but it's satisfied on my terms. I changed from thinking I was done with education at 16, believing I was stupid after achieving very average leaving cert results, to putting myself through college twice and developing an insatiable appetite for knowledge. I shifted from having no career expectations beyond working on a factory-line at 17 to starting my own business at 25 and paving the way for a career in health and wellness along the way.

Openness to self-development allowed my mindset to shift from wanting to change everything about myself. I didn't want curly hair, freckles, sticky-out-ears, glasses or big lips. With work, I became confidently comfortable with who I am. I went from having low self-esteem to a genuine self-belief and an, "If somebody else can do it, why not me?" attitude. I also moved from believing that my "place" in this world was fixed and quite limited to accepting that I have a world at my feet. This in turn, led to travelling to some of the most beautiful, interesting and amazing places on the planet.

A new way of thinking taught me identify fears or doubts, so I could limit their power and effect, instead looking at them as challenges and opportunities that would help me grow stronger and wiser. It aided me in letting go of a judgemental attitude where I looked at much of life as "black or white" and 'right or wrong', instead becoming far more open-minded and accepting of how things are. A clearer perspective taught me to trust that life happens for us and not to us, even if I don't fully understand what's happening in the moment. I don't need to worry so much about the future, instead looking forward to whatever it brings.

Change can indeed be difficult. I have certainly struggled to let go of old habits, at times, through fear of the unknown. Although it took effort, these changes were far easier than remaining as I was. They have allowed me to become more healthy, energetic, creative, open-minded, confident, positive, calm, loving, fulfilled and content. I'm now doing things that I thought would be impossible for me such as writing books, illustrating, singing, song-writing, performing, travelling, coaching and running my own company.

The biggest plus is that none of these take away from my most important jobs, i.e. that of being an involved and active parent to my children, maintaining friendships and running a home. It was possible to incorporate many positive changes while still living a normal life. We don't have to become monks to meditate, Olympic athletes to exercise, nutritionists or chefs to eat well, starving artists to develop our creativity or quit our jobs to travel the world. These can all fit into a normal life with some simple modifications. I've learned that change can be very good for us and that we can enjoy being open to all the possibilities the future will bring.

There is always more to learn, do and experience but where I am now is so much better than where I used to be. We're made of the same stuff, you and I, so if I can get to that place, so can you. "What to do with Stardust?" can help to show you the way.

You Matter

Chapter 2

An Almost Life-ending Experience

"To live or not to live?", that is the Question!

Have you ever felt like you were a slave to your own thoughts, unable to shake off worries or doubts? I certainly have. While a beautiful, life-changing experience at thirty allowed me to clearly see the wonder of life and gave me the understanding that all is ok, there was a time in my younger days when my viewpoint was far darker. My mind was so clouded, in fact, that I made the decision to end my own life. The vast majority of this book is positive and hopeful, and for very good reason. There is much for us to be optimistic and hopeful about. This chapter encourages understanding, trust and communication but it does involve a visit to a place and time where I believed I was devoid of hope. Perhaps truly appreciating the light required a trip through darkness. Of all the chapters in this book, this one may save a life.

DANGEROUS MIND-GAMES
This terminal decision was not a one-off moment of madness, it was spurred by a build-up of the weight of many moments. These prevented me from enjoying life or looking forward to a happy future. I didn't want to continue living that way. In truth, I almost finished this book without adding this story. Of all the information contained within, this was the most difficult for me to write and put out there for all to read. Revisiting this situation picked at scars of the past and brought back memories of an extremely challenging time. It stirred up some of the feelings I felt, and raised fears that I may find myself subject to some ridicule for revealing my inadequacies.

However, I also found it quite therapeutic as I put words on old feelings and looked at the situation from an older, perhaps wiser perspective. I found I could accept that there may be those small few that mock. I chose, in advance, to not take it personally, understanding that they probably carry more issues than most, issues they are too scared to address. Instead of dealing with our problems, sometimes we shame others to draw attention away from ourselves. Alternately, since no topic is off the table for the Irish when

17

it comes to humour, some will make a joke of it just to poke fun. Most will respect it for what it is i.e., revealing a personally challenging life-lesson to demonstrate how the mind can make mountains out of molehills.

I chose to add this section because I couldn't honestly write a book that encourages people to face fears, believe in change and embrace a happier life without talking about a situation that almost led to me taking my own. I could not expect you to believe me when I say it is possible to feel hopeless, largely because of your own mind-set, and then truly hopeful once your viewpoint becomes clear without explaining how I have experienced just that. Nor could I expect you to be brave enough to seek help and free yourself from the fears that obstruct you from peace and prosperity without challenging my own fears of being judged or criticised for my own percieved 'flaws'. Of all the positive-thinking, health-promoting and life-affirming sections in this book, this one could be the most important for some.

START OF THE NEAR-END

To set the scene, I was a quiet kid, lacking in confidence. I know now that this was more common than I would have realised then. I felt I had lots of reasons to feel awkward or ugly. I wore glasses from age 8, before they were trendy. I had freckles, curly hair, and big "rubber-lips". I was not a cool kid. "Four eyes, fatty, curly head of cabbage". I heard those a lot. It's funny now but as a kid, and a bit of a softy, they stung! I was a nerd and certainly not one of the popular kids that excelled at sport, played music or talked the talk! Please don't be offended if you're a nerd. I'm still a nerd but now I've embraced it!

Due to shyness from confidence issues in my mid-late teens, I didn't have a girlfriend and, aside from a rare kiss at a disco, I wasn't at all experienced with the fairer sex. I got into fitness training at a time when, in Ireland at least, very few were going to the gym regularly, and by the time I turned 17 or 18 it showed in my physique. This fitter body added a little to my confidence and drew more attention than I was used to.

I found myself, unexpectedly, in a relationship at 17 that progressed quite quickly to the promise of sex. I knew my new partner had experience that I, as a shy teenager, didn't. Of course, I didn't admit that I was so inexperienced and shy. I found myself thinking about how I would perform. Of course, I knew the basics of how it all worked and what went where but I pressured myself to perform as if I had experience. This mind-set was totally unrealistic and unfair to myself, but nonetheless, that's how it was.

When we got back to her place, after a night out, my mind was racing. I was excited at the prospect of what was to come but also worried she'd realise I was inexperienced or that I wouldn't be any good at it. This thought took over and performance anxiety kicked in, so much so that I couldn't perform at all! My body didn't react the way it should have, the way it had earlier in the night when we were slow-dancing together. No big deal, right? Sure, doesn't it happen to every guy at some stage?! Maybe it does, maybe it doesn't, but it was happening to me and I was mortified.

an almost life-ending experience

I was still just a shy kid, not the experienced man I wanted to be, and it hit me hard. How I felt on the night in question was awful but what came after was so much worse. I beat myself up over it, mentally. I questioned it and my manhood repeatedly with thoughts such as - "What kind of a man can't perform with an attractive woman?", "The opportunity was right there in front of you, but you couldn't do anything about it!", "What a joke you are!". It rocked my masculinity and sense of self to the core at a time when I had only dipped my toe into adulthood.

I was still only a teenager, only ready for teenage romance. I had time to figure out all that goes with adult relationships, but I just couldn't see it that way. My expectations of myself were far too high but, because I didn't speak to anybody to get some sound advice, I couldn't have known that. My partner didn't give up on me, but she didn't really understand it either as it had never happened her before. Knowing that didn't help my mental state, it just made me criticise myself even more.

Our time together was bitter-sweet. When just hanging-out, I had no issues with feeling amorous or my body reacting appropriately, and I could enjoy that time. However, when a situation arose where an actual "performance" was needed, anxiety would kick in and stop me in my tracks. The expectation of failure seemed to be always lurking in the background of my mind for an opportunity to knock me back every time.

PERFORMANCE ANXIETY

Such a response is far more common than is obvious in relation to sexual activity. It's equally common elsewhere. The singer that feels anxious about performing is not worried about the quality of their singing. If that was the case, they would feel the same anxiety when singing alone, in the car or in the shower. The anxiety only comes when there is the possibility of judgement from the audience. It's the "Will I be good enough in their eyes?" factor. A similar effect applies to public speaking and sporting performance.

Understanding the basic workings of our nervous system is something I feel everybody needs, as we are affected by it every day, in every moment. This system's state greatly influences our sense of wellbeing and how our bodies function. We have two sides to our autonomic nervous system. Autonomic is the part we don't have direct conscious control over and is also known as our involuntary nervous system. One side of this autonomic nervous system is called the Sympathetic Nervous system (SNS) which is the system in charge when we are stressed. By stressed, I mean any situation where we believe we are threatened, afraid, nervous, anxious, uneasy or under pressure.

The SNS creates the necessary changes in the body to help us to survive a threat to our lives or wellbeing. These engage the fight, flight or freeze response that helped us survive a genuine physical threat such as seeing or hearing a nearby predator. Physiological changes include increased heart rate, pupil dilation, decreased digestion, contraction of muscles and the diversion of extra blood to the working muscles. The SNS focuses on short-term survival. For simplicity, I'm going to refer to it as our Stressed Nervous system.

The other side of the autonomic nervous system is our Parasympathetic Nervous System (PNS) which is the system in charge when we are at ease. By this I mean peaceful, calm, relaxed, content, comfortable etc. The "Peaceful" Nervous System creates an environment in the body that promotes long-term health and well-being when we are safe and content. These changes include digestion of foods, the growth of new, healthy tissues, production of immune cells, lower heart rate and increased libido. This prepares us for long-lasting health and vitality and long-term thriving over surviving.

These two systems are essential in each situation and indeed do interact and work with each other. However, we can find ourselves in the stressful nervous system mode far more often than we need to be and that creates problems. Our surroundings or our state of mind will generally activate one mode or the other and decide to what extent i.e. ranging from a little fearful to terrified, or a little calm to blissfully at peace.

AGE-OLD ANXIETY

Anxiety, you see, has quite a powerful effect on the whole body, which I didn't understand at all at the time. If I had understood this effect sooner, it would have saved me a lot of suffering and self-criticism. That understanding helps me greatly now and I expect will do the same for you.

Anxiety triggers our Stressed Nervous System, which rules our "fight, flight or freeze" survival-mode. This is part of our primitive survival systems that are still part of us today, despite our ongoing evolution. When we are stressed or in danger, our body prepares to fight off the attacker, "fly" (run or climb) as fast as possible from danger or freeze by staying quiet and still until the danger has passed. It does this by increasing the breathing and heart rate to get more oxygen to our muscles and diverting blood-flow to our legs and arms for fighting, running or climbing. This redistribution of blood takes blood-flow from areas that are not immediately essential for survival, including blood flow to our digestive systems and sexual organs.

To give an example of why this physiological response to stress or danger was essential for the human species survival, here's a scenario. A caveman and cavewoman meet some 400,000 years ago and like the look and smell of each other. They get together to make some little cavepeople and help keep the species going. They get closer and their bodies react in the way young lovers do. Blood starts flowing to their sexual organs as they get excited. All else is forgotten as they get down to baby-making business in the long grass of the Savanna.

Suddenly, they see a Sabretooth-tiger stalking nearby. Now, not even the sight of a huge tiger with 7-inch teeth might stop our passionate caveman from finishing the job he started, when much of his blood is diverted from his brain to his nether regions! Our cavewoman is enjoying herself just as much, so neither one wants to stop to get out of harm's way. If they continue, the tiger gets an easy meal and our species loses two of its members and the possibility of more. For the sake of the survival of humanity, something's got to change and quickly. Luckily for us, it does, and they live to fight another day.

an almost life-ending experience

Our caveman's body switches gear, into the Stressed Nervous Systems survival mode, due to the instinctual fear of impending danger. His body stops feeling amorous and it redirects the blood-flow to the muscles in his legs and arms from his erection. Something similar happens to our cavewoman as the pleasurable sensations and urge to carry on dissipates. The main difference being that its effects are less visible on her.

Now fully in survival mode, he jumps off her, and they run like the wind through the nearest bushes to safety. Luckily, since his manhood is no longer at full mast, it doesn't get caught and damaged on thorns or bushes as he runs. Once they escape and are truly safe, their bodies can switch back to the Peaceful Nervous System "thrive-mode" where our caveman, his manhood and our cavewoman are safe to pick up where they left off. This fight, flight or freeze response, necessary for survival, is passed on genetically to their children and the subsequent generations, right down through our ancestors to us modern-day humans.

Yes, we still have that survival mechanism in us today. Sabre-tooth tigers are no longer a threat to our lives, but in stressful times of famine, drought or war, pregnancy could result in the death of both mother and child through starvation or an inability to flee from danger. As such, our fight or flight response is still relevant and important for our survival. In modern times, the need for such a survival system could go on for long durations, suppressing our sex-drive for weeks, months or even years until the threat has passed.

Now, for many of us thankfully, famine, drought or war aren't a threat but through the power of the imagination and our mind-body connection, fears and worries can stimulate that very same fight, flight or freeze response. We get stressed by financial concerns, work deadlines, achieving through sports, grief, body-image issues, bullying, worrying about world issues etc. These can initiate our Stressed Nervous System just as the life-threatening stresses of the past did, unless we learn to deal with these issues either internally or by taking appropriate action externally.

Stress is a common cause of infertility, impotence and many other health issues, for both men and women. In my case, performance anxiety was my initial trigger and, while simply not thinking about failing would have been fantastic, it's very difficult to not think about something.

KILLER PENGUINS

Just not thinking about it would have been the ideal answer to my problem. It seems simple, and it is but it's not so easy. I'll ask you to try this. Don't think about a penguin! Can you do it? My guess is you're probably thinking about a penguin!! Our brains ignore the "don't" part of that order, instead they focus on the object i.e. the penguin. Trying to "not think about it" will almost always result in focusing completely on it. I know now that one of the best ways to disempower fear or anxiety is to accept all will be ok even if my fear is realised, but I was to learn that lesson far later in life. As time passed the 'penguin' was in my head more and more. As it progressed, if I saw other couples, I would feel inadequate in comparison to the men that I was convinced were more capable than me of performing.

I didn't realise it at the time, but I was feeding my issue daily by thinking about it, growing it more and more out of proportion. It began sparking anxiety in me simply by seeing an attractive woman. I found I was telling myself that I should get turned on by her because I would if I were a 'real man'. Of course, that was ridiculous but because I still hadn't spoken to anybody about the problem, that train of thought continued.

I was functioning well in other areas of my life. I was fit, physically healthy, productive at work, sporty, had friends and a social life but, in this one area, I was struggling big-time. As time went on and that relationship ended, I couldn't bring myself to even try to get involved in another relationship. I hadn't the courage to face the shame of not performing again, having her maybe think I wasn't really interested in her, or worst of all, have her tell anybody else about it.

In my head, it was bad enough for me to know I wasn't a "real man" but if others knew too, I felt I would be a laughingstock! That's what I believed so I didn't even confide in a friend or family member. I wasn't comfortable talking about personal issues then. This was a skill I would learn later as was the confidence and trust needed to do so. My foolishly stubborn and independent nature combined with shame meant this would be my cross to bear for some time.

As more time went on and months turned into years, my anxious train of thought fed the issue so much that I believed I would never have a relationship again. Sex is an important part of a relationship and when you are 20 it is the foundation of a lot of relationships. Again, this is what I thought, so I avoided any kind of intimacy or encounter that might lead to a situation where I could embarrass myself again. Being quite a naturally affectionate person and knowing, even then, that I would want a family at some stage, the belief I would lead a solitary life hit me very hard. I thought I was alone, and I was going to remain alone. I was depressed, I'm sure of it, although I was never clinically diagnosed, I can't think of a better word to describe it. I found no joy in life. I either felt sad, lost, ashamed or numb.

NUMBNESS

I remember the numbness being the worst of all. I guess is a mechanism much like our survival system that allows us to function quite well, short-term, to get through challenging times. We can get on with our daily lives, often with a smile on our face, but with no real feeling about anything. A smile is the greatest mask there is. As with our survival mode, it's not meant to be a long-term state. I often say to my clinic patients, in relation to the physical body, that numbness is worse than pain. When in pain, at least you're feeling something, and you know the body part is still alive! I believe the same holds true for emotional health. Pain is difficult, but numbness is like being in a state of limbo. It's a nothingness and if we humans are meant to do anything, it's to feel.

I'm not even sure now exactly how long it was since my issue began but it was long, too long. Somewhere around 3 years, which amounts to over 1,000 days and nights criticising myself and feeling a weight on my chest. A heavy heart one could say. I fully accept that we all can get days where we're a bit down or anxious. That's perfectly normal and part of life but when there's something on your mind constantly, with no break from it, it gets tougher. I guess it's like lifting weights at the gym, which is great for building strength. But if we don't let go of the weights, instead carrying them with us, 24/7, eventually they'll wear us down and we are going to have bigger problems.

With emotional baggage, the sadness builds, weighing you down until you forget what it felt like before, when you were light-hearted and care-free. I tried some hypnotherapy to see if it could take away that one thought that was the root of my problem. It didn't work for me, at that time, although I do believe it can be very beneficial for some. Maybe I didn't give it enough sessions. I'm sure I also needed some counselling. When hypnotherapy didn't fix my problem, it strengthened my conviction that this was it, this would be my lonely life, forever. I occasionally attempted the odd chat-up at nightclubs when alcohol gave me some courage, but the anxiety was always there, lurking, so I never took it further.

A LOGICAL END

I didn't want to keep living like that and concluded, quite logically, that if I couldn't continue as I was and yet couldn't get 'fixed', then I should end it. I remember setting a 3-month 'deadline'. By this time, if I didn't improve, I would take my own life. I had planned to do it in a way that would look like an accident. I didn't want anybody close to me to know it was intentional. Nor did I want them to carry any guilt about what they should have or shouldn't have done to save me. They had no idea, I hid it too well.

I won't detail my plan here in case it plants ideas in anyone's mind. Looking back, it would probably only have resulted in cuts and bruises but still my intent to end it all was real. It wasn't going to be a cry for help. Reaching out still never occurred to me as my best option. It was going to be over, once and for all. I have often heard that victims of suicide find peace in the lead up to their deaths following the decision to end their suffering. I can totally relate to that. There was a strange sense of relief in knowing the anxiety, numbness and mental self-abuse would finish soon.

Before making that decision, there was an over-riding sense of hopelessness. To this day the saddest thing for me, when I hear of a suicide, is knowing that person had lost all hope for life to be good again. I imagine them weighed down by a problem that they believed to be far greater than it was. I see them consumed by it and so distracted from the beauty of life that ending it was, to them, their only logical solution. I believe they sought relief from the torment of their own thoughts and feelings. On some level, they believed that the world was better off without them. If only they had talked to the right people, asked for a little support and learned to develop a different mind-set, they might have seen their value and found a reason to live.

23

MY GREATEST FAILURE

I'm still here 20 years later so I obviously didn't meet my deadline. My main reason, at that point, for not taking my own life was the pain I knew I would leave my family members in. I also believe that regular fitness and karate training gave me outlets for my frustrations along with the endorphine boosts that are proven to be beneficial in treating depression. I was self-medicating with healthy eating and exercise, so I didn't reach breaking point. I will always believe in the benefits of a balanced exercise program and diet for development of a healthy body and mind.

I have heard people say that suicide is a cowardly act. I don't believe that to be the case, not for an instant. Our survival instincts, in most situations, will do all they can to keep us alive. It takes intense pressure and pain to over-ride our built-in survival system and take that ultimate step, truly but misguidedly believing that those left behind and the world itself will be better off without us.

The rate of suicide in males tends to be close to double the number of that in females around the world. While there are many factors that account for people choosing to end their lives, the difficulty men have in showing vulnerability seems to be one of the major problems. There is a misguided belief in males that vulnerability of any kind means weakness, that we should always be strong and tough. It seems to be more acceptable for a man to get angry than upset or scared. Aside from the death of a very close loved one, it's almost as if men should never cry, although crying is a natural human response and the first thing that we all do when we're born.

I eventually went to a doctor about it and got some medication to help with arousal. The medication probably had more of a placebo effect than physiological, but I needed something to convince me that I could perform. I then found myself in a long-term relationship and no longer needed the support of medication.

If I had my time over, knowing what I know now, I would have talked about my worries and trusted sooner that I would find understanding and support. Once I eventually had the courage to face the possibility of failure, support and understanding was all I found. I would have changed the storyline that was playing out in my head. Instead of seeing my "Penguin" as huge and unbeatable, I would have seen myself as the Iceberg, cool and impenetrable, on which the penguin was only an annoying inconvenience. I could have saved myself a lot of discomfort and stress and freed myself to enjoy life far more than I did at that time.

Tough situations can leave an emotional mark on us, just like old physical injuries can leave scars. Like an old war wound, my old anxieties have occasionally surfaced at the start of a new relationship. By explaining the situation and trusting that all would be fine, the anxiety passed very quickly, and normal business resumed.

Sometimes healing is about learning to be at ease with our scars and to accept that while fears may arise in us, we don't need to give them any more power than they deserve.

EVERYTHING IS OK

That's the sad part of the story finished, any other challenges life has brought my way since were minor in comparison. I'm so grateful that I have lived long enough to see what I would have missed. My children, my family, friends, travelling, music, sports, work and a multitude of experiences that would have been lost to me had I taken that ultimate step. I've had the opportunity to help raise two wonderful people, to support others as they return to health, to coach sports, sing, laugh, eat, drink, travel and to love. I've also learned that my life had purpose, even when I thought it was meaningless.

I guess my main reason for explaining all of this is to tell you that things are ok even when you feel and believe that they are not. Your problems only seem insurmountable because you believe they are so. There are always people that will offer love, support and guidance. There is always hope, even when you feel there is none. You make a real difference even when you think you don't. You are strong even when you are vulnerable. You count in this world, you are needed, you are wanted, and you are loved.

Hang-in there if the chips are down, get some help, let the healing begin and watch the magic unfold.

You Matter

Chapter 3

A Life-changing Experience!

In the words of the great Freddie Mercury, "This could be heaven for everyone". Maybe all it takes is a little clarity and love to make it so.

In 2008, just after my 30th birthday, I had a profound experience that has affected every aspect of my life since. To say it was mind-blowing is an understatement. It took me some time to get my head around it although I never once doubted its validity.

To set the scene briefly, I was a father to a 6-year-old daughter, and almost 5-year-old son. Their mother and I had separated two years previously and they lived with me almost half the time. I ran a small physical therapy business and was lucky to be able to balance my working hours with quality family time. I also made an effort to keep physically fit and healthy while maintaining a social life on the weekends I wasn't on "dad duty".

I had many positives in my life, but something was missing. I decided to take stock of my life and asked myself an important question, one that perhaps we should all ask regularly. I asked, "How do I feel?". I realised that I wasn't particularly happy, not terribly unhappy but in a sort of limbo. I was often stressed and tired. I put up a good front and nobody would have noticed I was finding it tough to juggle everything. This is a façade I'm sure most of us use at some point. I knew that my general life situation wasn't the problem because my finances were adequate, and I liked my work. There were still some ongoing issues with access to my children not being finalised yet, but I was still seeing them regularly. Also, I had friends and family I could turn to if I needed support. Since the block to my happiness wasn't outside me, I knew the problem lay within. I just wasn't sure how to fix it!

I had often heard about finding inner peace through meditation. This sounded like a pretty good place to start. I Googled 'meditation' and the first link that came up was a Chakra meditation guide. I printed it off and went to my bedroom. I pulled the curtains closed as it was early in the day and I didn't want anybody to see me. I sat on my bed and assumed the most basic version of the lotus position I could comfortably manage, using pillows for support. I then followed the meditation guide as best I could.

27

LOOKING INWARD

I began with slow, deep-breathing exercises to calm my body and mind. I noticed that I became more aware of the sensations within my body. I then felt the areas where I was holding tension in my muscles and could let some of that tension go. I have a very active mind but noticed it was less busy while I focused on how my body felt. I later realised that I would need regular grounding practice such as this to maintain an easy mental and emotional balance.

Next step in the meditation guide was for awareness to be brought to each of the seven chakras, one by one. Each had its own accompanying word to be chanted and a hand gesture or mudra to be held. The chakra awareness exercise started at the root chakra, located at the base of the spine, working up to the seventh chakra at the crown of the head.

With each chakra focus, I noticed my body relax and my mind calm a little more. It wasn't so much that I stopped thinking, but my background thoughts surfaced and became more organised. My feelings about them became clearer also. You could say I was more conscious of them, almost as if I was looking at them on a screen. This is a practice I often now use to take myself outside of a situation and look at it from a more neutral and unbiased perspective. I noticed that many of my thoughts were ones that made me tense and unhappy. These included fears of the future, self-doubts and even petty grudges that I held. Some were recent, others from as far back as childhood. I knew that while carrying these inside, I couldn't truly be at ease.

I remembered reading once that "holding a grudge is like holding a hot coal, waiting to throw it at an enemy, all the while you are the one being burned!". I decided to let go of these grudges, so I could stop burning myself. I also knew that releasing grudges involves more than taking the moral high ground. I would have to rationally and logically work through them, with a measure of compassion, so I could genuinely accept and let them go. I decided to take a closer look at each one.

Where I was insulted by another's comment or behaviour, I looked at the possibilities that maybe they were joking, in a bad mood or in a tough place in their own life at the time. Maybe I was just too sensitive and took the insult on board because deep down I also believed it to be true. I now understand that an insult only hurts us if it confirms to us what we already believe but cannot accept. Otherwise, it's simply fact or fiction and will run off us like water off a ducks back!

I reminded myself that if the insult was true, then it was good for me to hear it, accept it and decide if I wanted to do something about it. If the perceived affront was not true, then it wasn't my problem. The lie said more about its creator than it did about me. I accepted that I played the bigger part in being insulted by taking it on as truth. I forgave myself for this and imagined a scenario where I thanked them for what I could learn from their comment and its effect on me. I imagined myself shaking hands with some and hugging others that I had previously held grudges towards. This allowed me to let go and I noticed, as each grudge was resolved, I felt a little better.

a life-changing experience

As I continued the meditative practice of breathing deeply and analysing my own mind, I noticed thoughts regarding my abilities surfacing. I looked at my self-doubts and wondered why I had them despite all the successes I already had in my life. In my physical therapy clinic, my success rate was over 90%, so I questioned why I would always seem to remember the few patients I couldn't help. Despite the many patients that were very happy with the service, my focus was on those few I couldn't fix. Why was I so hard on myself?

I wondered how I would view someone else that put themselves through college twice while still working, once while also raising a young family. I wondered what I would think of a single parent that built up a small but successful business from scratch without any form of grant or loan, made a big effort to be a good father, kept fit, and tried to be a pretty honest, decent and fair person in general. I realised I would certainly be impressed by those achievements and attributes in someone else. Yet I didn't seem to be so in myself. My expectations were too high.

I questioned why I was so self-critical, expecting that I should be more or do even more than I was already doing just to be "good enough". I decided to give myself a break and be a little nicer, to believe that my best was indeed good enough. If I fell short of my best occasionally, so what? Nobody can give all they have, all the time. This "letting go" also lightened the stress load and I felt a little better.

With every stressful thought I resolved, another one seemed to surface. It was like closing down one computer window or phone app to see another waiting behind. No wonder I was stressed with all of these operating in the background! I looked at the fears that arose in me for the future. Would I find a long-term relationship? After all, I was a single parent and would put commitments to my children ahead of any romantic relationship. Would somebody want a thirty-year old with two children. Did I want to start a relationship with another single parent and find myself in a "Brady bunch" situation, turning two families into one?

Would I ever have job security? I worked for myself, by myself and should I somehow find myself unable to work, I'd have no income. With self-employment there was no safety net. I worried about my relationship with my children weakening over time or possibly ending as I have seen happen to other fathers, following a separation. These thoughts created tension in my chest and disrupted my inner peace, so I looked at them more closely and talked myself through them. I chose to take different perspectives on each issue that would work for me rather than against.

RESOLVING FEARS

Firstly, I looked at the positives of what being a single parent brings to a relationship. Having kids teaches selflessness, compassion and understanding. Parents know that it is normal to put another's needs ahead of our own. We know how to live with other people, care for them when sick and the power of a hug or a kiss. Kids help to keep us young at heart, as they show us

29

the world through fresh eyes again. They remind us of the magic of watching a line of ants at work or examining flowers up close. Kids teach us to use our imaginations and bring fun into the simplest things like turning chairs and sheets into a tent, building sandcastles or making a bouncy castle from mattresses. Having kids has made me more than I ever would have been without them. I figured there had to be women out there that would see all those qualities as positives, rather than baggage. I chose to believe that my family situation didn't have to be a barrier to finding a relationship again.

As for professional and financial security, I realised that I had never gone a day without food to eat or a roof over my head. At 30 years old, I had lived for almost 11,000 days and nights and was never hungry or homeless! My finances have been tight at times, but I've always had enough to get by. I had no legitimate reason to believe that should change so I decided to trust it would continue. I also accepted that if I were to go hungry once or found myself sleeping under the stars, I would manage. I had already been luckier than a great many on this planet. Again, I felt a little better.

With each resolution of a fear, doubt or worry and the resulting change of attitude, I noticed a little tension leaving my body and I felt lighter in my chest. I became aware that I felt my body tingling - like when you get goose-bumps from an inspiring piece of music or movie. This tingling was moving from my feet to my head but was particularly strong along my spine. The buzzing continued and grew as if some energy, that had been blocked, was now moving again.

Still, some tightness remained in my chest, a heaviness that was more obvious now as the rest of my body had become more relaxed, loose and free of tension. It was then that I got to see my greatest fear unfold in my mind's eye i.e, the fear of losing my kids. This is common to all parents, I'm sure, but possibly exaggerated in my case due to the guilt I carried about not being there for them full-time, and the fact that the separation from their mother had been less than amicable.

This one I struggled with more than the rest. How could I let that fear go? Convincing myself that it would never happen wasn't going to work for me. Logic told me it was possible that I would lose them, however unlikely, as fathers' rights are often placed well below those of mothers' in Irish courts. I couldn't simply visualize happily waving my children goodbye and living a normal life without them. They are my favourite people in this world and, as a typical Cancerian, family is very important to me. I thought to myself "Surely loving your children means it's natural to be terrified of losing them?!"

As much as this is a logical and very human fear, I could feel that it was getting in the way of my inner peace. To remove the block, I wondered if loving my children didn't have to mean being fearful, choosing instead to be grateful for whatever time I had with them. I decided to trust that, if despite my best efforts they weren't to be in my life for a while, or even for the rest of my life, that was how it was meant to be. In my mind, I was talking to God, so I said, "You're running a whole universe and all that happens in it. I believe that we have a soul and that you look after that too. Whatever your plan is,

I'm going to believe in it, even if it means losing my kids. I trust you'll take care of them, and me".

In that moment, when I replaced that fear with trust, I felt more than a little better. I felt all fear, doubt and worry leave me, replaced by a sense of peace and bliss, the like of which I have never experienced before or since. The heaviness in my heart was replaced by a feeling of pure love, infinitely greater than anything I could ever have imagined. My eyes were still closed but there was no darkness. I was surrounded by a warm, bright, golden light. In fact, it was more than around me, it was also through me. I was part of the light and it was part of me. The word "heavenly" certainly comes to mind. I felt as if every cell in my body, every facet of my being and all around me was buzzing with this golden energy infused with love. The energy was love. Everything was love! I have often wished since that I could somehow download that memory and share it with everybody else on the planet.

In that state, I had a crystal-clear understanding that absolutely everything is ok! I remember one thought coming to mind. It was, "Duh! How did I forget this?" It wasn't some new discovery that I had stumbled upon. I had merely remembered the truth that everything is ok and that we are loved so completely, absolutely and unconditionally! It was a truly wonderful experience and I just sat in that state for a while.

Did I have a spiritual awakening? Maybe. Did I take my mind to a point where, with the absence of conscious worries, my nervous system shifted completely out of "fight-or-flight" mode and fully into a state of calm and peacefulness? Perhaps. Was this nervous system shift accompanied by a surge of the neurotransmitter dopamine, one of our major feel-good chemicals? Possibly. Who knows, maybe it was all of these. Either way, it was real, and it was profound. It showed me what is possible when we choose love and trust over fear. I wanted more.

HAPPILY EVER AFTER?

So, like all the great fairy-tales, I lived happily ever after! Well this isn't a fairy-tale and, it wasn't quite as simple as that. I found myself 'coming back around' on my bed after a time and returning to, I suppose what you could call my normal state of consciousness. I felt good but certainly dazed and a bit confused as to what had just happened! I would remind you that I was new to meditation and didn't know it could lead to experiences like this. I was also unsure as to what I was supposed to do about it. It was a big deal surely, to have a mind-blowing experience like that. I found myself thinking, "Should I tell people or keep it to myself?". "Would anyone believe me. Would they think I'm crazy, or on drugs?".

There certainly were no drugs involved, by the way, nor the possibility of the after-effects of past hallucinogenic drug use. Drugs were never my thing. It was the most real, most true experience I've ever had. I have a healthy dose of scepticism at the best of times and I could hardly believe it myself, but I could never be convinced that this experience was anything other than how I have just explained it.

As the days, weeks, and life in general went on, I saw that old habits die hard. I found myself getting tangled up once more in common fears, judgements and doubts. I was feeling some weight in my chest again too. These were just my normal, common worries really but having felt such peace and clarity, even everyday stress was far more obvious now that I could tell the difference. This annoyed me, in fact it really pissed me off. I was totally conflicted between the experience I had and my 30-year-old habits. I would remind myself that I now know the truth, that everything is ok, all is love and there's nothing to worry about, but the old habits were still there despite that.

I even felt a little guilty and ashamed for not being calm and peaceful all the time as if I should now become some kind of saint or guru, following my blissful experience! I thought, "shouldn't knowing such a profound truth be enough to give me inner-peace for life?". I would try to return to the blissful state again during meditations, only to get more frustrated. I wanted to know why I would get a glimpse of "heaven", feel such peace, then go back to the comparative "hell" of stress, judgement and worries.

I came to realise that I created the discomfort myself by choosing fear over love. That choice was habitual and sub-conscious rather than intentional. A newfound awareness of my thoughts allowed me to see it happening, but it didn't stop me from doing it, at least not straight away. When I had allowed myself to let go of the worries, trusting completely whatever will be, I had felt bliss. When I worried or believed that I or my life should be other than what it was, it created tension and distracted me from peacefulness. I suppose I had beginner's luck, like when I got a hole-in-one the first time I played pitch and putt. It was going to take regular practice to be able to do it more consistently, especially when the pressure was on.

It took me quite a while, but I eventually started to accept the simple message I got from my experience i.e. "everything is ok". I explored it more from a practical point of view so that I could try to reconcile it with 30 years of believing that things are not always ok. Sure, I believed some things were ok like kindness, "good" behaviour, honesty, generosity etc. But what about the things that weren't ok? From a very young age we're told what's bad and what's wrong such as lying, breaking things, being greedy, using swear words, being too noisy etc.

BLACK, WHITE OR SHADES OF GREY

We get older and learn, through media, advertising and those around us, that we should look and act a certain way to fit in or to be good enough. This suggests, by default, that we don't fit and we're not good enough already. We also discover more extreme "bad", possibly even "evil" behaviours like stealing, murder, wars and abuse. We learn about all the various punishments dished out for being bad, from bold steps, grounding, being shouted at, having our stuff taken away to corporal punishment, prison, purgatory and eternal damnation! We build up a list of what's right and wrong, black and white. We are given lots of reasons to be afraid, self-conscious and to believe that the world is simply not ok.

a life-changing experience

We're not always taught to look deeper. I remember being very black and white about right and wrong until I got older and everything faded to grey. We don't learn that lying is part of our social development and used by intelligent children to avoid getting in trouble or that cursing can relieve stress and is usually funny to the adults that are chastising it. We're not always told that we may need to raise our voices to be heard, that people sometimes steal to eat or kill to survive.

I'm not suggesting we stop parenting, but maybe we could do a better job of "separating the sin from the sinner" by explaining situations rather than painting them as good or bad. Finding the reasons behind unpleasant behaviour is often overlooked and instead they are simplified to right or wrong. We all want to be peaceful, calm, understanding and loving but when we believe so much is wrong with the world, the people around us and ourselves, it's hard not to be judgemental, stressed, angry or afraid much of the time.

If everything is genuinely ok, as my experience showed me, then there cannot be right or wrong, nor can there be good or bad. There can certainly be pleasant and unpleasant, productive or counter-productive, constructive or destructive. All our actions have consequences, but it's really what we hope to achieve and our belief system that dictates whether we perceive them as right or wrong.

I found that if I wanted to bring more peace and bliss into my daily life, I needed to change my perspective on many areas. I began to look for reasons why those situations that didn't seem ok, needed to be just as they were. I at least wanted to understand what circumstances led to them in the first place. Having felt such love, I couldn't believe that whatever divine consciousness or universal intelligence created us could simply abandon us to our own devices. Nor could I believe that we are punished for being "bad" the way we, as often flawed and fearful, humans punish each other. There had to be a reason for why it all happens. Likewise, I couldn't believe that any soul was evil. Damaged egos, misguided beliefs and frightened humans capable of destructive and terrible things, certainly, but not evil.

Accepting that everything is ok was hugely freeing for me in many ways, albeit challenging at times. It meant that I didn't have to be so hard on myself for the goals I had not yet achieved. What I already had and where I was at in my life was ok! I eased off on the self-judgement and the judgement of others and looked for reasons to accept and love.

Knowing that all is ok also meant there was no wrong way to live my life. This presented me with choices, so many choices! I now had the freedom to live whatever way I wanted, I could break away from my old habits and get out of my proverbial box to try something new, knowing everything was still going be ok! It gave me more peace of mind regarding the future. I was free to live and act the way I wanted to and let it all unfold.

When I face challenges now, I apply an, "Everything is ok" mentality, to try to understand the situation, and why I'm resisting it. I try to consider the perspectives of others involved and to be more patient. Patience doesn't always come easily to me, so 'everything is ok' helps, a lot!

33

I now compare the blissful experience to having stumbled onto a perfect, peaceful meadow in the middle of a wood, receiving a glimpse of what it offers, then leaving again to experience and explore the rest of the forest. It's an opportunity to learn to enjoy the forest as much as the meadow. The goal isn't simply to find my way back to peace and bliss.

While the meadow may be heavenly, the forest has lots to offer that the meadow doesn't. There are challenges to overcome, dangers that bring excitement and there is mystery. There are sights, sounds, smells and tastes not available in the meadow of bliss. The forest is a gift, a vast playground to entertain us. We can choose to experience it fully or in part, love it or hate it. We can spend all our time wishing we were back in the meadow, searching for it or we can simply enjoy the forest until it is our time to return.

I now know the peaceful meadow is there for us, always has been and always will be. Our right to go there doesn't have to be earned. It's where and what we come from. We remain connected to it always, even when we're out in the woods up to our necks in dirt! We can dip into its peace and draw from its love, but the forest is where life is waiting to be lived. I believe that when our time in the forest is done, we will all go back to bliss, no matter how we have spent our lives. Our focus only needs to be on how we spend our time in the forest.

So, to clarify, this book is not meant to provide some spiritual healing, save your soul or make you a better person. Your spirit, soul or essence is just fine, it can't be any other way for it is pure and perfect. My hope is to help you to let go of some of your unnecessary fears so you can live more consciously. I want to remind you to take care of your wonderful self, to dive into your life experiences fully and squeeze the most out of the time you have on this earth!

"What to do with Stardust?" is, again, a question you must ask yourself now that you understand you have the freedom to choose.

a life-changing experience

You Matter

Chapter 4

The Importance of Feeling Good

"I only know that what is moral is what you feel good after and what is immoral is what you feel bad after" - Ernest Hemmingway.

It seems like feeling good should be the simplest of habits to form when we have every reason to do what is pleasurable and creates positive feelings. Yet how many of us give ourselves permission to genuinely feel good? Do we fully accept our right to it and live our lives accordingly?

Since this book was greatly inspired by a moment of feeling unbelievably good during meditation, feeling good is one of its foundations and a thread that runs through every section. I have struggled in the past with believing in my right to feel good and as a result, I often didn't give myself permission to live and act in ways that made me feel that way. In this chapter, I hope to show you why feeling good is not just pleasurable but key to living our best lives. It is in the feel-good zone that we rise above simply surviving into the realms of thriving. This will encourage you to invest in your feel-good-factor. This is possibly the best indicator of our quality of life and worth increasing whenever, wherever and however possible.

WELLNESS SCALE

Both happiness and suffering are necessary for a full experience of living and have their benefits. Happiness generally tells us when we're on the right track and suffering tells us something must change. Much of the happiness and suffering we experience results from our own choices, habitual actions and how successful we perceive our lives to be. In this chapter we will look at simple ways to bring more joy into our lives.

To get our overall sense of well-being into perspective, I like to think of an old-fashioned weighing scale. One side holds our suffering i.e. any unpleasant thoughts, feelings and experiences. The other side contains our happiness i.e. all the pleasant thoughts, feelings and experiences. There is an arrow between them that points straight up at zero when both sides are filled evenly. As the suffering side is added to, the arrow tips towards minus one, then minus two, all the way to minus ten if we are weighed down with suffering. As the happiness side is filled, the arrow moves towards plus one, then plus two, all the way to plus ten if we are full of joy. Our overall well-being score depends on how much we put into each side, moment-to-moment and day-to-day.

We choose, consciously or unconsciously, which side we fill, via our thoughts and our actions. Some suffering in life is unavoidable so we must consciously take time to bring in more happiness to tip the scales towards wellbeing. We want to live our lives in the plus side of the wellness scale, in a positive state of mental, emotional and physical wellbeing. I believe that we can all add to the plus side if we give ourselves permission to act on what makes us feel good.

This is simpler than you might think. We can choose to let go of old beliefs, grudges and habits that create suffering, thereby removing them from our scale. We can choose to see past challenges as character, strength and wisdom-building exercises. We can do things every day that we enjoy. Every moment added to our happiness is a moment that nothing is added to our suffering. Once we add enough happiness to our lives and get our scale firmly into the plus side, even a major challenge won't keep us down for long. With a healthy measure of feelgood-factor saved up, the sheer weight of our positive thoughts and actions will tip us back into wellbeing again. We can build this by creating a habitual attitude of looking on the bright side. We can also develop mental, physical and emotional fitness. We can build close personal relationships. We can join clubs and groups to meet others that enjoy the same activities as we do. Committing to our wellness is the greatest investment any of us can make.

OUR RIGHT TO FEEL GOOD

Our need to feel good is hard-wired into our most primitive survival systems for individual and collective wellbeing. It is still one of the key factors for realising our full potential. Our physical bodies are designed, using comfort and discomfort, to tell us if they are healthy or in distress. Pain tells us if we are injured or are doing something that is likely to cause us harm. All our senses advise us to feel good whenever possible. If we touch something that's too hot, too cold, or too sharp, we feel pain, so we instinctively pull our hand away to minimise the damage caused. Tolerable and safe temperatures and surfaces are more pleasant. Noise that's too loud or lights that are too bright cause discomfort. A harsh, loud noise in humankinds past probably meant danger from a falling tree, landslide or came from the screeching of other creatures when a predator was nearby. Soft and calm sounds meant safety.

Extremely bright light would have told us the full strength of the midday sun should be avoided until it was safer for us to venture out in. Natural foods that are poisonous to humans are often very bitter or unpleasant tasting and smelling, so we don't eat them. Foul-smelling food is probably already over-grown with bacteria that would make us ill should we ingest them. Fresh, ripened fruits, vegetables and nuts at their most nutritious are often the sweetest or most pleasant tasting to us.

the importance of feeling good

The feeling of tiredness is unpleasant and leaves us more susceptible to disease and danger through poor concentration. We sleep to avoid this unpleasant sensation. While doing so, we give the body an opportunity to rest, turn short-term memory into long-term memories, repair physical damage and grow new healthy cells and tissues, so that we feel good once more. We also get an insight into our subconscious and the chance to dream.

When our 'gut-feeling' or intuition tells us that something is not quite right about a person or a situation, we act accordingly to save ourselves from trouble. We aim to spend time in the company of those who give us a 'good-vibe'. These are generally people who make us feel safe, appreciated and supported. We want to be with those with whom we have fun! When we are physically, mentally and emotionally well, we feel good. Feeling good is necessary for wellbeing, surviving and more importantly, for thriving.

MORE BENEFITS OF FEELING GOOD

Beyond our day-to-day survival, we look for other ways to feel good and reap its rewards. We dress to look good, to express our personalities which can help us to find "our tribe", those with whom we fit in and share interests. Our style may attract a partner, improve job interview success or gain the respect and admiration of others to improve our social standing. We socialise to have fun and develop new and stronger relationships. Social contact and close personal relationships have been found to be extremely beneficial for our health and longevity. Such relationships appear to be greater predictors of a long-life than even healthy eating, exercise or not smoking! The Beatles told us, "All you need is love". We need a little more than that, but they were on the right track.

The feel-good-factor of helping other people means that they benefit but so do we. It's a win-win situation for all! Even when we appear to be putting others needs ahead of our own, it's often because it feels good to help another human out, especially if we care for them. Co-operation has been one of the secrets of humanities success and will always continue to be so. I'm sure you're getting a clear picture now of how important feeling good is to you in many aspects of life. It's so important that I'm going to give you even more reasons, so you can cultivate an intention to feel good wherever possible.

Feeling good has an extremely health-improving effect on our bodies' ability to heal. The placebo effect explains this perfectly. A placebo pill may simply contain a plain, non-medicated, filler rather than any real medication. They are not really a drug. Placebos, because they contain no actual medication, are used when researchers perform studies to test the effects of the real drugs. Some patients are given the genuine drug being tested while others in the study are given a pretend drug, the placebo, to compare the results.

Placebos have been found, on average, to be effective in a third of patients with illnesses where it is possible for the body to heal itself. This means that by taking a pill with absolutely no medication that 1 in 3 patients would be expected to improve. What does this tell us? By taking a pill, which the patient believes will heal them, the patient will start to think more positively, believing that they will recover. As the worry of being ill or getting worse subsides and a more positive attitude takes hold, the body starts returning to the influence of the parasympathetic (peaceful) nervous system.

Remember earlier we discussed the sympathetic part of the autonomic nervous system (or Stressed Nervous System)? It's our mode for surviving right now by fighting an attacker or fleeing from danger. The parasympathetic mode (peaceful nervous system), often nicknamed "rest and digest" is geared more for long-term health. This mode is focused on the absorption of nutrients, building of healthy tissues and immunity, removal of wastes, resting, reproduction etc. These are all necessary to improve health and to survive long-term. When we feel-good, our healing powers are heightened!

Based on that, anything we do, that makes us genuinely feel good, can also help our body's own natural healing processes. This understanding is not new, it has been known and recommended for health in many ancient forms of healthcare. On a trip to Peru, I learned that Peruvian shamans would ask their patients four main questions. "When did you stop dancing? When did you stop singing? When did you stop being enchanted by stories? When did you stop being comforted by the sweet territory of silence?". In physiology terms, the shaman was asking when the patient stopped doing those things that naturally make us feel good and thereby enter the Peaceful Nervous System mode! Without its long-term benefits, the patient's body was unable to maintain or restore health and illness crept in and took hold.

Obviously, our aim is to feel good both in the short-term and the long-term so let's be a little sensible about this. Partying and excessive alcohol consumption may feel like great fun at the time but will probably lead to a nasty hangover lasting several days. I'm fond of a good night out myself but let's do the math. Hours of fun weighed against days of sickness, does not equal feeling good overall! If this occurs weekly, the body is unlikely to be healthy for long. The same can be said for the short-term satisfaction of junk food which can be followed by guilt, energy slumps and health problems. If a pleasant tasting food leads to any discomfort or stress on the body such as bloating, cramps, obesity or energy slumps, it's not a feel-good food. Extreme levels of addiction cause havoc for everybody involved, all for a quick buzz.

This weighing-up of the overall feel-good factor can also apply to the endorphin buzz of exercise. Overtraining can result in pain and injury to the muscles and joints and a weakened immune system. Think about the little picture and the big picture when adding to your feel-good-factor, bring some balance to your day and make choices that let you get the best of both worlds.

Finally, to help you avoid any guilt you may feel at making your own feel-good-factor a priority in your life, I'll ask you this - Is this drive that humans have to feel good, self-serving? Most definitely. Is this bad, wrong or negatively greedy? Most definitely not, especially in the case of our health. I believe that we should be positively greedy about achieving the highest quality of health possible! Our drive to feel good can be of great benefit to us and those around us. If we focus on what truly feels good, both short and long term, our self-serving nature can be "self-full" rather than selfish.

HAPPINESS SIMPLIFIED

I'm a fan of keeping things simple and practical so let's look at some of the simplest and most effective, tried-and-tested ways to add happiness to our lives. We'll discuss each one in more detail in later chapters.

Health

Take care of your physical, mental and emotional health. Invest some of your time and energy into it and you will reap the rewards now and in the future. Move your body regularly and rest it when tired. Nourish it with delicious and nutritious foods and kind thoughts. Surround yourself with people that feel good to be with.

Appreciation, attention

Pay close attention to the things that you already have, and you will find that you already have most of the important things in life and would not trade them for anything. Upon realising this, you will feel lucky, perhaps even rich. Your talents and energy are abundant, but your time has limits so pay attention to where and how you spend your precious time. Use it where you are appreciated and valued.

Positive attitude, Patience

Trust that everything happens for a good reason i.e., Life happens for us and not to us. Approach your endeavours with a belief that it will work out for the best. If something isn't going your way, trust that there may be a better way than you can currently envisage. Be patient and in time you will see that what's happening now is for your own good. Be patient also with yourself, if you are already doing your best. Be patient with others. They're probably doing the best they can with who they are and the abilities they currently possess. Even if you've got to light a proverbial fire under someone to get them going, patience will help you to inspire or encourage without burning them or your relationship in the process.

Pride

Take a little pride in your accomplishments. Be proud of all the medals you've won, certificates you've earned and lessons you've learned. Remember the achievements that at one time were your top goals and are a testament to what you can do when you try. They will remind you of your ability to learn, grow and overcome challenges. They will also encourage you to follow new dreams.

Interests

They say variety is the spice of life. Involve yourself in several different interests, some group-based and some that you can enjoy solo. You will gain new and varied groups of friends and have options so you're comfortable in the company of others or alone. If any of your hobbies are seasonal

41

or come to an end, having several on-the-go means you will still have plenty more to bring you pleasure.

New experiences, Nutrition

"Knowledge comes from books, but wisdom comes from experience!" You can never know if you'll enjoy something until you try it. Seek out new sensations, travel to see unusual places and cultures and observe new sights, even on your own doorstep. Taste new flavours. This world has more to indulge your senses than anybody could fit in one lifetime, so get moving, don't delay! Every new experience you try will broaden your horizons and give you memories with opportunities for interesting conversation. Feed yourself well. Nourish your body by consciously choosing foods that bring ease to your body and mind.

Education , Easy

Open your mind through learning! Formal education provides the paperwork that is often necessary to get a career but there are many ways to learn. Visit libraries, take courses and talk to people. The internet gives us access to a world of information in an instant. Listen, observe and learn all that you can. Remember that knowledge is no load and whether you have the credentials or not, you can still use that knowledge to benefit those around you. Not everything needs to be a struggle, so take the easy path sometimes. Evolution strives for efficiency and you can too. Take the easiest route to achieving your goals whenever possible and make life easier for yourself in any way you can.

Simplicity, Sip water

Keep it Simple, Stupid! This is known as the K.I.S.S. principle. We often already know the answers to our questions and, once we calm the mind and remove all the complications, solutions become apparent. Ask yourself what feels good and what feels right to you when faced with choices, then follow that intuition. Simplify your life where possible. Reduce your workload if you need more rest, minimise your living space so that you have less to clean, organise and maintain. Re-evaluate complicated areas of your life. A simple life has been professed for many ages, through various religious texts and philosophies, to be fundamental to a happy life.

We often speak of how our parents and grandparents were happier people as life was simpler in their time. I know in Ireland we say, "They didn't have anything back then, so they didn't have anything to worry about!". There is some truth in that statement. It seems that our happiness levels reduce when we are faced with too much choice. The problem comes from our tendency to imagine that the options we didn't choose are better than what we have picked. 'The grass is greener on the other side of the fence' mentality always suggests that we are missing out on this side!

Sip water, 2 litres or more, throughout the day and enjoy the many, many benefits that this essential, life-giving nutrient provides.

the importance of feeling good

Serve a purpose, Sleep
You're here for a good reason. Use the talents and gifts you've been blessed with to make your world a nicer place while also proving, to yourself, your own value and importance. Rest well each day by developing a healthy sleep pattern and taking powernaps when required. People have known the benefits of a good sleep for many years so remember these oldies but goodies - "go to bed on the day you got up", "an hour before midnight is worth two after", "a good night's sleep and a good laugh will cure what ails you".

Remember that allowing yourself to reach a state of happiness is one of the most health-improving decisions you can make. This allows the body to activate the parasympathetic (peaceful) side of the autonomic nervous system. In this relaxed mode, the body reduces blood pressure, encourages digestion, produces hormones that heal and repair damaged tissues and builds the immune system. All this newfound happiness may lead to a few extra smile and laughter lines as you get older to wear with pride!

SUFFERING SIMPLIFIED
In Buddhist philosophy, the Buddha teaches that attachment is the greatest cause of suffering to mankind. To release attachments is to free ourselves from unnecessary suffering. This can help us to avoid adding to the suffering side of our wellness scale.

An underlying cause of many of our personal dysfunctions is the attachment of our happiness or self-worth to something. This happens when we believe that our happiness is dependent on something outside of us or possibly even an aspect of ourselves. For example, if I were to believe I will be happy if this book becomes a world-wide success, I would place my happiness in the hands of other people and their opinions. My happiness would depend on sales, reviews and publishers. I would literally be handing over my happiness to many other people.

Even if I were to decide that I will be happy if this book helps 100 people, or 10 or even 1, I would still risk a portion of my wellbeing. I would set myself up for the possibility of losing that happiness if this book didn't achieve what I deemed necessary for it to be a success. I would also delay my present happiness by pushing it back to a later stage when the book reaches the goal I've set.

As a result, I would invite suffering. I would suffer if the book "fails". I would suffer the anxiety of wondering if the book will achieve my goals. I would suffer the stress of having attached my sense of self-worth and personal value to the opinions of others about this book. I would then suffer every criticism of the book as a personal attack on me, my writing ability and my knowledge. This would be unfair to me for, as John Lydgate said, "You can please some of the people, some of the time, but you can't please all of the people, all of the time!".

Such criticism need not cause me suffering if I keep my happiness separate, see it as constructive criticism and use it for my benefit by developing my writing skills further. I am human and subject to the same self-doubts as anybody else but knowing this fact helps me to avoid much suffering. I can still care for the opinions of my readers and believe in the potential of this book to be helpful without such attachments.

However, by realising that I was here, and happy, before this book existed, I can know for sure that my happiness doesn't depend on it. I can also enjoy the process of writing, the research, the knowledge I've gained and the fact I've achieved something I would have thought impossible only a few years ago i.e. to publish my own book! I have some say over how good I feel throughout this process if I accept that my happiness is my own.

That's just one example of how attachment can be an underlying cause of suffering. In later chapters we will discuss, in more detail, other areas where attachment causes many of us to suffer at some point in our lives.

Here are some simple ones you may identify with and wish to change;

Solitary confinement, sloth

Humans are social, community-based creatures not the solitary kind. Some time to ourselves is good but in general we are better together. It has always been our intellect with our ability to cooperate and care for each other that makes us strong, giving us an edge over other creatures. Some of the most crucial factors found to help us live to a ripe old age are social contact and having close personal relationships. Sometimes we need a little TLC and it is good for us to give it to others.

Sloth, also known as laziness, is one of the "seven deadly sins". While I don't believe these "deadly sins" have any say over an afterlife, they certainly can impact our current life experience. Lack of physical movement and exercise have detrimental effects on the physical body. It stiffens, weakens and becomes tired more easily. Waste builds up in our soft tissues and we struggle to complete even simple tasks. We must use our bodies to keep them finely tuned and feeling good. Laziness prevents us from bringing our gifts to the world through action and can make us feel useless and unnecessary. Doing things that make a difference to the world shows us our importance and value.

Under-achieving, unrealistic goals

We've already got to grips with how amazing and full of potential we are. Wouldn't an eagle suffer if locked in a cage and prevented from soaring high, as is its nature. Doesn't it stand to reason that you would too if you're not shining as you are meant to and sharing your talents with the world? Reach your potential for a greater sense of fulfilment. For balance, set realistic goals that are achievable, or you will suffer the feeling of failure. Once one goal is reached, you can always plan another so that you make steady progress and enjoy lots of success along the way.

Finding fault

This is a form of non-acceptance of reality i.e. believing that things are not ok, just as they are. When doing so, we miss the beauty and the benefit of a situation by looking for problems with it. Sure, there may be a better way but perhaps how it is, is how it must be, at least for now. Struggling against reality is akin to struggling against the current of a river when we could go with the flow instead. Accepting what already is, through understanding, compassion and a broader perspective can greatly reduce our suffering.

Fear, food

Our greatest fears are usually of the unknown. We can generally deal with what we understand but the unknown worries us. Worrying is imagining what we don't want to happen and causing our body and mind to experience that situation as if it is real. Being realistic about the likelihood of our fears coming true can reduce their power, as will accepting that all may still be ok, regardless. The human body is so amazing that it can survive on poor nutrition for lengthy periods, but it simply doesn't thrive without adequate nutrients. Many common illnesses are a result of nutritional deficiencies and food intolerances. A simpler, cleaner diet can often reverse these illnesses and restore a healthier state.

Engaging in drama

Energy flows where attention goes. By engaging in drama, we feed and encourage it in others and ourselves. This goes beyond dealing with "dramatic people", most of whom are rarely aware that they are in fact "drama-junkies". Engaging in drama includes listening to drama-filled radio programmes or watching dramatic television programmes or movies. The news also tends to be dramatic by its nature, highlighting the worst of what is going on in the world while showing very little of its beauty. They will show the failures of health services but rarely the successes. It will show murders but not explain that for every person that would take a life, there are many more that would strive to save one. It will feature extreme weather from around the world, but we may forget that for every storm there are many more fine days. We feed our minds through our eyes and ears just as we feed our body through our mouths. While we can safely handle a little "entertainment-junk", it should be kept to a minimum, favouring that which makes us genuinely feel good and at ease.

Reliving past hurts

The past absolutely should be learned from, to help us avoid repeating problems in the future. It is also sometimes necessary to refer to the past to explain or understand a current situation. However, living in the past when holding on to traumatic experiences can sometimes subject us to the same hurt again and again. While another person may have been responsible for our hurt initially, we are responsible for that suffering in the present moment when we choose to relive it. It's a little like picking at an old wound and then wondering why it is not healing. Perhaps if we leave it alone, and give it some time, it will heal. The past belongs in the past. Take the lesson, resolve it to build a bridge to get over it and then move on.

Identifying with the ego

The ego, according to some Eastern philosophies can be described as the part of us that believes we are separate from everything else, convinced that we are finite and alone. It is this ego that fears, that believes we are unworthy of love and the ego that creates loneliness. The ego does play a vital role, however. It helps to keep us safe from genuine physical danger. However, believing that we are our egos and nothing more, causes unnecessary suffering as it can lock us into survival mode rather than a peaceful state. We are so much more than just the ego. If the meditation experience, I described in chapter 3 taught me anything, it's that we are loved beyond our wildest imagination and we are truly connected to everything.

Nonsense

The main problem with common sense is that it is not all that common! We are gifted with the ability to apply logic yet so often we choose not to use it. To know what is good for us but to act and live in ways that we know are not are not good for us makes no sense. Smoking, excessive drinking, unnecessarily late nights and engaging in abusive or unsupportive relationships These are nonsense as common sense tells us there are better ways. Living and thinking nonsensically will always bring some level of discomfort or cause us problems that could have been avoided had we simply used our good sense.

Greed

Usually stemming from the attachment of our self-worth to material objects or money, greed encourages us to accumulate possessions in an attempt to feel secure, worthy or good-enough. This is a futile endeavour for, without accepting our innate value, the entire world is not enough to fill the "unworthy" void. Greed may also arise when trying to guarantee security and status for ourselves and our loved ones. Many of us already have all we need, just perhaps not all we want. On the other end of the spectrum, choosing poverty to become more "saintly" or spiritual is just as likely to fail. Believing that giving up all our possessions makes us worthy is an equally foolish notion. It still carries with it a belief that our self-worth is somehow connected to our possessions. Giving all our possessions away simply means we have less to dust and polish. If we are lucky enough to have abundance, we can enjoy it, share it even, knowing we are worthy regardless of the sum of our possessions.

Avoiding these sources of suffering allows us more time and energy for habits that bring more happiness, wellbeing and living our best lives.

the importance of feeling good

PART 2

Health Matters

Health Matters

Chapter 5

Health is Wealth

Health is "more than simply the absence of disease" Jocelyn Elders M.D. and U.S. surgeon general.

Our bodies are the most valuable things we own, and our health is of utmost importance. Being healthy means more than just not being sick. It involves many of the attributes we often associate with youthfulness, i.e. vitality, energy, ease of movement, physical comfort and more. Health must play a big part in any plan to reach our potential and live our best lives.

I've seen, throughout my career in health and fitness, a general acceptance of low to average health as normal and an over-reliance on others to take care of our health, rather than taking personal responsibility for it. This chapter aims to explain what health is and what it is not. We will also discuss how our healthcare systems are often more focused on disease-care. Vast amounts of time and money are spent researching diseases and medications to treat their symptoms. If the same was spent on studying healthy people and their habits, I believe we would find the answers we seek. I feel a shift is needed to encourage an attitude of self-care, so we only need hospital and medical services as a last resort. By the end of this chapter, I hope you will evaluate your health expectations, get a little greedy about the level of health you want and choose to commit time and energy to improving yours.

YOUR HEALTH IS YOUR WEALTH

Everything we do in this world, throughout our lives, we will do in, with and through our bodies. The condition of the body will dictate the places we can go and the activities we can engage in. Our state of health will also largely determine how good we feel as we go through life. If feeling wonderful, a simple walk around the house can be a very pleasurable experience. If feeling terrible, walking on the worlds' most amazing beach by the most stunning sunset would bring little or no joy. Good health will give us a far greater quality of life and allow us to take on many more opportunities while mostly feeling good throughout. We can go further, achieve more and be at our best, when in a healthier condition. Good health gives us so much more than any material thing we can acquire during our lives. We would trade it

51

all in a heartbeat for health, if we were to become ill. Remember that a body must last us a lifetime, so it is worth investing in our health early in life to give it that chance to serve us well throughout.

We can look and feel younger than our years as caring for our health gives us some sway over the aging process. Each tissue type in the body is made of many cells which are replaced regularly with new copies when the old ones stop working so well or die. While in one sense we can say our bodies are very, very old i.e. made of atoms formed billions of years ago, in another sense, many parts of us are very young i.e. only days to weeks old, as those cells have just been created. Improved health and nutrition allow the body to make better quality cells, which can last longer. Since the rate of turn-over of new cells plays a large part in our aging process, longer lasting cells slow many effects of aging. What I'm saying here is that our chronological age, the time that has passed since our birth, is only one factor in determining the age we look and feel. There are many others that we will discuss in detail over the next few chapters.

EASE OR DISEASE?

The simplest way that I have found to describe health is this – "Ease or Disease". The word disease means dis-ease or a lack of ease. If any aspect of the body, mind or emotions is not working easily, functioning efficiently or capable of handling a reasonable amount of stress, we say quite rightly, that it's dis-eased. The word disease, in everyday language often carries with it a sense that a disease is something we get or have, through bad luck and as such is something we must simply accept or try to treat. This is true some of the time, but our lifestyle habits play a part in our level of "health-luck".

Do we look deeply enough into our diets, sleeping patterns, stress levels and thought processes in the months and years leading up to diseases, to see if perhaps they could have been avoided? And do we really consider our role in the common but manageable dis-eases such as headaches, indigestion, bloating or flatulence, tiredness, irritability or moodiness, difficulty sleeping, mild anxiety, joint stiffness or aching muscles? They certainly are diseases, perhaps not immediately life-threatening, but dis-eases, nonetheless. They are often the "warning-shots" given by the body to alert us to problems and will almost certainly lead to more serious issues if a healthy balance isn't regained. There are often ways of restoring ease by removing the restriction to normal healthy function, thus supporting the body's own healing systems.

If a lack of health is called dis-ease, then our goal must be the opposite i.e. ease. If we can move our bodies easily, performing physical activity without pain or restriction we can say that we're physically fit. The same applies to how easily our digestive, hormonal, cardiovascular, nervous systems etc. are working, and whether we are mentally or emotionally at ease. If we want ease, we must invest time and energy into developing it!

Ultimately, we are largely responsible for our own health levels through the lifestyle choices we make. Think again of the wellness scale. On one side we have all those things that encourage ease in the body and mind like healthy eating, drinking fresh water, taking adequate rest and relaxation, a balanced exercise program, positive thinking etc. On the other side we have all those that create dis-ease like junk food, poor sleeping patterns, not enough or maybe too much exercise, negative and fearful thinking, prolonged emotional stress etc.

Our daily choices and lifestyle habits will tip the balance to ease or disease, either a little or a lot. Does an amazing Stardust body deserve to be given the best of care?

HEALTHCARE OR DISEASE CARE?
The resources available through our western healthcare systems are primarily geared towards disease care i.e. treating those that are already sick and keeping them alive. To be fair to them, our healthcare systems have become very efficient this, as can be seen in the increase of the average lifespan of humans to almost eighty years. Survival is the necessary starting point but often our medical system's resources are limited to restoring only a basic level of health. Ideally, we would fix our attention and resources on developing true health and ease so there is very little disease to treat.
I want to be clear in that I am not saying that we should just turn away from western medicine and switch completely to a holistic, complimentary or alternative therapy. Be mindful that, if seriously ill, we will need disease-care to survive long enough to return to health. Some exercise, a meditation session and a handful of goji berries is not going stop and reverse a heart attack, shrink a life-threatening tumour or replace a worn-out hip! The purpose of this section is to bring clarity to the limitations of all forms of healthcare, including our medical services and promote more realistic expectations.
I also want to remind you of the power we already have over our own state of health. Learning from the habits and lifestyle choices of healthy people is likely to be more beneficial in the restoration and maintenance of health than simply treating diseases and symptoms when they present themselves. Luckily for us, there are people that have observed wellness for thousands of years and passed on their combined knowledge. Some of the simplest and most effective elements of what I've learned over the last twenty-eight years can be found in this book. I would highly recommend that you continue to learn about self-care.

ALTERNATIVE CARE
All developed countries have healthcare systems to provide for the needs of their people. You probably have availed of their services at some point, I know I have. Before these current systems were put in place, we had other forms of healthcare. These included medicine men and women, shamans, druids and various other healers that used their knowledge of foods, plants and herbs, massage, psychology and the subtle energies of the body to care for the ill. Theirs is the foundation for all medicine as we know it and yet they are referred to as "alternative therapies".

I would like to remind you that alternative means another choice or option. Indeed, many of their practices have survived to this day and are enjoying a resurgence as we realise that much of their knowledge is still useful. This section is not intended to undermine the knowledge gained or the excellent work done by our modern medical systems, but simply to identify them all as part of a great pool of knowledge that we can draw from. I look forward to the day when the benefits of all forms of healthcare are equally respected and all healthcare practitioners can sit around a "round table" of wellness, working together, pooling resources and learning from one another.

OUR ATTITUDE MATTERS

Our personal attitude towards health also plays its part in our ability to achieve it. Focusing on the cause of any dis-ease is necessary to instigate change, but the disease should not be given all our attention. Remember that energy flows where attention goes. Our main focus should be given to the ease of the body and mind. There can be a tendency, for some of us, to wallow in the "diseased" state, possibly playing the powerless victim's role. These, I have found, are the patients least likely to restore health. They don't seem to truly want to be well.

Comparing scars and moaning about our problems will not promote a healthy attitude and bring us into the healing parasympathetic nervous system mode. Instead it will increase stress levels which, in turn, will slow or prevent healing. On the flip side, I have seen patients with significant injuries but with a very positive expectation of returning to health, achieve it far more quickly than average. These people tend to acknowledge and focus on any and all improvements from each clinic session. They choose to see these as proof that they will reach their goal. Their positive attitudes allow their bodies to remain in the nervous systems' relaxed parasympathetic state, which is conducive to healing.

SYMPTOM RELIEF OR CURE?

Symptom relief alone is like putting a sticker over the warning light on your dashboard that tells you that your car is low on oil. The warning is removed but nothing has been fixed.

The human body has its own healing mechanisms. It wants to be healthy and fully functional. When a health issue arises, it is often because the body's own ability to heal is prevented or overwhelmed. In these days of instant gratification where few of us can spare the time to be sick or slowed down by illness, our first response to feeling unwell is often to get some symptom relief. This comes commonly in the form of painkillers, anti-inflammatories or anti-depressants. Here I'm going to explain why these should be used cautiously, short-term and only when necessary.

PAINKILLERS

I remember reading, in a Sunday magazine as a teenager about a woman whose two sons had a rare medical condition in the form of congenital insensitivity to pain, which meant they felt no pain, ever. At first, while reading it, I thought how amazing that would be to feel no pain, no matter what. It sounded like a super-power! As I read through the article, I realised it was anything but a gift. Her sons were regularly admitted to hospital, for all manner of injuries, as they had no safety mechanism to make them take better care of themselves. Normally, when a child gets hurt, they will cry and go to an adult for help. They will learn, through the pain experienced, what is unsafe. This knowledge limits the amount of damage they will inflict upon themselves in future. Without the gift of pain, yes, I'm calling it a gift, they can endure far greater damage before stopping. The children would often attend the hospital for minor injuries but need a full array of tests to find out just how much damage there was.

This article showed me the importance and benefit of pain and why we should moderate our use of painkillers. Anaesthetics are, of course, essential for surgical procedures and beneficial short-term, while undergoing a treatment plan but painkillers are not a treatment in themselves. If painkillers are required long-term, this suggests that healing is not progressing and another form of treatment to support healing should be sought. Pain is a warning, it tells us of damage or dysfunction present and forces us to protect the area while it heals. The more extreme the pain, the more severe the injury so it will tell us to seek out extra help if the body is unable to heal by itself. If we use medications to reduce this pain level, we will feel better than we truly are and may stress the injury more than it is ready for.

Once health is restored, pain will be relieved naturally. I have had clients that were told by their healthcare providers, when still suffering pain after treatment, that the treatment was successful and that they were indeed healed of their injury. It was stated that the reason for their discomfort was that the body still remembered the pain. This, I have found to be untrue in every case I encountered as I would find another cause for their physical distress. If our bodies remembered pain, then surely we would still feel every bump, bruise and scratch we ever had and spend our days in agony! Their issue was simply outside of the previous practitioner's training and knowledge base. We should, as healthcare practitioners be able to admit when we don't have an answer and send the patient elsewhere. Remember that no single specific form of health care or therapy can cure every human illness. If one could, then all providers would practice that form.

ANTI-INFLAMMATORIES

Inflammation, like pain, has been given a raw deal without due appreciation for the vital role it plays in the body. Getting rid of it with anti-inflammatories is not always the best thing for us.

Inflammatory fluid is the same substance that causes swelling around a sprained joint, builds up under the skin in a blister, creates a lump on a forehead from a bump on the head or that builds up on the brain from a concussion. Inflammation is an essential part of the healing process. It is called the inflammatory response as it is the body's response to trauma or damage.

Inflammation is involved in many functions, including the sealing of damaged blood vessels to prevent bleeding, the elimination of bacteria that could cause infection, the replacement of damaged tissue with new healthy cells by stimulating cell division and the safeguarding of the injured area by increasing tenderness which forces us to protect it or seek treatment.

There are times when anti-inflammatories should definitely be used, just not always. In situations where inflammation may cause more harm than good such as concussion or compression of the brain or excessive fluid affecting other organ function, inflammation should be reduced through medical means. However, for most of our typical aches, pains and injuries, I believe it is best to focus on resting the affected area while the internal repair work is completed, along with any form of treatment that aids or supports the healing process. This could include massage of the surrounding tissues to promote blood and lymphatic flow and improved nutrition and dietary habits to support new cell growth, remove allergens and improve gut-health.

Healthy gut bacteria balance has been found to help regulate the inflammation process while also helping to improve our mood! Other means include acupuncture, chiropractic therapy to re-align bones that have shifted out of their natural alignment, reflexology and energy therapies. Let's not forget the mind-body connection. Counselling to release mental stress can reduce physical tension in the body. Ideally, we want to support the body's own systems so that the inflammation can subside naturally. In the case of non-life-threatening issues, medication or surgery are definite options when simpler, non-invasive methods have proved ineffective.

ANTI-DEPRESSANTS

Anti-depressant use has increased consistently over the years but so have depression rates. We need to ask if they are truly getting acceptable results or if we should look at the alternatives.

The most commonly prescribed anti-depressant medication known as SSRI's and SNRI's, work to keep more serotonin in the brain. Serotonin is a neurotransmitter that regulates depression among other things and would normally break down or be reabsorbed after it's released and used. Keeping it from breaking down is helpful but doesn't address why there are low levels of serotonin to begin with. SSRI's and SNRI's also carry warnings for increased risk of suicidal thoughts and other unpleasant side-effects.

Another approach may be to focus on supporting the natural production of Serotonin. The idea being that if we have plenty and are making more every day, the natural breakdown and reabsorption of Serotonin won't lower our mood. Some recommended means include dietary improvements. We can get more vitamin B6 from foods including chickpeas, beef liver, tuna, salmon, spinach and bananas. Natural carbohydrates such as potatoes and grains can help with serotonin production while also feeding the brain the glucose it needs as fuel to work efficiently and balance our moods. Yes, food affects mood. Ever notice how hangry i.e. hungry-angry, we can get? Fermented foods, drinks and probiotics improve our gut-bacteria balance which, among other things, improve our digestion and absorption of nutrients necessary for serotonin production.

We can exercise daily to boost serotonin levels. We can destress with mindfulness, meditation and massage to reduce cortisol, nicknamed the stress hormone, which interferes with serotonin, and increase serotonin levels. How about enjoying some sunshine to stimulate specific areas of the retina that trigger the release of serotonin? Try eliminating or at least significantly reducing sugar from the diet. Over-consumption strips us of the vitamins needed to digest and process it. Sugar can also create imbalances in the gut bacteria as it feeds certain types that we want to keep in-check. Generally following the earlier advice on bringing more wellbeing and happiness into our lives can reduce our need for anti-depressants. If already taking prescription anti-depressants, engage with health professionals to work towards restoring health so they won't be needed in the future.

HOLISTIC HEALTH

Every part of us is important. Improving any area of our health improves our overall wellbeing.

'One day all the body parts were having a discussion about who among them was most important. The lungs announced that they bring oxygen into the body, which is essential for life, so they must be the most important. Many of the other parts met this with agreement. The heart declared that without her, blood wouldn't carry oxygen, or any other nutrients for that matter, around the body so she must be most important and again many thought that she had a right to claim the title. The brain then made its case based on the many essential functions that it regulates in the body and, it seemed there was a winner! Suddenly, the bowel piped up "I think I deserve the title of most important body-part". This was followed by howls of laughter at the ridiculous notion that the bowel could compare in importance, to the lungs, heart or brain. "Fine" responded the bowel stubbornly, "let's see how you manage without me" and went it on strike. After a few days, when they realised how much crap the bowel dealt with, the rest of the body came to appreciate the bowel.'

Holistic means whole. The holistic approach to health refers to the health of the whole body, or more-so the whole being i.e., body, mind and emotions together as one unit. As I continue to learn about wellbeing, holistic health is the only approach to healthcare that makes sense to me. While we have different charts to show the various systems, organs and tissues and we have individual experts for each, there isn't any separation between them. They cannot function alone, all our parts must work together synergistically for a positive state of health to occur. To add to that, we have trillions of bacteria that outnumber the cells in our body, most working symbiotically with us to maintain health and wellness. All systems, parts and bacteria are important and if any are missing or working poorly, general health will be affected.

Physical, mental and emotional health are equally important and completely intertwined, therefore any attempt to improve health should involve all three. A simple demonstration of the direct connection between mental and emotional health can be seen by looking at the effect of dreams. We instantly feel as if this is happening for real even though it has been created entirely in the mind. When we wake, the emotions experienced will still linger and we can feel wonderful or terrible depending on the type of dream. Following a nightmare, we may wake with increased heart rate and sweating, the same response we would have if we were in a real-life dangerous situation.

Another simple demonstration of the mental and physical connection can be seen in what we call body language. Experts can read what's going on in the mind of a person by our subconscious movements. In fact, we can all tell the moods of people closest to us by their facial expressions, posture and the way they move. We don't teach babies how to cry yet crying is the physical reaction to discomfort natural to all human races. Smiling and laughter also demonstrate muscular reactions to the emotional state of happiness.

The connections between mind, body and emotions work both ways therefore, if we feel physically unwell, the mind tends to think less positively, and we may feel emotionally more fragile. Alternately, when we are feeling physically fit, we tend to think more positively and feel more emotionally balanced and at ease.

Now you understand why we must take responsibility for our own health rather than neglecting it and then relying on others to fix it. You also understand that improving any aspect of our health can affect the rest so you can see it's worth investing time and energy into self-health-improvement.

All forms of healthcare have benefits and all have limits. Combining the best of each them increases their benefits but reduces their limitations. We are responsible for creating our good health and for seeking out those that can help us to restore wellbeing when needed.

health is wealth

Health Matters

Chapter 6

Healthy Habits

"Healthy habits are learned in the same way as unhealthy ones – through practice" – Wayne Dyer

WHAT REALLY WORKS FOR US?

There is so much advice out there telling us what we should and shouldn't do to improve our health. Much of this advice is conflicting and confusing. Foods can be viewed as healthy one minute, bad for us the next. Exercise forms seem go out of fashion quicker than the clothes we wear while doing them. Opinions vary on what is the best mattress to sleep on and how to meditate. There are supplements and machines that often claim to be the 'wonder-cure' for all that ails us. Rather than tell you what to do in this section, I'll tell you how and why. This will give you a greater understanding of your body's needs and the power to choose more effectively.

If you would like greater energy levels, mobility, peace-of-mind and wellness, try these top 5 tips on for size. I have found these to be particularly beneficial both personally and with clients. You will not be surprised by any of them as they feature on most healthy advice lists but perhaps you might be amazed by the difference adopting these habits can make to your wellbeing. Such changes can be introduced quite easily with visible progress likely within days to weeks.

1. WATER AND HYDRATION

Drink fresh, clean water to improve digestion, muscle function, athletic performance, concentration, mood, energy levels and protect your joints. Water tops my list of healthy habit changes that can be immediately introduced to our lives. It is essential for life as we know it as all living organisms need water to live and function well. In humans, severe dehydration can cause muscle cramps, rapid heart and breathing rates, irritability, confusion and lethargy! Even mild dehydration adversely affects our digestive system, mood, concentration and energy levels. I can easily tell when my physical therapy clients are dehydrated by the tightness of their muscles.

Approximately 2-3 litres of water or water-rich fluids a day is recommended for the average adult. More may be required if we're active, living in warm climates or working in dry environments. Preferably, our drinking water should be obtained from a clean and natural source. Other beverages and foods with a high water-content can contribute to our requirements but should not completely replace the water we drink. Natural fruit juices and teas are generally better options than beer, spirits, fizzy or sugary drinks and copious amounts of coffee!

2-3 litres each day may seem like a lot and we could be forgiven for thinking we'd spend half our lives in the toilet when consuming so much. However, it's worth remembering that we not only lose water through our urine, but also through our breath and skin as we breathe and perspire throughout the day and night. We won't see the moisture we exhale unless it is cold, or we breathe on glass but it's there, nonetheless. Nor do we notice perspiration if it evaporates quickly enough from our skin or through our clothes. All of this needs to be replaced along with providing sufficient water to flush toxins, carry water-soluble vitamins and nourish our cells.

"CLEAN WATER"

I personally avoid tap water where possible and get my drinking water directly from a local natural spring that has been tested for purity. My reasoning for this, other than the amazing taste of the natural spring water and the weekly excuse to go to the beautiful location where my well is situated, is that tap water is treated with various chemicals to purify it. Chlorine, fluoride and aluminium are commonly used in the purification process, all of which have come under scrutiny for their possible health and environmental implications. Tap water may also contain elevated levels of copper or lead if the pipes and pipe fittings it passes through contain these minerals. These have the potential to cause heavy-metal toxicity which can have adverse side-effects for the body and mind.

Chlorine's purpose is to kill the bacteria in our tap water, and it does so with great efficiency, to help prevent the spread of bacterial diseases. This is necessary for our water systems to remain free of such disease. A possible issue is that our digestive systems rely on healthy bacteria to function optimally. We don't want those bacteria destroyed by the chlorine in our water. The average human is estimated to have about 100 trillion bacteria living in and on the body. Most of these live in the intestines and are a major part of our immune system. The growth in the food industry of probiotic supplements, drinks and yoghurts to help promote our gut bacteria health, demonstrates our understanding of its importance. A natural, clean, source of drinking water from a tested spring, or bottled provides your bodies nutrient needs without harm to the digestive systems helpful bacteria. Use of a probiotic supplement may also help to restore balance if tap water is your only option.

In a report published in The Lancet Neurology on Neurobehavioural effects of developmental toxicity by Dr Philippe Grandjean and MD Philip J Landrigan, MD, Fluoride is listed as a neurotoxin linked to neurodevelopmental disabilities, including autism, attention-deficit hyperactivity disorder, dyslexia, and other cognitive impairments. We have the ability to protect our teeth now without a need for Fluoride in our drinking water, so we can safely avoid it if we choose.

DEHYDRATION

To self-assess for dehydration, we can check to see if we are thirsty or look at the colour of our urine. We are thirsty if there is any dryness of the lips or mouth, which should be obvious, but I've often found that my clients only notice their mouth dryness when I mention it. I find that when very dehydrated I can even feel dryness in my fingertips, like the leaf-tips of a dried-out plant. Requiring lip-balm regularly for dry lips, without spending time in cold or breezy conditions, would suggest a near constant state of dehydration. Chewing gum may also disguise mouth dryness as saliva is released into the mouth but created from the body's own stored water rather than introducing more. Note that as we age, our thirst sensitivity to dehydration may be reduced i.e. we might not feel thirsty even when semi-dehydrated so we should consider creating a habit of drinking water regularly regardless of thirst.

Some of the water we consume is used to flush waste products from our bodies through urination. Urine colour is a strong indicator of our hydration levels and should be almost clear or straw coloured. A stronger orange colour, and odour, indicates a very high concentration of waste, suggesting that there is less water available to flush through the body. Note that some vitamin supplements can add strong colours to urine. Aim to drink enough water daily i.e., two litres or more, to have clear urine and prevent dry mouth.

Remember that water alone is not enough to rehydrate your body stores. We also require minerals and carbohydrates to allow certain cells to use and hold that water so adding a tiny pinch of natural salt to your water and eating some natural sugars contained in fruit or vegetables will replenish your bodies water store more efficiently. I sometimes dilute one-part orange juice with two parts spring water to rehydrate quickly, especially first thing in the morning after losing fluids through the night.

CONSTIPATION, CONCENTRATION AND CRAVINGS

A steady water intake aids easy movement of waste through the digestive system. When dehydrated, the body prioritises its water usage for other bodily functions and reabsorbs water from waste passing through our intestines. As the waste dries out, it becomes more difficult to pass through our intestines causing constipation. Drinking more water flushes toxins and waste products from the body more quickly and easily. Even mild dehydration affects cognitive function so a balanced water intake can improve mood, prevent headaches, improve memory and concentration.

Cravings for sweet foods is another sign that we may be dehydrated. Our liver keeps a store of sugar, in the form of glucose, to be released into the bloodstream when we need a little extra energy. Dehydration makes it difficult to release this glucose so craving sweetness would naturally drive us to find sweet, juicy fruit that contain natural sugars, vitamins, minerals and a high water-content. In modern times, we have created junk foods that are high in sweetness and sugars but are not nutritious. Without satisfying our nutrient needs, hunger and thirst will remain and may result in overeating, obesity and metabolic disorders such as diabetes.

PERFORMANCE

We can make life easier for ourselves by drinking more water. Dehydration affects our physical performance. Even at 2% dehydration, a low level that would be barely noticeable to us, our endurance and motivation can be reduced. Perceived effort level may increase further during rigorous activity so demanding work seems even harder than it should! Muscle tissue contains approx. 75% water and when dehydrated will become stiffer, tighter and less elastic. This makes movement more difficult so aim to keep your general and athletic performance at a higher level with a steady, adequate intake.

Water can help protect the cartilage in our joints, which is more brittle and susceptible to damage when dried out. Water keeps our body fluids balanced and most of the chemical processes that occur in the body take place in the fluid of the cells. An sufficient daily water intake can also help to keep nasal congestion and headaches at bay.

Singers are, or at least should be, aware of the effect of dehydration on the voice. The vocal folds are naturally moist. Dry them out and they won't vibrate as sweetly as they should. The hoarseness that follows a night out is often as much to do with dehydration as the talking or singing.

2. SLEEP AND REST

"An hour before midnight is worth two after", "A good laugh and a long sleep are the two best cures for everything". "Go to bed on the same day you got up". Irish proverbs.

Kids get cranky when they're tired, and so do we! Sleep is next on my list of healthy habits because of the detrimental effect a lack of sleep has on us within a short space of time. The average person sleeps 7-8 hours per night but since few of us are truly average, this will vary from person to person and depend on activity levels, stress etc. We, like every other creature have a natural cycle or clock, called our circadian rhythm. This rhythm tells us when it is time to sleep or wake.

I shifted my sleep pattern to approx 10pm – 6am several years ago and found it to be of great benefit. My energy levels increased, and my immune system strengthened to a point where I can't remember the last time that I caught a cold, even when those around me are sniffling, coughing and sneezing. Now, the only time I feel myself starting to get even a little sick is when my sleep pattern is disrupted, and then I get run down. An early night or two to catch up on some quality sleep and I'm back to my energetic self again with a strong immunity that can handle whatever comes its way.

ANCESTRAL SLEEP

Humans are generally diurnal creatures, as opposed to nocturnal, meaning we are active during daylight. The ideal time for most of us to sleep is roughly between 10pm and 6am. Our species evolved and then spread out from the warm areas closer to the Equator, where temperatures are suitable for us to survive in our bare, naked and natural state. We lived there for many, many years and became attuned to the daylight and night-time rhythm where it is generally dark between those hours.

Back in our caveman days we would have risen with the sun and maybe stayed awake by the fire past sunset but not for very long. If, in modern times, we had no artificial lights or entertainment to keep us awake, we would probably still go to sleep when it gets dark and would wake when the sun rises. We're designed for this. Our eyelids are thin enough to allow sunlight through when our eyes are closed for that very reason. The increased light levels detected through closed eyes stimulate the brain to wake up.

In the past, we would also naturally have taken a siesta around 2-3pm when sun and heat levels are strongest to avoid over-exposure. Many people today still notice a 3pm "slump" where they feel tired and need a coffee or sugar boost to keep working. A powernap can be the ideal solution to this to give our batteries a quick recharge and help us power through the day.

AYURVEDIC SLEEP

In ayurvedic medicine, 10pm – 2am is said to be under the influence of the Pitta dosha, the energetic dosha of fire, digestion and transformation. Under ayurvedic principles, if we don't get to sleep before this energetic cycle begins, we are likely to get an extra burst of energy, probably the late-night munchies and will find it hard to go to sleep before the pitta phase ends at 2am! Equally, in ayurvedic medicine, the time between 6am and 10am is ruled by kapha dosha i.e. earth and water, and states that if we wake during this phase, we are likely to be more sluggish and tired than if we rise at or before 6am. If your sleep pattern is closer to 12pm – 8am, simply try going to bed and getting up earlier for a few days and allow that to become your normal pattern.

IMPROVE YOUR SLEEP PATTERN

If you have kids and normally get jobs done at night when they are asleep, leave these jobs till morning. Go to bed early and get up earlier, using the extra morning hour or two you've gained to complete them then. You will be fresher, more alert and probably find you can do these jobs more quickly. If you find yourself working nightshifts, use black-out curtains when sleeping during the day to trick your eyes and brain into thinking it is truly night-time. Most importantly, try to find a sleep pattern that works best for you. Always remember to wind down before going to sleep. Mental stimulation of a dramatic, exciting book or tv programme can make it difficult to relax fully so use the hour before bed to calm and set yourself up for a great night's sleep. Soft music and lighting, comfortable pyjamas and sheets, weighted quilts or duvets and gentle meditation to empty the mind are great ways get into a calm, cosy state that is ideal for deep, restful and recuperative sleep so you wake fully refreshed in the morning.

Take power naps during the day. 20 – 30 mins of sleep can recharge and rejuvenate the body and mind, while improving mood just as it does with children. We're the very same. Some things never seem to change.

SLEEP FOR HEALTH

Sleep is more than just an opportunity to recharge our batteries as the body diverts its energy and resources to promoting long-term wellbeing. Much of our growth occurs while we sleep. Proteins are produced to help repair cell damage and, particularly in adolescents and young adults, growth hormones are released to grow new cells and tissues. This explains why teen-agers and babies require extra sleep when they go through growth phases. Immune cells are also produced during sleep to help us fight infection and viruses but when we are tired or run-down, we become more susceptible to disease.

Bed rest is very important when we are sick to aid recovery. Nowa-days, with our hectic lifestyles, we often don't want to stop because of minor illness so we take over-the-counter medications to cover up the symptoms. Simple logic should tell us to listen to our bodies and rest when feeling un-well. In my experience, we can boost our immune systems far more effec-tively and within a day or two through adequate sleep than with any vitamin supplement!

At more extreme levels, exhaustion from sleep deprivation affects concentration and mood and can even lead to hallucination, depression and suicidal thoughts. It increases our cortisol levels (stress hormone) and can even lead to the onset of diabetes. It's not a case of all or nothing with sleep however as minor sleep deprivation still has a negative effect. Losing an hour or two every night for weeks or months, could lead to the more extreme symptoms. Sleeping but not reaching the deeper most recuperative states of sleep due to mental stress or physical discomfort can have a dramatic effect too. Quality and quantity count.

SLEEP FOR PRODUCTIVITY

A well-rested mind can concentrate better when problem-solving or studying new information. It is also thought that, during sleep, our short-term memory is converted to long-term memory so that we can remember it in fu-ture. Staying up late to study when already tired appears to be inefficient and counterproductive overall. It may work well in the hours or days leading up to an exam but if we will need that information down the line, in our profes-sions, this approach will not work for us. Going to sleep earlier and studying while fresh and alert should be more effective. Improved concentration in general makes us more efficient and less likely to make mistakes.

CHOOSING YOUR MATTRESS
You will, or at least, you should spend about 1/3 of your life in bed so buy a quality mattress. If you can, test it before you buy. In the shop take time to lie on it, in every position you may sleep in to make sure it's comfortable and supportive. If you find you had a great nights' sleep at a hotel, check the brand of the mattress and buy one for yourself. Very soft memory foam mattresses have been advertised as beneficial for spinal health. I would disagree with this in general as a soft mattress allows us to sink into poor postural positions. However, if you already have excessive spinal curvatures or skeletal deformities that cannot be corrected with treatment, you may need a soft mattress to accommodate your body comfortably. Invest a little extra money in quality bedsheets with a high thread count. They will probably last longer than cheaper alternatives, so they won't cost you more, long-term, and they'll feel so much more comfortable, helping you achieve quality sleep.

Visit highestpotential.ie for more sleeping tips and guided sleep meditations.

3. EXERCISE AND FITNESS
We get one body to last us a lifetime. We must care for it if it is to serve us well.

We've already mentioned several benefits of owning a fitter body, but some are worth mentioning again. We can engage in many more activities and enjoy higher energy levels. We can sleep more soundly and help protect our cardiovascular system. We can increase serotonin levels and general feel-good-factor. We can help prevent obesity and its related diseases. We can improve our posture, physique and self-confidence levels. We can use our fitness to go places we could not otherwise manage.

The body is, in lots of ways like a vehicle we use to travel through life. When it is well serviced, driven with care and properly fuelled, it can be reliable, efficient and fun to drive for many years. The potential for fitness of the human body is astounding. Look at the variety of sportspeople around the world from distance runners to sprinters, powerlifters, gymnasts, swimmers, long-jumpers, high-jumpers etc., to scratch the surface of what is possible for our species. These athletes, competing at the Olympic level, demonstrate the top end of the fitness spectrum.

Perhaps you have the potential to reach such a level or maybe your expectations are more modest. But, if another human can run a marathon, 26.2 miles or 42 kilometres, in just over two hours, couldn't most of us expect to be able to walk or even jog comfortably for 30 minutes at our own pace? If a powerlifter can lift objects several times his or her own weight, surely the ability to lift our own bodies out of chairs, bed or up a flight of stairs with ease is possible for the average human. If a gymnast can jump, somersault, roll, cartwheel and do handstands, isn't day-to-day functional movement i.e. bending, twisting and reaching well within the realms of possibility? If a bodybuilder can sculpt a physique to the most minute detail, surely a regular person can improve posture, muscle-tone and body-fat levels. An expectation of functional fitness and wellness should be, I believe, our norm.

USE IT OR LOSE IT

The human body is so efficient that it will only maintain the body in a condition that is required regularly. This means that if we don't use our strength, we become weak. If we don't use our flexibility, we become stiff. If we don't use our stamina, we lose the capacity for endurance. If we don't use good posture, we lose that too. Moving the body daily, in ways that keep it tuned up and highly efficient, is necessary to enjoy physical wellbeing. 30 minutes per day is recommended and should include a variety of exercises including walking, swimming, stretching exercises such as yoga and strength training.

We will cover this in more detail in the "Body Matters" section.

REPAIR WORK

After 15 years in clinic practice, I must mention the value of treating our injuries for genuine physical wellbeing. In my experience, if an ache or pain lasts more than two weeks or is recurring even once or twice per year, it needs a helping hand. This applies to back pain, headaches, muscle strains and many joint pains that are diagnosed as arthritis. Carrying injuries is unnecessary for most and is an indication of a lack of self-care. I find that most injuries are resolved within 3-5 sessions. If not, we are well on our way to restoring health or have identified an issue that needs to be treated by another form of therapy. If you have an ongoing injury, seek out assistance. If one form of treatment isn't working, find another.

Go to www.highestpotential.ie for extra links and videos.

4. MEDITATION MINDFULNESS AND POSITIVE THINKING

MEDITATION

I began practicing meditation at the age of thirty having realised that despite the benefits of eating well, exercising regularly and striving for a work-life balance, I was still more stressed than I would have liked. Meditation has proved to be one of the most health-improving and life-changing habits I have ever encountered. As with other forms of fitness, I find it's a case of "use it or lose it", so regular practice is now and always will be part of my life to enjoy greater peace, contentment, self-awareness and understanding.

The best description I have heard about the "right" way to meditate stated that, "Meditation is a state rather than an act". In this meditative state, we are more centred, focused, present, observant, peaceful and generally more loving. Whatever we do to help us achieve this state can be called meditative practice and it can be achieved through various means. These can include sitting, breathing, chanting, visualisations, walking, listening to music, engaging in art, spending time in nature or any means that works for you.

I feel that this explanation makes meditation far more accessible to everyone by bringing a flexibility and range to how it can be enjoyed, rather than tying us to a specific form of practice. There are also quite disciplined practices that have been developed over hundreds, perhaps thousands of years, to reach more profound and deeper meditative states. I'll leave those to the most dedicated practitioners as not everyone can incorporate them into their lives. A freer approach to meditation allows all to enjoy its benefits.

WHERE TO MEDIDATE?

It can helpful to create a pleasant, calm space for meditation in a spare room or quiet spot in your garden. We can also go to a local park or nature spot. However, most of my meditative practice and I would say the most beneficial, is done sitting up on my bed before I go to sleep. This allows me to let go of any stress I might have picked up during the day, calm my busy mind and sleep more soundly. Sometimes I'll practice in the morning to set a calmer and more positive tone for the day. Occasionally I'll practice outside in a natural space like the beach, in the woods or on a mountain peak during a hike. I've often done it without anybody else even noticing on planes, trains, buses, in airports and stations by sitting comfortably, closing my eyes, breathing gently and going inward.

CAN ANYBODY DO IT?

I believe that the meditative state is natural to us but that the mind often distracts us from this state of being. It does so by imagining reasons to not be peaceful and content. If habitually distracted by worrisome thoughts, finding ways to let them go and become centred and balanced again, can restore that calm state once more. Without the distractions of fears, judgements and expectations, we can gain a clearer perspective and a more positive viewpoint. I have often found in my practices, insights "pop up" that I can carry into my daily life to use when situations trigger my mind to distract me once more.

I should clarify that I am not always calm, peaceful and present, but I experience these far more often than I would without regular meditation. I am also now more acutely aware of times when I become distracted as the accompanying stress, tension or negativity differs so much from a caring and peaceful state. Stress sticks out like a sore thumb now where before it was probably my default setting. This contrast encourages me to identify the distraction and then attempt to resolve it.

A SIMPLE PRACTICE

Meditation is often practiced sitting or lying in a peaceful space with minimal disturbance, to delve into deeper levels of our consciousness. Physical comfort while practicing is important as pain may distract the mind from ease. I personally prefer to use earplugs when I practice at home so that I hear less noise around me.

Begin with a body-scan. Feel each body-part internally from the toes, right up to the top of the head. Slowly bring attention to each area, notice any tension and then let it go. Then bring awareness to the breath, the diaphragm which is under the front of the ribcage, and the belly. Allow the breath to flow with ease. Observe it and all the sensations that come with the breath.

Health Matters

When thoughts cross your mind that distract you from the sensations in your body and observation of the breath, acknowledge them but choose to deal with them after you finish your practice. This will allow you to stay more present and take a break from the busyness of life. Spend as long as you are comfortable in this practice. I would recommend starting with 5-minute sessions, then work your way to 20-minutes or more. Daily short practices can be far more effective than one long session each week. There are many free guided meditations and relaxing music tracks available on YouTube and online sites to help you reach such calm states.

Remember that for most of our species evolution, we didn't have mortgages, job-deadlines, how we looked in the mirror or Instagram likes to worry about. By temporarily stepping back from the outside world, we can more easily access what we could call our inner presence. At the deeper levels of the meditative experience, we may even be able to let go of our sense of having an individual consciousness, to feel and know that everything is part of one greater consciousness.

MINDFULNESS

Mindfulness has become one of the buzz words of recent times among those seeking wellness. Mindfulness is a new term for an old concept, in fact it has been practiced for many years. It is often used by people who never even heard of the term! Mindfulness refers in particular to being present, non-judgemental and compassionate. It allows us to become more aware of our feelings, sensations and thoughts and to pay full attention to our current experience without the distraction of being somewhere else in our heads. Put simply, it means tuning in to our senses, our feelings and our thoughts. Through mindful living we can fully experience each moment and therefore life itself. What is a life fully lived, if not many moments fully experienced?

MINDFUL PRACTICE

You can do this right now by scanning through your body to notice your physical sensations. How do your feet feel in your shoes, socks or bare? What position or posture is your body in? Are you seated, standing or lying and how does that feel? Is there tension or relaxation in the muscles of your body or face? Notice the temperature of the air around you and any breeze or draught. Notice the smells, perhaps of the book you're holding, food or flowers, cut grass or perfume. Listen for the sounds of nature, voices, machinery or even your own breath.

Become aware of the emotions you feel right now in this moment and notice any change that comes simply from bringing attention to them. Listen to your inner voice as it reads these words or the sound of mine. Look at the thoughts and memories that arise as you become more mindful. Are they pleasant, constructive and beneficial to you or something else? This self-assessment is about identifying where we are at in our experience. Change may or may not come about as a result, but non-judgemental acceptance of our current reality is often a consequence of the practice of mindfulness.

To those focused on using meditation to let go of the self and reach beyond the human experience, these moments may seem inconsequential but if our lives and our experiences do indeed have purpose, as I believe they do, mindfulness is a gift through which we can embrace them. Mindfulness when eating intensifies the flavours, textures and aromas of our food by focusing our attention. Mindfulness when holding a conversation helps us to listen fully and hear what is being said. It can also help us to pick up more of what is being expressed through subtle cues of facial expression and tone of voice. Mindfulness can certainly help us to clarify what we want to say, before we speak.

Such focused awareness while working can improve our efficiency and the quality of our work. When studying we are more likely to understand and retain information if totally focused on it. Mindfulness when exercising improves coordination, balance, posture and awareness of how the body feels. We then know to ease off if we are pushing it too hard and risking injury. When driving mindfully we will be more conscientious towards other drivers and more aware of hazards around us. If fully present when looking at art or scenery, colours and shades often appear more vibrant and detailed. When listening to music or nature sounds, we can become more immersed in them to truly appreciate their beauty.

BALANCING MINDFULNESS WITH DISTRACTION

I find that a mindful state is easier to achieve when we feel good and our environment is pleasant. It is not so easy when we are uncomfortable, in pain or in an unpleasant and stressful environment, which is why many of us distract ourselves to avoid the unpleasantness of our lives. Physical pain gives a good example of this. Many people tend to feel the pain of an injury more intensely at bedtime when no longer distracted by the activities of daily life.

We sometimes relieve our mental and emotional discomfort in the very same way by focusing on something other than where we are or how we are feeling. These distractions could come in the form of work, family responsibilities, hobbies, social media or other forms of entertainment. These can keep us busy from morning till night, so we don't really have time to deal with what's going on inside. Alternatively drugs and alcohol may numb us to avoid or help us to escape our reality.

If you find being present uncomfortable, there may be areas in your life that need some attention to restore balance. Once you have noticed discomfort, identified the cause and found a solution or a plan to bring about a resolution, mindfulness might need to be balanced with distraction. You may find it necessary to 'take your mind off' your issues while you follow a programme or plan and healing takes place. It's the equivalent of post-surgery self-care where we alleviate pain as we heal. Such alleviation may include prescription painkillers, antidepressants or other prescribed medications in more extreme cases. For some, a distraction will suffice i.e. spending time with friends to help get you through a tough emotional experience, taking on a new hobby to occupy your mind, reading or watching something enjoyable.

In such cases distraction can be an aid to our wellbeing as there is nothing extra to be gained from focusing on and intensifying the pain while we heal. Healing is a process and time is an essential part of that process. There is no need to be a martyr. Extreme and unnecessary suffering will not make us more spiritual, enlightened or wise! I would say the wisest course of action is to be kind, gentle and caring toward yourself to heal far more quickly. Allow the healing and growth process to be pleasant where possible.

POSITIVE THINKING

"The glass is half full.", "Look on the bright side", "Hope for the best".

Wouldn't it be nice to instinctively see the positives in life? I can vouch for this as somebody who has worked on developing and applying a more positive outlook that makes my life more pleasant and more productive. The concept of positive thinking is simple and yet isn't always easy in practice. Finding the positive in a situation may be challenging, if we're not used to thinking that way. Even if we can find it, sometimes it's hard to focus only on the silver lining. When worrying about the future and so many possible outcomes that we don't want to become real, it can be difficult to ignore them in favour of the positives.

Our life experiences and our most prominent influencers including family, friends, scholastic and religious educators shape our world view. These program our tendency towards positive or negative thinking. Our own internal voice and thought processes strengthen this viewpoint until it appears true. We develop a story of how life is and then we live our lives within that story line. The truth, as I would see it, is that life contains many possibilities, pleasant and unpleasant, desirable and undesirable. We may see them as fair or unfair, lucky or unlucky depending on our perspective or how we choose to look at them.

Should we choose to, we can trust that everything is ok, even if it is unpleasant or undesirable. We can believe that life happens for us and not to us. Instead of seeing failure when we don't achieve a goal, we can see various degrees of success. We can accept that every experience is a new addition to our overall life-experience and makes us a little wiser.

Applying such mantras to past scenarios that we believed were mistakes or unlucky can help us to resolve them but also makes it easier to adopt a more positive mindset in the present when faced with challenges.

FAITH

A little faith can help us to see the glass as half-full and some trust helps us to feel supported. I don't necessarily mean religious faith, although many gain great solace from it, but a belief in something that can override our doubts and fears. This can include faith in ourselves, our value to this world and our ability to achieve our goals. It could be faith in other people to help us when we need it. Perhaps faith in our society as a whole to pull together and work for a common good. Maybe it's faith in a system, program or plan that, when followed, will achieve the desired result. It could also mean having faith in a god, a divine plan, universal power or greater consciousness to guide us when lost, catch us when we fall and love us even when we don't feel worthy of it.

Without faith of some sort, we could find that we are at odds with ourselves, other people and our world. We can struggle with acceptance of political and societal structures and even with the biggest question of all i.e. "why are we here?". Without faith we could feel alone in a universe where lots is wrong and we feel powerless to make it right. I feel that I should stress here that I'm not encouraging a blind faith in any religion or organisation. Religions are man-made and, while founded initially to encourage faith and connection to something greater, often, if not always become corrupted in part by human weaknesses. All organisations, religious or otherwise are run by humans and as such are subject to human weaknesses and error. I am suggesting cultivating an underlying faith in ourselves, humanity or divinity, whatever brings you a sense of connection and security.

I personally find that faith in all three, gives me more scope to think and feel more positively about my life and world. I work on these regularly to feed that faith by looking for proof in my life where my strengths, other people and divine intervention were there when I needed them. Sometimes I could see that evidence immediately and at other times it was revealed through hindsight.

Refer to the chapter on "Developing Mental Fitness" for more on positive thinking.

Visit www.highestpotential.ie or highest potential on Youtube for more links and information on meditation and mindfulness.

5. FOOD AND NUTRITION
Food and nutrition are 5th on my top 5 list of healthy habits. There is a lot of information worth considering when choosing what to put in our mouths, so I've decided to dedicate the next chapter in its entirety to this topic.

Health Matters

Chapter 7

Food and Nutrition

"Let food be thy medicine and let medicine be thy food", Hippocrates

Food plays a significant role in our lives. It can give us instant pleasure and the opportunity to socialize with friends, have some quality time with family and maybe even start a new romance on a dinner date. Aside from these, food has some essential functions that can sometimes be forgotten about. It provides us with the energy we need to move and think. Food gives us the materials we need to grow and repair our cells. From the foods we eat, our bodies make hormones that are very much involved in how we feel. We have many choices to make each day about what we should eat, how we should eat and even when we should eat. In this chapter we'll look for some clarity around why certain foods habits are more beneficial than others.

Food choice can add greatly to our state of wellbeing but also has the ability to cause illness. Diets are ten-a-penny and there is no 'one size fits all' so I won't even attempt to give you a specific diet to follow. I will admit that, of all theories I've come across, eating in a manner close to how our ancestors did resonates most with me. The aim here is to help you develop a healthy relationship with food through a greater awareness of what food does for us. I hope this section will make you more conscious of what you eat and why, ultimately giving you more power to choose what will work best for you.

WE ARE WHAT WE EAT

There is so much more to this saying than "eat fat, get fat". Food must create your body before that same food fuels it. Your body is being created piece by piece every day from the foods you eat. What you eat today becomes part of your skin, hair, muscles, bones, blood and more. The average adult is made of roughly 50 trillion cells. Apart from a small percentage of cells such as heart muscle and some brain cells that can last a lifetime, most of the cells in our bodies are replaced with new ones on a regular basis. Your body is not the age your birth-certificate says it is. Much of you is newly formed from the food you ate in recent days, weeks and months.

75

Our bodies grow about 200 – 300 billion new cells every day, to take over from the cells that have become damaged or can no longer function efficiently. These new cells make up our physical body, as we are now. To be formed, these cells require many nutrients which we could think of as raw materials or building blocks. These include water, proteins, fats, carbohydrates, and a variety of vitamins and minerals. A healthy diet containing an assortment of natural foods, will provide a variety of high quality raw materials needed for better built and more efficient cells, tissues and organs.

I like to compare this process to a house where we replace everything in it, over time, when worn-out or broken. Imagine changing a light bulb here, a door handle there, a chair, tv, floor tile, brick, coat of paint etc., with newer versions. If we use high quality products, made from top-quality materials, our house and everything in it will be likely to look great and work as we wish. We can count on our new tv to switch on and tune in, our chair to hold us comfortably when we sit on it and our doors to open and close easily. We'll love our home and spending time in it. If we use inferior materials, our house won't look so good, our appliances won't work so well and will be more likely to break down sooner. Home won't be a particularly nice place to live or somewhere we can be proud of.

Now apply this to the human body and you get a clearer picture of what food does for us. Food replaces your current stardust with new stardust. It does provide us with energy to think and move and some flushes waste from the body, but it also makes new skin, hair, nails, muscle, bone, blood, hormones, etc. That's how amazing your body is. It turns food into you. The quality of your body can only be as good as the materials you use. Ask yourself each time you are about to eat something, "Do I want this to become part of me?" because it will. This is your choice to make.

YOUTHFULNESS AND DIET

Food and fresh water can be the best anti-aging products you will ever buy. We've already discussed how our new cells are made from the foods we eat, and their quality is largely determined by our nutrient supply. As such, the current condition of our skin, hair, muscles, brain tissue etc. is influenced by the food we've recently eaten. We typically associate aging with degeneration of bodily functions and link youthfulness to a body that functions at a relatively high level i.e. strong, agile, energetic and mentally sharp. Those who are sound of body and mind at any age can enjoy more of the benefits of youth. Who doesn't want to look and feel younger?

Now, if we could just keep making new and fully functional cells to replace the old ones, we could potentially live forever and never age. It's not that simple for lots of reasons, but we might be able to slow the process a bit and maintain our more youthful attributes a little longer. As time passes, when a cell divides to create a new one, the cell "copy" loses a little of its quality compared to the previous one it replaced. Stress, poor nutrition and environmental factors can also weaken our cells. Those of you mature enough might remember the older printers or ink stamps where the first copy was very clear but as the ink ran out, they became more faded. For us, this "fading" of our cell copies means that bones become less dense and muscle cells become weaker, so we lose strength among other things. Also, as we get older, not all cells are replaced as quickly as they are lost. As their numbers reduce, our memory and cognitive functions can be affected.

Let's say hypothetically, that a muscle cell lasts on average for one year before it becomes worn out and needs to be replaced. Let's pretend also that after 80 replacements, the muscle cell copy is so "faded" and jaded that it is unable to function well. After 80 years, a body full of such muscle cells would be weak, immobile and prone to injury. Now, let's imagine a person with a nutritionally poor diet whose body can only make muscle cells of an inferior quality. Due to their condition each muscle cell might only last, we'll say, nine months or 25% less, before becoming worn-out and in need of re-placement. In such a situation, they would need to renew their muscle cells 80 times over 60 years. At the tender age of 60, they would find themselves in the condition of a typical 80-year-old.

If, on the other hand, we took a person with a high-nutrient diet and well developed and fed muscle cells, we would see a far better scenario. If their cells could last 15 months or 25% longer than average, it would take 100 years for their cells to divide 80 times. Therefore, at the ripe age of 100, their muscles would have the qualities of a typical 80-year-old or an unhealthy 60-year-old. It seems that a healthy supply of proteins, essential fatty acids, B-vitamins and antioxidants can help to heal and repair both the cell structure and the DNA strands that provide the blue-print for how each cell is made and should work. Eating fruit, veg, nuts, seeds, wholegrains, oily fish and lean meats can help provide these truly anti-aging nutrients.

While the above-mentioned lifespan of muscle cells is not accurate, as they are estimated to last somewhere between 10 to 15 years, it gives you a sense of how the body renews itself over time and shows how we can affect our aging through food choices.

We can even roll back the body-clock when we switch to an active, healthy lifestyle as we stimulate the body to adapt to our extra activity and then nourish it with all it needs to transform itself. I have seen many gym clients do this by providing the body with the nutrients it needs to create healthier new cells. Combined with exercise to tone muscles, improve posture and burn excess bodyfat as fuel, they looked and felt years younger within months. Remember this when you are buying and eating your food today, tomorrow, next week, month and next year. What we eat today will become part of us, possibly for the rest of our lives! No face-cream or anti-aging gimmick, that I know of, can offer the same results.

EATING FOR HEALTH

Food can play a significant role in our wellbeing, feel-good-factor and how we look. We can help to stabilize our blood sugar and therefore energy levels through food choices to enjoy greater health. Sweet, sugary foods and carbohydrates that are broken down to simple sugars rapidly in the stomach will enter the blood stream more quickly. This may cause a spike in blood sugar levels. Our body wants to regulate its blood sugar levels, so it releases insulin to pull the excess sugar from our blood stream. There are several possible destinations for this sugar.

Firstly, insulin pulls sugar into our muscles' glycogen stores, so they have fuel ready for our next high-intensity activity. If we haven't emptied our muscles' energy stores recently through high-intensity exercise, they will still be full and have no room available for this sugar. Next up, insulin will store some sugar as glycogen in the liver, again if there's room in the livers' glycogen storage cells. If both our muscle and liver stores are already full, the sugar pulled from our bloodstream must be stored as fat. This explains why regular high-intensity exercise like weight training, aerobics, boxing and sprinting are so effective at reducing our body-fat levels i.e. after these activities, the sugars we eat are more likely go into our now empty muscle stores rather than filling our fat cells.

Regulating our blood sugar levels by eating a high-fibre and high water-content, vegetable-based diet can have dramatic effects on bodyfat levels. Combining these with proteins such as beans, nuts, seeds and lentils, fish, eggs or lean meat ensures a slow and steady digestion of naturally occurring sugars. It also provides a high variety of vitamins and minerals. A major hidden bonus and something that's only becoming better understood in recent years, is the effect of a plant-based diet on our microbiome i.e., the bacteria that live on and within our bodies. Our gut is filled with bacteria, mostly helpful, that are involved in digestion and play a big part in development of our immune system. A healthy diet nourishes us but also feeds our helpful bacteria. There is also some suggestion that the bacteria within us can play a role in how we store our food as bodyfat.

Limiting our refined sugar intake protects our teeth longer. Sugar feeds bacteria in the mouth which produce tooth dissolving acids. If we want to keep our pearly whites for longer, we must act when we're younger. It has also been suggested that sugar in the bloodstream may attach to proteins that cause skin to lose its elasticity, causing more wrinkles and premature aging. How many more reasons do we need to eat a wide variety of deliciously simple, natural foods and use our bodies, in ways we enjoy, to keep them looking and feeling great?

NUTRITION STARTS IN THE TROLLEY

Aside from the select few that can grow all their own food, most of us rely on supermarkets and shops for food. What we put in our shopping trolleys and baskets will form the bulk of our diets. To make healthy eating easier for us and avoid self-sabotage, I would suggest eating before shopping. If hungry, we are more likely to reach for high-energy, convenience foods than healthier options that need some preparation. Make a list before going to the shops, while there is no temptation from less healthy options, and stick to it. Avoid those junk-food aisles completely if possible or just be disciplined until you are out the door.

Buy foods that are easy to prepare for situations when time is limitedand you need fast food. Tupperware containers can be a healthy eater's best friend, allowing you to prepare good food for when you're on the go. Create a fruit, veg and nut counter in your kitchen so that these are within easy reach and never out of sight. I did this recently and I'm eating more of these as a result. It's like having a sweet counter only better! Because they're in full view, it also means that they don't get a chance to spoil so I'm not wasting money on them.

Keeping the foods that you know you don't want to eat out of your home saves you the hassle of temptation. If we get a sudden craving and junk is readily available, we'll have it eaten before we even think about it. If we must go somewhere else to buy it, we'll probably just eat the healthy option instead and feel much better as a result.

WHAT ABOUT THE FLAVOUR?

Initially, switching from sugar-dense, high-salt, fatty and flavour-enhanced processed foods to simpler, more natural foods can seem like we are sacrificing flavour for health. We just don't get the same kick from it. This happens when our taste buds are already desensitized by overexposure to excessive sugars, salts and flavour enhancers, becoming unable to appreciate the full flavour of natural food. The lifespan of taste bud cells is about ten days to two weeks. After eating naturally for such time, our taste buds are replaced by fresh, unaffected ones. At this point we can truly appreciate how great real food tastes and could even find artificial flavours overpowering and sickly sweet. 'Diets' are often seen as arduous tasks that require strict discipline, but this couldn't be further from the truth. There are so many pleasant tasting herbs, spices and natural flavours available that healthy eating can be very satisfying and enjoyable. Believe it or not, you can love your healthy food even more if you give it a chance!

COMFORT EATING

Many of us are inclined to comfort eat when feeling low i.e., low in energy, low in mood or both. It's all too easy to get caught on a rollercoaster of highs and lows. Understanding this process can empower us to put on the breaks and get off the ride.

As discussed earlier, one of our primary drives is to feel good and, since taste is one of our 5 senses that we can instantly please, food is a handy way to give ourselves an instant buzz! There's more to the impulse to tuck into a tub of ice-cream, the greasy burger or box of chocolates than the pleasurable taste. Eating fats and carbohydrates can quickly change brain chemistry, producing opioids, the same chemicals as those provided by narcotic drugs, and stimulating extra serotonin, a feel-good hormone, production.

When stressed, emotionally or physically, our bodies will produce cortisol, often referred to as the stress hormone. Cortisol increases our appetite and has an effect of helping the body create more mature fat cells in the abdomen and under the skin. In the distant past, when human's stressors were immediate life-threatening animal dangers or longer-term struggles such as famine, the trigger to overeat when food was available could help us to survive. If we found food during a famine, we would have gorged on it, consuming as many calories as possible to nourish us until we found our next meal. This let us build an energy reserve to help us survive through the famine. For our survival, stress made us eat more and then store the extra calories as fat.

Overeating was an integral part of our survival mechanism. The problem today is that we often go into our survival mode without any genuine life-threatening situation. The imagination brain can dream up reasons to be nervous and trigger our stress response. In modern times, we can find ourselves in a near-constant stressed state but without the physical exertion of escaping danger or the effort of having to go hunt and gather food. Combine this lack of activity with an almost limitless supply of high saturated fat and refined sugar foods available for a feel-good kick and it's not surprising we would consume far more energy-dense foods than we actually need to live on.

The gorging that once helped us to survive, may now deprive us of nutrients, fill our fat cells, upset the body's natural mineral balance and create disease and more stress. We can find ourselves caught in a vicious cycle as the food-kick from junk-food is short-lived and followed soon after by a blood sugar and energy slump. For some, overeating brings guilt and shame for our lack of discipline to avoid such food or a sense of embarrassment at our own body if we believe we are already 'out of shape'. These only add to the mental and emotional stress that triggered the overeating in the first place!

ALTERNATIVE MOOD-BOOSTERS

A far more effective solution, to avoid the need to use junk food for a mood boost, is to engage in other mood-improving measures. This creates an effective cycle of behaviour and wellbeing. Our bodies reward us with feel-good hormones when we engage in activities that are beneficial for our health and long-term survival. Being well rested and alert would have given us a better chance of surviving back in our caveman days so a regular sleep pattern, ideally 10pm to 6am, was and still is very beneficial. Some daily exposure to sunlight, especially in winter months increases vitamin D production and grants us the mood-enhancing effects of these golden rays. I'm sure this doesn't surprise you as we've all seen the effect of a sunny day on the faces and friendliness levels of the people around us.

Get exercise high! Serotonin, one of our top feel-good hormones is released during exercise and for some time after. This has been linked to reductions in depression levels. Again, no surprise to hear that we feel good after a walk, hike or workout. Once, the fitness gained from the daily physical exertion of walking, foraging, climbing and hunting for food was a key factor in the survival of humans before supermarkets, refrigerators and cupboards. If we didn't move ourselves then we starved. The fitter we were, the better chance we had of finding and eating a wider variety of good foods and living longer. A stronger, fitter body was more likely to escape and survive an attack too. Many people that engage in exercise or sports love the buzz that follows for hours or days afterwards. Tap into that buzz, to avoid the need for a comfort eating buzz, with some regular exercise and feel the difference. If starting back into exercise, work at your own pace and build your fitness slowly.

Find somebody or something to care about. Humans relied heavily on intelligence and their communities to survive. Caring about each other meant we would work together, combining our individual skills to protect ourselves, find food and care for our sick until healthy again. The feel-good-factor that comes from helping each other out, being part of a group and feeling affection towards others are just as real today as they were in our past. Making those part of our life can give us a dose of daily mood-boosters.

Get entertained. Put on some upbeat music that makes you want to tap your feet and move your body. With Spotify, Youtube and various other music platforms, we can access music from all genres and decades. Pick your favourite songs that bring you back to good times or modern ones that pull you up to into a happier state. Watch some stand-up comedy or funny programmes and movies to get the joy that comes from laughter and pressure release of taking life a little less seriously. All the above methods can be used to replace the urge to comfort eat and still get the feel-good buzz we all need. If these methods are brought into our daily/weekly routine, we should find the overeating urge goes as we become fitter, healthier and happier.

90-10 RULE

Sure, we can survive for quite a while on artificially processed foods that we know are laden with sugars, salts and fats. Certainly, a little of them will not do us any great harm as a healthy body can tolerate them. Remember that this is only because an abundance of healthy foods may counteract the effects of a little of the others. We shouldn't kid ourselves by thinking that junk food belongs to a healthy diet. Junk is junk. If you want to give your body the healthy chance it deserves, I'd suggest aiming for at least 90% natural, minimally processed and healthy foods. Weigh that against the other 10% junk and we're operating at a healthy 80% overall. That gives us far better odds of enjoying health and wellbeing.

HUNGER GAMES

Food should provide us with all the nutrients we require such as proteins, carbohydrates, fats, water, vitamins and minerals. We need these to build and provide energy for every cell in the body while also supporting their day to day function. Hunger is our body's way of driving us to take in those nutrients by eating food. If we do not eat, or if we eat food that is lacking in essential nutrients, we will remain hungry until our nutrient need is satisfied. I believe that many of us overeat due to poor nutrient quality in our choice of foods. It is possible to eat very large amounts of junk foods, every day, without getting all the nutrients we need for optimum health. This can leave us almost constantly hungry as the body craves nutrition. We will also become unwell as the body struggles to process the unhealthy foods and probably become overweight as the extra calories are stored as bodyfat.

WHEN TO EAT

There are many guidelines and opinions on when we should eat. Professed for years as the ideal approach to healthy eating, "three square meals a day" is said to have begun during the industrial revolution to keep manual worker's energy levels up but also to standardise food breaks for factory productivity. If every worker was to go for food at various times, a production line might never have a full complement of workers. If they left at the same time and returned together, work could go on unhindered. Intermittent fasting, where all meals are eaten within an 8-hour period e.g. 12 noon to 8pm, has gained popularity recently claiming benefits such as helping muscle building, fat burning, reversing type 2 diabetes and more.

Then we have the proponents of the 'little and often' approach, aiming for 4 to 6 smaller meals per day rather than fewer large ones. Some even suggest that we should only eat one large meal a day which would reduce our overall food intake and perhaps help with weight loss. There are studies showing the benefits of each of these approaches so rather than focusing on one, we'll look at how you can make your mealtimes work for you. I would say, above all else, to choose the eating pattern that works best for you in relation to your energy levels, the quality of the food you will eat and what is workable within your daily schedule.

Our stomach organ is the same size in the morning, afternoon and evening and has the same volume of digestive juices available to break down our food. Overloading the stomach with a huge meal at any one time could make it harder for digestive juices to break down our food. We can also find ourselves quite tired following a large meal as the body diverts extra blood flow to the digestive system to absorb nutrients. I know I always am after Christmas dinner! This should be avoided at any time when we need to be active and alert immediately after a meal.

Increasing our stomach's gastric capacity i.e., making our stomach organ bigger, by regularly filling it to its maximum may lead us to feeling dissatisfied with a healthy portion size. As the natural "I'm full, stop eating" response becomes desensitised, we can then find ourselves going for the larger portion or seconds, just to feel like we've eaten enough. For that reason, if portion size is out of control, eating smaller but more regular meals will allow overall stomach capacity to reduce. This approach can also help to stabilise our blood sugar and energy levels. It can also help us to be more selective of our food choices as, with smaller fasting times of 3 hours or so, we are less likely to get very hungry and reach for a quick but unhealthy fix. We could also help prevent 'hanger' from taking us over!

For those that simply cannot eat first thing in the morning until the stomach 'wakes up', or last thing at night if it affects quality of sleep, intermittent fasting might be ideal solution. However, with fasting, more consideration to quality and variety will be required to ensure maximum nutrition. As with all healthy diets, planning and food preparation is key to this. Tupperware and easy-to-prepare snacks and meals are your best allies to creating consistently good habits and give you more control over your dietary needs.

food and nutrition

Chrono-nutrition (time-based eating) is a relatively new term but one that ties in with the Ayurvedic approach, a form of Indian medicine that has been practiced and developed over thousands of years. Both are based on the idea that the human body has natural rhythms and cycles during which it performs various processes within the body. Ayurveda suggests that the hours between 10am and 2pm are influenced by the Pitta dosha (the elements of fire and water). Ayurveda states that during these hours our digestive powers are at their highest. Interestingly, proponents of Chrono-nutrition believe that those who eat their large meals early in the day are less likely to experience obesity, compared to those who eat the same calories but later in the day.

MOST IMPORTANT MEAL OF THE DAY

As it can take a little time for our digestive system to "wake up" in the morning, a lighter breakfast may suit best. Drinking a glass of room temperature water, with some lemon juice if you choose, when you wake can gently stimulate the stomachs digestive enzymes to prepare it for the first meal. If exercising in the morning, consider waiting until after to eat solid food and avoid stomach cramps. Try to eat 2-3 hours before exercise, if later in the day. Aim to have your last meal 2-3 hours before sleep so much of the food's digestion is complete. When you wake, you will want to eat breakfast reasonably early and start the day on the right track. If you find you are hungry late in the day, it may mean that you didn't eat enough earlier, or that you have created a habit that you need to change.

I aim to eat some protein in most meals, especially when actively exercising. If I want my body to develop more strength or stamina, it needs the materials to do so. I personally aim for about 30 grams per meal but that will vary according to your body weight, lifestyle and fitness goals. I get my protein mostly from fish and nuts but do eat a little meat. There are many theories on what we need to survive, grow muscle, excel at sports and for wellbeing. I recommend trial and error to find what works best for your body. I also include healthy fats such as those found in nuts, seeds, oily fish and some vegetables and carbohydrates from rice, corn, fruit and vegetables. As our entire meal is digested together, the presence of protein and fats will slow the digestion of sugars for a more gradual release of sugars into our bloodstream. Blood sugar balance is good! I would highly recommend that you contact a nutritionist for a tailor-made program to suit your lifestyle, goals and nutritional needs.

HOW TO EAT?

How common is it for us to be so busy or distracted by TV, reading, smartphones or conversation that we become totally unaware of the pleasure of eating? To get more gratification from our food, we can be more mindful as we dine. This lets us focus our attention on the sensations provided by two of our primary senses, taste and smell. Dark dining has become popular in restaurants around the world, where customers eat in complete darkness and often in silence. By removing the distractions of sight and sound more attention is paid to the smell and taste, enhancing the experience.

Mindfulness includes taking longer to chew our food, 20 - 30 times per mouthful. This allows us to appreciate flavours fully while ensuring food is broken down into easily digestible small pieces, aiding our stomach's digestive juices. Chewing also produces salivary amylase, an enzyme which starts digestion of the sugars in our foods. Taking more time to eat our meals increases the likelihood that we'll stop when we have had enough, rather than realising when it's too late that we have overeaten. Taking time to eat more slowly with a little grace may also make you a more appealing dinner date!

For links to more on this, go to www.highestpotential.ie

EVERYTHING IN MODERATION?

There are many slogans and phrases bounced around in health and wellness circles. 'Everything in moderation' is one of these, suggesting that we can eat or drink a little of everything and still enjoy good health. There is some truth to this, but only in that some junk food will be tolerated by the body as small part of a healthy diet. It does not mean that we can eat a little of everything available. You see, there is an abundance of heavily processed food more readily available in supermarkets, restaurants and corner shops than simple healthy wholefoods. If we were to eat a little of all of these, our diets would inevitably become quite unhealthy.

I'd like to go on record here to say that I don't blame supermarkets, fast-food restaurants or the multi-national sugar-dealers as they do not force us to eat unhealthy foods. While they do make their products very appealing by tempting our eyes, noses and taste buds, they simply sell what we choose to buy, and we should take personal responsibility for our purchases. Take the shelves of a typical supermarket as an indication of what we, the public, consumes most. The beverage section will stock some water and fruit juices, but the vast majority tend to be sugar-laden soft-drinks, so called "juice drinks" that also contain sugar and artificial fruit flavours, and aisles filled with beers, wines and spirits. If we were to spread our liquid intake evenly between all of these, we would certainly find ourselves heading for health problems.

Go to the frozen-food section and it's typically the same! We'll find some frozen fruit, vegetables, meat and fish but the majority is battered, bread crumbed, cheesed or covered in pastry or sauces. These tend to be calorie-heavy but nutrient-poor. Of course, we also have freezers full of frozen desserts. We see the same in the breakfast cereal section where sugar in its various forms tops the list of ingredients. I'm sure we can agree that refined sugar probably shouldn't form the bulk of 'the most important meal of the day'! Likewise, when we go to the bread or bakery aisles with rows and rows of white bread. Then of course there's the obvious 'treat' aisles filled with buns, biscuits, cakes, chocolate and crisps. The fruit and veg sections are the only ones that resemble the simpler foods that our earlier ancestors ate for hundreds of thousands of years. If we could fill most of our trolley from there, and add in some fish, meat and eggs, bobs your uncle, we've got a diet closer to what our bodies have evolved to thrive on!

84

PROCESSED FOODS GOOD OR BAD?

Natural food is quite simply, food that is in much the same state as it was when picked from the tree or bush, pulled from the ground and fished from the sea or river. In the case of animal products, the meat, organs or milk would be packaged, tinned or bottled in its natural state. Most of us cannot hunt or gather our own food anymore so we rely on others to do this for us and send it somewhere for us to collect i.e. the shops. Such food may be sliced, diced, ground, minced, peeled, chopped, pressed or juiced. This is mechanical processing which will change the shape, size or texture of the food but the ingredients remain the same.

Food may be frozen, cooked or dried to prevent bacterial spoiling and are therefore processed using temperature but still they only contain the original ingredients. Some food is treated with a preservative to give it a longer shelf-life i.e., to make it last longer on the shelf before it spoils or goes off. Salt is a commonly added preservative and sugar is often used for jams and preserves. These are forms of chemical preservatives. Humans have cooked food, used salt and sugar as preservatives and ice or cold storage, where available, for millennia. All of these can be referred to as food processing and unless our salt intake is excessive, these forms are generally safe for us.

There are benefits to such practices as we all enjoy a greater variety of foods and at prices that would be impossible otherwise. Freezing fruit and veg when freshly harvested can keep them at a higher nutrient level than without freezing for days. Of course, many foods taste better and are easier to eat when cooked compared to their raw, natural state.

On the other hand, there are foods that have been processed or denatured to a point where the benefits of eating them may be outweighed by the health risks. Artificially produced colours, sweeteners and flavours are often used to make some foods look and taste like the foods we instinctively know are natural and beneficial for us. Unfortunately, they don't contain the same level of healthy nutrients. A bag of apple flavoured sweets is not likely to keep the doctor away. Orange-flavoured, sugar-filled "juice" drinks do not compare favourably with an actual orange. Such processing intensifies the "hit" we experience in our mouths and brains in ways that natural food cannot. Thus, it becomes more difficult to make the healthy choice. We still don't know the full extent of what these artificial chemicals are doing to our bodies so I would suggest keeping them to a minimum and focusing on minimally processed foods.

Refining natural sugar from plants to extract maximum sweetness by reducing fibre and other nutrients also means we get a buzz from such foods but at the cost of our health. Foods with a high sugar content tend to be calorie-dense but nutrient poor. These give us an instant hit but leave us dissatisfied and often hungry as our bodies still crave nutrition. I recall a radio interview several years ago in which a nutritionist was discussing a very sweet chocolate and nougat bar whose advertising was aimed towards children. Its advertising slogan suggested that eating these wouldn't ruin your appetite. "Food is supposed to ruin your appetite", he exclaimed as he explained that a food that doesn't satisfy hunger isn't doing its job. Excessive consumption of refined sugars is believed to increase risk of obesity, diabetes and heart disease. Sticking to foods that naturally contain sugar, but also fibre and other nutrients for our occasional sweet treat is likely to be more beneficial.

TRUST YOUR GUT

Gut feeling goes beyond intuition. It appears that the health of our gut, influenced by our diet, affects our moods too. This connection between the gut and brain is referred to as the "Gut-Brain Axis". Put simply, the gut communicates information to the brain just as the brain communicates with the entire body.

The Enteric Nervous System or ENS is made up of over 500 million neurons spread over the entire digestive tract. This system controls our gut and is sometimes referred to as our second brain, not to be confused with our mammalian brain which is the second part of our actual brain. The ENS is connected to our CNS or Central Nervous System, i.e., The "gut brain" is connected to the spinal cord and "head brain" via the vagus nerve which is an information superhighway between the brain and the gut.

The New York Times bestseller 'I am multitudes – the microbes within us and a grander view of life' by Ed Yong, explains the symbiotic relationships between bacteria and their hosts in amazing detail. His book shows links between gut bacteria and behaviour of the host. It also shows how these bacteria are involved in disease, immunity, obesity, reproduction and more. It even suggests that brain chemical levels in mice could be altered by exposing them to certain microbial bacteria.

Up to 90% of serotonin, a brain neurotransmitter that influences mood, is estimated to be made in the digestive tract. Think about that for a moment - feel good chemicals are made in the gut! Happy gut = happy person? It's worth noting that most anti-depressant medications work to increase serotonin levels. Research at the California Institute for Technology or Caltech, published in April 2015, found that mice lacking in certain microbes produced 60% less serotonin than their 'germ-filled' counterparts. These bacteria appear to work with the host body to make serotonin. Other research suggests that some bacteria make it all by themselves.

This form of research is still in its infancy but looks very promising. However, utilising bacteria to promote health is nothing new for humans. Fermented probiotic foods and beverages such as beer, bread, wine, yoghurt and kefir have been used for over 10,000 years. I have personally used kefir, the water-based kind as I have an intolerance to dairy, seeing almost instant improvements to my digestive system. Kefir contains many helpful bacteria, is thought by some to be more beneficial than yoghurt and is very easy to make at home. We can also eat fibre, which passes undigested to the gut where it then feeds these bacteria to keep them healthy and balanced. It seems that if we look after our gut bacteria, they will look after us. Fibre rich foods include wholegrains such as wheat, oats and barley, beans, lentils and seeds and should be included in our diets if we can tolerate them.

TRUE V FALSE FOODS

Imagine if all processing of foods were to suddenly stop and we were to go out into the world, only eating the foods we find growing in nature. If limited to foods that taste good to us in their natural state, what would we eat? Obviously, that rules out all fizzy drinks, bread, biscuits, pizza, pasta, sweets, chocolate, crisps etc. We could really only eat fresh, ripe fruit, nuts, berries, vegetables, mushrooms and herbs which, as it happens, are often considered 'Superfoods'. I use the term superfoods loosely as it is generally applied to more exotic foods which tend to cost outrageous sums. I believe that Himalayan goji berries and blackberries from our own hedgerows are equal, in fact the freshly picked blackberry will probably beat the dried out and processed goji every time.

In nature, true foods draw us to them by appealing to our senses so that we will eat them. In doing so, we get an abundance of nutrients needed to nourish the body. These superfoods appeal to our eyes with their strong or vibrant colours when at their ripest and most nutritious. This attraction to colour is a trick that clever food packaging designers use to draw our attention. Notice the equally strong, vibrant colours used on soft drink cans and bottles, chocolate wrappers and sweet packets that suggest to our instincts that these are good for us. Be conscious that legally, food labels may use words such as nutri, nature or healthy, with images of fruit, veg or healthy foods on the packaging and still be heavily processed and sugar laden. They are free to put such images on junk food wrapping once the ingredients are accurate. Armed with this knowledge and a little discipline, we can choose not to be fooled. Read the ingredients instead, or better yet, choose the true food that is packaged only in its own skin!

Our attraction to a variety of colours in true natural foods makes us eat a greater variety of fruits and vegetables. The reds, yellows, oranges, greens and purples of real food form the original "pick'n'mix" of the hunter gatherer. This gives us a more complete range of nutrients as no one food contains all that we need. Aside from the packaging, artificial colours are used directly in food processing to make them look like they would be good to eat. We rarely see true food coloured a dull grey unless it has spoiled. Meats in supermarkets often contain chemicals to keep their vibrant red colour, suggesting to our brains that this meat is fresh.

Real superfoods appeal to our taste buds with sweetness to tell us they are safe, ripe and highly nutritious. In nature, sour or bitter flavours usually mean they've not yet ripened, have spoiled or are poisonous to us. Food producers add refined sugars and artificial sweeteners to mimic this sweetness that tricks us into using our primal urge to eat ripe fruit.

The same can be said for the aromas and textures of foods. We don't like foul smelling foods or slimy consistencies that suggest they are gone off. Preservatives are added to foods that prolong their shelf-life while true natural foods will begin to spoil as soon as they are exposed to air and the bacteria that naturally feed off them. If bacteria can't thrive on them, is it safe to assume that we can? The priority of many processed food companies, as businesses, is to give us what we think we want rather than what we genuinely need. We must assume that responsibility ourselves.

SUPPLEMENTATION

"Eating the rainbow" i.e., eating a wide variety of foods should supply us with most of our nutritional needs, most of the time. There may be times however, when our diets need the support of supplementation to keep us flying high. In parts of the world away from the equator, winter not only reduces the number of hours we receive sunlight each day but also its strength. We rely largely on our skins production of vitamin D from direct sunlight to meet our needs. In summer 15 – 20 mins of facial and forearm exposure may be enough. In winter, we are unlikely to get enough exposure and a vitamin D supplement will be required to make up the difference. Approximately 1,000 – 2,000 iu is recommended per day from October to March.

I have seen clients benefit greatly from the use of a magnesium supplement to help with muscle cramps. I recently had a "twitchy" muscle beside my right eye that made me look like I was winking when it got going. Not ideal when you're speaking to clients about their physical ailments and about to give them a massage! I took a few magnesium capsules and the twitch disappeared, as did the awkwardness of explaining to clients that I'm not in fact winking at them.

Sports people and amateur fitness fanatics commonly use protein powder supplements for an easy option to add to their daily intake. These powders come from several sources including whey from milk, pea and rice proteins. Aside from the potential for increased gas, they are generally harmless and not at all to be confused with steroid use or other performance enhancing supplements and drugs. While I stick to wholefoods now, I did use whey and rice protein powders when I trained at higher intensities.

Our lifestyles, stress levels and health issues may dictate the need for other forms of supplementation. Those on restrictive diets may require Iron supplements to top this up and those with muscle cramps may benefit from additional magnesium for example. Follow the advice of qualified nutritionists and dieticians if you feel you are lacking or deficient in your diet.

FOOD INTOLERANCES

Awareness of intolerances to foods has exploded in recent years compared to even five short years ago. Health food stores catered for the intolerant then but now most supermarkets have a "free-from" section. Almost every menu now includes indications of potential allergens and food-packaging highlights them on the ingredients list. Asking if a meal is gluten-free, rather than being an embarrassment, is now sometimes seen as the "in-thing". Dairy which was once hailed as a superfood and the ultimate source of calcium is now recognised as a cause of health issues in those that cannot tolerate it.

For some, being intolerant is a new group to belong to. For others it is validation that the health issues they experienced for many years was not just in their heads. I am one of those people and while I have never been tested for coeliac's disease or other intolerances, I know through trial and error that there are foods that make me ill. I suggest keeping a daily food diary for a few months to note the food you eat and how you feel within hours to days. If you have food intolerances, you will notice patterns and see what you must avoid. If you do need to attend a nutritionist or dietician, such information will be extremely helpful to them in developing a food plan to suit your needs.

I have only recently encountered FODMAP's, after an interesting chat with a nutritionist. FODMAP stands for "fermentable oligo-, di-, mono-saccharides and polyols". It relates to foods whose natural sugars pass through to the intestines and feed our gut bacteria. The bacteria produce gas as they digest these sugars which can upset our digestive tract causing symptoms often connected to IBS or Irritable Bowel Syndrome such as bloating, pain, diarrhoea and flatulence. The list of foods that are high in these FODMAP'S, is the closest I've come across to the foods I've already identified as triggers for my own digestive issues. They include wheat and milk but also onions, garlic and cashew nuts to name but a few. It is suggested that these foods are avoided for a period of time and then slowly introduced to see if the body can tolerate them after a break. If not, they should be avoided completely. I will be interested to see if changing the microbiome or balance of the gut bacteria can reduce the effect of FODMAP's on intolerant individuals.

EVOLUTION OF OUR DIET

Homo sapiens i.e. humans, haven't changed very much, physiologically, in about 120,000 years, i.e., we are still built roughly the same now as we were then. Up until about 10,000 years ago we were hunter - gatherers, living off the fruit, vegetation, fish and animals we found seasonally. We then began to work the land to grow specific foods, we domesticated animals and created permanent settlements. This is in stark contrast to the nomadic lives we led for over 100,000 years, moving around to find the best fishing and hunting, gathering fruit and vegetables as we went.

This change to agriculture gave us more control over immediate access to food by storing grains and using our domesticated animals for eggs, milk and meat. Unfortunately, we traded the freedom to roam for the safety of walls, a wide variety of foods for a few staples, optimum nutrition for adequate calories. Labour intensive farming didn't allow much time for hunting and gathering and our farms and storehouses couldn't be picked up and moved with ease. Growth of civilisations and populations won but nutritionally we lost. Until now that is!

With irrigation, improved farming techniques, worldwide transportation and a global market, the farming of a wide variety of foods is now the norm. Much of the world now has access to natural foods of all colours. We are becoming more aware of the negative effects of pesticides and are turning more and more to organic produce. This trend will grow "organically" if we spend our money on organically grown foods, which will inevitably become cheaper as more is produced. We are entering a new era of being able to have the best of both worlds. It's our choice to enjoy it.

FISH TALES

Most human civilisations and the smaller tribal ones grew near seas, rivers and streams, not just because of the need to drink fresh water or for transport by boat, but also for the access to fish and seafood. If we suddenly had to find our own food, we would find it far easier to fish than to go hunt wild animals for meat. Fish is also generally easier to mechanically digest than meat. Think of how easily most fish breaks up with a fork compared to a piece of beef. There's a reason we get a special knife, which is practically a mini saw, with our steak!

Farming practices have increased our meat consumption way beyond where it would have been in the past and we're now only realising the health issues that can arise with that. The International Agency for Research on Cancer (IARC), the cancer agency of the World Health Organisation, have said that "processed meat is now classified as a 'definite' cause of cancer and high consumption of red meat as a 'probable' cause of cancer". Meats processed with nitrites are deemed to be most harmful. There are also suggestions of links to kidney dysfunction and heart disease while the hormones sometimes present in meats may even trigger reproductive issues and early onset of puberty in pre-teens. I should mention that hormone use varies greatly from country to country. Agriculture laws in Ireland are very strict on hormone use so should be quite safe. While it is true that meat also provides protein and minerals such as Iron, it is important to reduce the risks where possible. In my own personal experience, a diet based on eggs, fish, wholegrains, fruit, nuts and vegetables with only a little meat works best. Such a diet is easier to digest and provides high quality proteins, carbohydrates, fibre, fats, vitamins and minerals.

FOOD POISONING

Food processing, synthetic pesticides and additives are all relatively new to this world. There are records of some organic preservatives and pesticides used as far back as 3,500 years ago but the synthetic chemicals we now have are only in common use since the 1940's. Real food was appealing to bugs and insects or pests as we might call them, and they would live happily on them. Now, much of our food is made poisonous to insects and bacteria, by spraying them with chemicals. One of the most widely used pesticides, Chlorpyrifos, works to destroy insects' nervous systems. In a report published in The Lancet Neurology on Neurobehavioural effects of developmental toxicity by Dr Philippe Grandjean and MD Philip J Landrigan, MD, Chlorpyrifos is listed as a neurotoxin linked to neurodevelopmental disabilities, including autism, attention-deficit hyperactivity disorder, dyslexia, and other cognitive impairments.

The amount of these chemicals in any one meal are far from fatal to us but may be harmful long-term, nonetheless. Buying foods that contain fewer artificial chemicals where possible means that we can reduce these and help to protect our environment. I understand that organic food is more expensive but hope that in time, with more people opting for organics, it will become more cost-effective for producers and cheaper for consumers. Washing our fruit and vegetables can remove some of the residual chemicals that sit on the surface but not the chemicals that have been absorbed through the ground. In relation to food additives and preservatives, a simple piece of advice is this – "if you don't understand what's on the ingredients list, think twice about eating it!". I suggest learning some basics of nutrition for yourself so you can read and understand labels. Know what you're putting into your body to make healthy, educated choices.

REAL FOOD?

What I term real food is the food that we humans have evolved over millennia to consume to give us the nutrients we need to thrive. These certainly include some foods that come directly from nature but remember that not everything that grows naturally or comes from animal sources is good for us. There are common foods, consumed by people every day, that aren't always as beneficial as we might assume.

Take cow's milk for example. Its natural purpose is to turn a calf into a cow, not to provide us with our daily requirement of calcium! That statement always made my female gym clients think twice about using it. Humans managed quite well for a very long time before we domesticated cows. I think it's fair to say that you probably wouldn't drink dogs or cat's milk or even human milk for that matter if it was offered to you? It's only because cow's milk has been consumed for so long, that we consider it normal to drink it. I wonder if the very first human to start drinking cow's milk looked a little strange. Perhaps he or she only did so from a desperate need to survive!

Some people can tolerate dairy well and get much benefit from its calorie and protein content. Some people are intolerant to dairy and know it doesn't suit them. Then there are those who are intolerant but don't realise it is causing their health issues. Drinking some cow's milk or eating some dairy probably won't kill you, even if you are one of the many people with an intolerance to it. In fact, many cultures have survived in climates where they may not otherwise because of cow's milk and other "not-so-natural-for-humans" foods. Are you thriving is, I feel, a more important question?

As mammals, humans do naturally drink milk, or rather breast milk, as infants but are then weaned off once we are fully capable of eating and digesting solid foods. It seems that many of us lose the ability to produce the enzymes necessary to digest milk adequately at about 3 years of age, as we shouldn't need to digest milk anymore. As such, many humans are intolerant to lactose, the natural sugar present in milk.

In recent times, health issues are recognised to be linked to the consumption of dairy products such as milk, cheese, butter, yoghurt and foods containing milk powder. These can cause abdominal bloating, pain, flatulence and diarrhoea and are suspected triggers of conditions including asthma and eczema. I should probably mention here that I ceased using dairy products years ago. I have seen only positive benefits since, including clearer sinuses and improved digestion. If you drink milk or use dairy products such as yoghurt and cheese and feel great, carry on. If you have the above symptoms, remove them from your diet for a month and see how you feel. Better yet, contact a nutritionist or dietician for more advice.

Wheat and oats are among other common foods that we would not eat in their natural forms and yet are commonplace in our diets. We are highly unlikely to look at a field of ripened wheat, lick our lips and go tuck in! Again, I accept that some human cultures have survived largely because of bread and that many people today can eat it without any negative side-effects. However, just because we grind it into a flour, mix it with some other ingredients and bake it to make it taste nice, this doesn't mean that we can all digest it and use its nutrients effectively. Many people have major intolerances to wheat, ranging from mild bloating and discomfort to the severe symptoms of coeliac disease. I personally have avoided food containing wheat flour and oats for many years due to the abdominal bloating, cramps and constipation generally followed by diarrhoea.

There are those that don't believe such intolerances exist, making them the butt of jokes, or attributing them to psychosomatic symptoms. I know that I had digestive issues for many years before I ever heard of coeliac disease or gluten intolerance. Until then I thought these widely available foods were normal and healthy. It was only when I learned of the possible issues and removed them from my diet that I saw great improvements. I have also seen dramatic improvements in client's health over the years having removed wheat products from their diets. Several reported significant weight loss that cannot be explained by calorie deficit alone. The reduction of intolerance related inflammation is the most obvious other likely factor.

I have not taken a test for coeliac disease. I don't need to as I know, from experience, the effect of wheat on my wellbeing. If in doubt, try it out! Take a break from all wheat products for one month. See how you feel and then decide if you're better off without it.

THINK BEFORE YOU EAT

In summary, you will become the food you eat today. It will affect how you look, feel and what you can do in this world for yourself and for others. Your choices can give you more energy and vitality to pursue dreams and goals, to really make a difference. You can renew your Stardust with the best Stardust available and give your body the chance for wellbeing it deserves. Choose wisely!

food and nutrition

PART 3

Mind Matters

Mind Matters

Chapter 8

Developing Mental Fitness

3 is the magic number!

The Celtic trinity knot is a symbol I like to use to represent holistic health and not just because I'm Irish! I even use it as my Health Matters clinic logo.

For me it demonstrates how the three points of Mental, Physical and Emotional health are of equal importance and completely intertwined, with one flowing into the next. It also shows how each are contained within the whole human being i.e. the circle. Those of a more spiritual inclination may view the circle as the spirit or consciousness experiencing life. Because they are interlinked, it is impossible to separate mental, physical or emotional wellbeing from each other in reality. To create a structure for this book, I will separate them into categories, but all will be mentioned, when applicable, within each section. As most of our actions begin with a thought that is either conscious or habitual, we will start with the mind.

TRAINING THE MIND

Development of a healthy mind is an important starting point when making any life-changes, long or short-term, as it is the mind that directs everything we do. A phrase that I encountered several years ago sums this up and we can apply it to all aspects of our lives. It states that "energy flows where attention goes". Repeat that in your mind or out loud as it is a statement worth remembering... ENERGY FLOWS WHERE ATTENTION GOES... This means that we invest our energy in the form of time, thoughts or action in whatever we focus our attention on.

We give energy to everything we think about. As we feed a train of thought, we reinforce our tendency to think like that, creating a habit. How we habitually think now, is influenced greatly by how we have been consistently thinking up to this point in time. It's like a well-worn pathway through a wood that we automatically follow. If we were to take another route and use it regularly, we would create a new pathway. The older and now unused one, would become overgrown and impassable. Habits, be they good, bad or indifferent, are created and broken in the same way, through practice and consistency. What is important, when choosing our habits, is whether or not they are desirable, constructive and beneficial to us.

Note - Most of us can safely work on developing our mental fitness but, if we are in a state of mental distress that poses any threat to our own life or the lives of others, we should immediately seek the support of professionals. Such experts can guide us through the more difficult terrain until we return to full health. The advice in this book is not intended to replace any programs already put in place by healthcare professionals. However, this advice may be beneficial as an aid to the restoration of long-term mental well-being.

Here is a short-list of tried-and-tested means to develop positive mental fitness which we will then explore further.

Practice awareness

Be mindful of our thoughts and actions. Be conscious of the inner voice we all possess and what it says about us and others. Take note of how we feel and what led to those feelings.

Develop an open mind

Look at life from other points of view along with our own to get a clearer view of reality and broaden our perspective. Accept that there are many ways to live and act in this world. Learn from others and their ways so we have far more options to incorporate into our own lives. Travelling is a wonderful way to do this as we will encounter diverse cultures, traditions and belief systems. Use what works best.

Let go of what you think you know

We are all wrong sometimes. Often, we simply have the wrong idea, belief or are not fully informed. Letting go of the need to be right creates space for new and perhaps more accurate knowledge that is more advantageous.

Learn something new

Treat the mind as a muscle that is only as fit as it needs to be. If we use it, stretch it, challenge it and develop it, we will find it far more capable than we previously realised. We also gain confidence in the knowledge that we are still capable of learning and that our mind will serve us well in future.

Practice gratitude

Look for the reasons that prove to us how lucky we are. Remind ourselves of the things we once wanted and now have. Note the things we desired but are now glad we don't have, as life worked out even better for us. Be thankful for the simple but important things we have that we would not trade for anything. These may include a body that works, close personal relationships, food, shelter, a job and more.

Practice positivity

Cultivate a belief that every experience may happen for us and not to us. This transforms our attitude from being a victim of circumstance to one who is lucky and looked after. Look for the positives in all situations. Find the silver lining, something that stops us struggling against what we believe to be "wrong". Look for the lesson to be learned to grow, evolve and mature.

Use positive affirmations

Overwrite and reprogram negative thought patterns and beliefs with positive statements. Repeat them until you believe them. We will discuss the above list in more detail through the remaining chapters of this "Mind Matters" section.

Get adequate rest

A tired brain will perform below its full capacity. Refer to the section on sleep in the "Healthy Habits" chapter for more on the benefits of rest.

Eat well

The brain relies on glucose as its main source of fuel and proteins and fats to repair and grow new cells. The health of our gut bacteria is also linked to overall wellbeing. I recommend little and often, with a wide variety of wholesome and natural foods to balance blood sugar levels and support gut health. Refer to the 'Food and Nutrition' chapter for more on this.

Mind Matters

Chapter 9

Awareness and Perspective

"The ultimate value of life depends upon awareness and the power of contemplation rather than on mere survival", Aristotle.

Assessment of the current state of our mind, honestly and non-judgementally, is needed before we can change our mindset for the better. To assess the mind, we must become consciously aware of how our mind is operating or thinking. You'll see that we think all the time, all day, every day, but not always consciously. We're often thinking several thoughts at once. One main thought may sit on the surface of our awareness but there may be others underneath. I often compare the mind to a computer, tablet or smartphone where our conscious thoughts are like the apps on the screen, but with several others running in the background. These hidden background apps are still using the device's energy and affecting the overall speed and performance.

The mind works in a similar fashion. We regularly find these unresolved background thoughts "popping-up" to the surface of our awareness. They distract us from what we want to focus on and from getting our important work done. This is often the difficulty for people with very active minds when they try to meditate. With eyes closed and no outward distractions, all the background thoughts come flashing into the mind's eye. This can make reaching the calm, centred and focused state of meditation quite difficult for us as the "pop-ups" don't shut down just because we want them to.

To develop awareness is to look at all the thoughts that are running in the mind, superficially or beneath. We can then decide to deal with them and close them down, freeing the mind for other tasks. Our productive and positive thoughts are worth running as they give us something we want. It's the more worrisome thoughts that drain our battery and give us only stress in return. These are the ones we want to resolve and shut down. It's very refreshing to take a complete break from over-thinking occasionally too.

We talk to ourselves in our heads quite a lot. This chatter is often referred to as the 'monkey mind'. The voice we will hear more than any other is our own. Becoming aware of what we are saying about ourselves and about others can be a real eye-opener as to where we're really at! Most of us would probably say, when asked, that we are positive thinkers. When you become aware of your own mental chatter you will almost certainly find many negative comments about yourself, others and the world in general. We all do it!

When observing internal chatter or inner voice, do so non-judgementally, as a form of self-exploration. Having judgemental thoughts about our judgemental thoughts only adds to them! You may start to see that you are overly tough on yourself and critical towards others. They go hand in hand. You will surely find yourself thinking things that you would never say aloud for fear of being considered crazy or downright horrible.

You may also find that you spend a lot of time in conflict with the world around you. I would remind you that every time we complain, we are conflicted with reality i.e., we're not accepting what is. Much of our energy is spent complaining about how much is wrong with the world rather than appreciating how much is right or that it is as it is for a reason! If this sounds like you, don't worry or feel guilty. This is normal and certainly doesn't make you a "bad person". You are just a typical human being that has fallen into a habit of judgement. Again, be gentle with yourself as you acknowledge these thoughts. Once you've got a clearer idea of how you're thinking, you can decide if it's working for you and if that's the mindset you want. Your next step will be to accept your habitual mindset or change it to one you'd prefer.

HOW TO BE THE OBSERVER

One simple technique I've found helpful for developing inner awareness is to sit quietly and comfortably with eyes closed. I personally use ear plugs to avoid distractions from outside noise. I then imagine I'm sitting alone and comfortably in a cinema as my thoughts are being displayed on the big screen in front of me. This allows me to be a little disconnected from my thoughts while I observe them. Rather than getting totally invested in what I see, which may be uncomfortable enough to quit the practice, I can just sit back and watch how each thought unfolds.

In this practice you will notice your conscious awareness tuning into all the thoughts the mind creates. You may see memories, future-plans and imagined scenarios or conversations, popping up on the screen. They can be very erratic and jumbled with your mind jumping from one thought to another quite quickly. Try to focus on one scene at a time though and allow it to play through fully.

The end-point of this exercise is to help you resolve any stressful beliefs, thoughts or memories, so they no longer cause you to struggle and can be put aside. That may take time. Some take longer than others. Your goal here is to sit and observe. You will have the opportunity to view each situation more clearly and reflect on it. Solutions may come to you straight away. As the observer, you can give yourself advice, just as you would give it to a friend. We're all great at giving advice to others. Act on this the next chance you get or create an opportunity to act. If the solution isn't immediately apparent or there is no way to change it at the moment, you can ask yourself some simple questions to help you find a way to be more at ease with it.

Is what's on the screen true or is it simply your perception of it? If it's a memory, could it be that you saw it differently because of your belief or mindset at the time? I remember trying to make conversation with a classmate I sat beside in secondary school. We were roughly fifteen years old at the time. I got little or no response. I figured that he was just too cool to talk to me, so I stopped trying. Years later we became reacquainted and were chatting. I joked with him about how he was too cool to talk to me back in our schooldays. His response surprised me. He said, "I was a weirdo back then. Nobody wanted to talk to me!". It was a simple misunderstanding. He thought nobody wanted to talk to him. I thought I wasn't cool enough for him to want to talk to me. Neither was true, or maybe we were both a bit weird and uncool. Who isn't at 15!

WE SEE THE WORLD AS WE ARE NOT AS IT IS

How we see the world and what is going on around us depends largely on what's going on inside us. Reality is filtered through our own beliefs and mental or emotional state. We see the world as we are, not as it is. If happy, we will see the world as a fun place, if scared we see the world as a place to be feared. If comfortable in our own skin, we can take a comment or joke in good humour. If self-conscious, we can be easily insulted when none was intended. Our own state of mind and emotions will greatly influence how we view any situation, so we often misread them.

A simple example of this is where we receive the same criticism from two people. One we consider a friend and the other an enemy. The friend's criticism will be taken on board as constructive, helpful and well-intentioned while the enemy's criticism will be taken as ill-mannered, insulting and possibly an act of aggression. Either way, the criticism may be something we need to hear and can be beneficial to us if addressed. Regardless of its source and intent, a friend's or an enemy's point of view can be just as positive for us if we are aware enough to put our guard down and listen.

TO WORRY IS TO IMAGINE A FUTURE WE DON'T WANT

If we are worrying about our future, there are another pair of questions worth asking ourselves i.e., "Is it likely to ever happen?" and "What is the basis for this story-line or scene?". Remember that we are the script-writers, and directors of our imaginations and the producers of our worries. Our own habits or fears can lead us to create scenarios that we don't want to happen.

The mind-body connection is so powerful that our body will react to what we imagine, in many ways, as if it is happening for real. Just as a pleasant dream can leave us feeling wonderful or a bad one feeling terrible, a fearful thought can create anxiety and nervous tension. Choosing to observe the worry from a logical perspective can allow us to resolve it, and let it go for good. We can accept that there may be a million to one chance of it ever actually happening and live our lives accordingly. We could look to understand where the fear stems from and address that root belief. We could trust that we will still be ok, even if our fear is realised. We could also choose to rewrite the script by imagining how we would wish it to play out instead.

To give an example, I found myself at one point worrying about my finances. As a self-employed single-parent, money was indeed tight at times. I believed I had good reason to be concerned about my financial future. The self-employed here in Ireland don't qualify for social welfare payments so, should I find myself unable to work, for any reason, I would soon be in financial difficulty! After noticing this fear popping up regularly, I sat with it, observed it and my thoughts, and worked it through.

I was in my early 30's which meant I had lived about 12,000 days and nights. In all that time, my finances were such that I had never gone one day without food to eat, a bed to sleep in or a roof over my head. At this point, even I should run out, I had done well so far, and I trusted that I would handle a little want. Also, I knew I could count on the support of family and friends. They wouldn't let me go homeless or starve so it really wasn't worth worrying about. Being realistic about this worry resolved my fear. I no longer felt a need to think about it and I'm grateful to say I've had no concerns since. I always seem to have enough. Sometimes I have a little more to spare. Sometimes I've got to 'cut my cloth to measure', but there's always enough to cover my needs.

WHAT PART AM I PLAYING?

The next question worth asking as you observe your thoughts in your 'home-mind-cinema' is, "What is each character, including you, hoping to achieve in your thought-scene?" If a thought keeps popping up in your mind, it must need some form of resolution. Is there some outcome you're hoping for that you need to let go of? Remember, to be totally focused on one outcome is to close off to the possibility of others. There may be endings far better, that you haven't considered than the one you currently want. Becoming more mentally flexible might be the key to resolving this.

Perhaps this outcome you want is very achievable but you're not taking the steps towards realising your destiny. Maybe others aren't fully on board and you need to follow through with your idea yourself rather than waiting for them? There may be blocks within you that are holding you back, that you need to get over before you can carry on down your chosen path. Being brave enough to observe, accept and address your own issues could be the answer. If the struggle connected to the scene is in dealing with another person, try to understand what they really want and why. You may find a way where both of you are satisfied with the outcome. If the scenario you conjure or remember insults you, look at the part you play in accepting the insult and the hidden benefits for you. Other people may force us to look at our own self-confidence levels or to stand up for our rights. They may poke at the vulnerable spots we have about ourselves and give us the opportunity to dress those wounds and heal.

Next, ask "How does the thought make you feel and what is this telling you?" A thought that provokes a powerful emotion needs to be acknowledged. If it's an unpleasant emotion, something needs to change because it's harmful. Either the situation needs to be addressed and changed or you need to genuinely accept it for it to be resolved. Our gut-feeling or intuition can tell us something that the conscious mind is not seeing clearly or maybe is ignoring. I find that if I have any uneasy feeling or tension around a thought, situation or person, even though it seems ok on the surface, there is always a reason for it. My goal is to figure out if the problem is me, the situation or the others involved. I have found that it's often me. It could come from my inability to accept the situation, frustration at a lack of efficiency or progress, or my lack of patience to wait for it to work out. I have worked a lot on these areas and will probably have to keep working on them for the rest of my life! The work I have done helps me to work better with others. When the problem isn't me, I see that I can choose to remove myself from the situation and direct my time and energies where they are better used.

MORE HISTORY LESS MYSTERY

What is the background of each character in your scene? If a current situation is frustrating because it doesn't make sense, looking at what went on in the past may bring clarity. The past is the past, but it has led to the present. "Once bitten, twice shy!" Seeing where our past experiences are influencing our thoughts and actions now can help us to understand why we and others act as we do. It may also save us from living in the past instead of the present moment.

Another set of questions when dealing with others is, "Are they doing the best they can?" Is their best good enough, even if it doesn't reach our standards or expectations? Is it ok for others to do it their way or does it have to be ours every time? Answering yes to these can allow us to work well with others. Compromising and working together has been essential for humanities success and will continue to be so. One group of people can contribute hundreds of years of experience and wisdom that one could never gain alone. A healthy mind will see and take advantage of this.

You will find other reasons for your stressful thoughts and other means of resolution. The bottom line is this - when we can resolve the thoughts that interrupt our peace of mind, we find the peace that was already there. Undistracted, we can focus our minds on that which is beneficial to us, our lives and our world.

PERSPECTIVE

The reality we experience sometimes has little to do with the facts of a situation. Our version of reality comes from how we read it from our own perspective. Again, "We see the world as we are, not as it is".

Here's an example of a situation. Imagine you arrive at a fine restaurant to meet some good friends to celebrate your friend's birthday. You walk in, see your friends across the room and start to make your way over to them. One of your friends looks up, notices you and gives you a wave and a warm friendly smile, happy to see you. You wave back, equally delighted until, slightly distracted, you trip and fall. You land on a table occupied by two well-dressed couples, mid-meal with full wine glasses and deep in conversation. There's a crash and a scream as you send the food and wine flying. You roll from the table onto the floor. Then there's silence, not just at the table but through the entire room. It lasts for only a second or two, but it feels like an eternity as you lie, frozen on the ground.

Your mind kicks in instantly to assess the situation and your inner voice starts talking, "You have just ruined the night for the couples at the table as well as your friend's birthday celebration". "Everybody in the restaurant is staring at you, thinking how foolish, stupid and clumsy you are. They judge you and are laughing at you". You are absolutely mortified. You wish the ground would open and swallow you whole. You want to die. In fact, you're thinking death would be a happy release. After what seems like an eternity, people come to pick you up. They ask if you're ok and you say you're fine, even though your ribs hurt, because you don't want to be any more bother. Your friends arrive eventually, and they try to bring you to their table. Your monkey mind tells you that you can't go on to enjoy the meal or the night, so you decide to make your escape and head straight for the door. You are never, ever going to live this one down.

Now take the same situation but from your birthday friend's perspective. You're sitting in the restaurant waiting for one of your closest friends to arrive. You look up to see them walk towards you, trip, fall, knock some food on a table and land on the ground. You instantly spring to your feet and run to see if your friend is ok. Before you can get there the couples at the table are already gathering around your friend, genuinely concerned. The room is still quiet as the other diners try to figure out what just happened. Your friend is already standing when you arrive and, aside from a small clothing stain and two bright red cheeks, looks to be ok. You say, "Are you ok? Don't worry, it could happen to anybody!" You are close friends, so you make a light joke of it. Your friend apologises for ruining the night and leaves, but you follow in pursuit. Luckily, with a little humour and a lot of coaxing, you manage to convince your friend to join your table and the celebrations. By the time you re-enter, the restaurant staff have cleaned the small mess. Aside from some sympathetic smiles, all is as it was, and everybody has returned to their meals and conversation. It turns out to be a great night and a funny story that brings a smile to you and your friend for years to come.

The point here is that we are often vastly over-critical of ourselves, chastising our actions in ways we would never do to another. If we can switch our own internal voice to friendly mode i.e., actually becoming our own friend, we get a totally different narrative. I'm talking about a proper best-friend voice here, the one that gives you an honest kick-in-the-arse when you need it, but always with a pat on the back. Be one that is there to support you. Developing our own self-friendship and self-love will take time and consistent effort. All true friendships take time to grow strong. Nurture it daily and you will always have a friendly voice to encourage you.

It's good to ask ourselves, in any situation, from what angle am I looking at this? What is my current mindset or belief? Is it realistic, positive, calm and caring or, is it unrealistic, negative, anxious and fearful? Does my perspective allow me to see the truth of this situation, clearly and logically or am I blinded by my expectation, my previous experiences or simply by being too hard on myself? This is a big one, "Can I be my own best-friend?".

Try this exercise to help gain a clearer, more positive perspective;
Sit or lie comfortably in a space where you will not be distracted. Take your awareness and relaxation to your feet and legs, taking slow, deep breaths as you do. Allow your neck, shoulders and head to relax, features softening, letting any tension in the face melt away.

With closed eyes, visualise a situation that you are struggling with as an independent observer i.e. watching the scene from the outside. Look at it from the eyes of somebody who trusts that everything, including this, happens for a good reason. Accept that there is some lesson or purpose behind your problematic situation. Remind yourself that even if you can't see it immediately, positives will come from this situation for all involved.

Now watch the scene as it plays out. Look at each person involved and remind yourself that they are doing the best they can with who they are and what strength, knowledge or experience they have available to them in that moment. Remember that each has their own perspective, goal and reason for acting or reacting the way they do. This allows you to be more open-minded, understanding and compassionate. They may even be unwittingly doing you a favour by forcing you down another path.

I have seen this in my own personal life. Others that I once believed held me back from pursuing a goal actually gave me more time and space to develop my ideas, before turning them into reality. Acknowledge that what is important to you, may not be as important to them, and that's ok! We all have our own goals, dreams and agendas. Accept that the others involved may still care about you or your needs but have an unusual way of showing it and that's ok too. This approach can reduce some of the hurt and frustration we experience when others don't meet our expectations.

Look to see what the situation is teaching you or doing for your benefit. Maybe it's showing you that you need to be more accepting or lenient, if you are trying to get your own way completely. Maybe it's showing you that you need to stand firm, find your voice and assert your rights, if you have been too lenient or people pleasing. Maybe it's preventing you from doing what you want but something better is around the corner. Maybe it's teaching you to trust that it'll work out for the best. The situation might force you to look deeper into the history of those involved to gain a greater understanding, making you wiser. It may cause you to let go of preconceived ideas you have carried through imagining yourself in another's shoes.

Look at the situation from every angle to allow you to be at peace with it or come up with a plan to resolve the situation, for the best possible outcome for everybody involved. Remember that if you have a right to be satisfied, content and happy with the outcome then so does everyone else involved. That would be the ideal end-result!

BIG PICTURE – LITTLE PICTURE

One great means through which we can bring more bring positivity, mindfulness, perspective and patience into our mindsets is to take a big picture / little picture approach. By 'little picture' I mean you and your current situation while 'big picture' refers to everybody else and the overall story. You could think of the 'big picture' as an entire jigsaw puzzle and your situation as the little picture on a single jigsaw piece. You certainly belong in the puzzle so never underestimate your importance. Your piece is as important to the whole as any other, because the big picture is incomplete without it!

Figuring out where our piece fits into the big picture is one of our major goals. We tend to struggle when we don't 'fit in'. In our youth, we won't always see where our piece fits, but if we are armed with the knowledge that it will fit somewhere, we can be ok with that. If we are patient enough and brave enough to try the options that come our way, we'll find the pieces that fit with ours. In this process, we'll learn much about ourselves and everybody else. We'll see that trying to fit in somewhere that isn't right for us just won't work. We can then try another way.

We'll also find our place in the overall picture, maybe in the centre, perhaps way out there on the edges but it'll be a great fit and right where we need to be! Those that we are looking to fit in with are looking for us too. Finding our "tribe", a tight-knit group that gives us support and a sense of belonging helps us to thrive.

Patience plays its part here too as we don't need to be in too much of a hurry to find our place. Not fitting in can be an interesting experience. We may show others that are pretending to fit in that there are other options. We've got an entire lifetime to figure out where we belong in the big picture. The fun in jigsaw puzzles is in finding a place for our pieces. Life offers us a series of opportunities to see where we can make things fit! So, if you're struggling to make sense of your situation as it is, take a step back, try out a few options, be patient and all will be revealed.

As important as we are to the big picture, acknowledging that it's not all about us can take some pressure off us too. All the pieces are equally important. We can see that it's not up to us alone to run the show or figure everything out. Others have their part to play. In real life terms, that will mean looking at everything that's going on around us before deciding if it fits us and if we fit there. Often it means seeing that what we're doing now might have purpose down the line. It could also mean looking to the past to see what lead to our current situations.

Mind Matters

Chapter 10

Opening the Mind

"I love keeping an open mind. It's liberating to know the universe and our existence are not limited to my understanding" Izey Victoria Odiase

LETTING GO

How often do we carry old programming, beliefs and grudges allowing them to cloud our judgement and influence our decisions? All the time! That time we 'put ourselves out there' and got shot down or ridiculed can hold us back from ever taking a chance again. The time we took a leap of faith and failed can tell us to stick with the safe option forevermore. The first impression we get of somebody can make us tag them with personality traits, applying those tags in all future meeting and dealings. The beliefs we learn from our families and traditions can lead to carrying on practices through life without ever even questioning why!

Letting go of what we think we know lets us clear our mind. This gives us an opportunity for clarity much as cleaning our spectacles does. I've been wearing glasses for 32 years now and I'm still amazed at just how dirty the lenses seem to get before I notice they need a wipe! The smudges and spots build up slowly. Because they're right in front of our eyes, we can't really see them, yet they distort our vision. Only once cleaned do we realise just how much our viewpoint was clouded.

Possibly the most valuable aspect of letting go, in relation to choosing what to do with stardust, occurs when we let go of our perception of who we are. We often take on roles and stereotypes within our families, social groups and work environment. We can play these roles indefinitely, even though we naturally grow and change throughout our lives. Within the family or social circle or job, we may be the smart one, the funny one, the quiet one, the loud one, the energetic one, the lazy one, the moody one, the calm one, the troublemaker, the peacemaker, the high-achiever or the average joe.

If we identify too strongly with these attributes, we can become bound by them and never allow ourselves the opportunity to try on other roles for size. Even though those roles may suit us better. Going to college in another city or travelling solo to other countries can give us freedom to stretch

111

our personalities. This is mainly because nobody in these new environments knows the role we played and won't find it strange if we act differently. Leaving home isn't necessary, however. Those that love us will accept us regardless, and we need not concern ourselves with those that liked us because of how we acted. They never really knew us to begin with. There are plenty more that will like our authentic selves, should we choose to express them.

RETURN TO INNOCENCE

A helpful exercise to let go of old programming, beliefs or stereotypes is to sit quietly and comfortably with eyes closed. Imagine yourself as having only entered the world, a perfectly clean slate, so to speak. Innocent. Babies, with their own natural personalities and instincts but no judgements, unnecessary fears or self-doubts have a wonderful innocence. They are the epitome of potential and possibility. This brings more space for joy, happiness and wonder. From this perspective with no prior knowledge of how things are, were or how they should be, we are ready to simply observe, learn and try stuff out.

We can ask if who we were and how we lived is who we are destined to always be. We can form new impressions based on our own experiences rather than what we were told. We can set aside other people's ideas and beliefs to decide for ourselves what seems to be the truth and what works best for us. We don't have to completely disregard what we learned before, but we can balance it with more current information and the insights gained from an open mind. Letting go also allows us to drop old grudges that bring negativity to our mindset.

LEARN SOMETHING NEW

Regularly learning new things works the mind and keeps it sharp. It also reminds us that we have the capability to learn at any stage, not just while we're in full-time education. The new thing you learn can be something that helps you reach one of your goals. It may simply be for personal interest which may in turn come in useful for reaching goals too. Interesting knowledge makes for interesting and more varied conversation which helps us to create connections and build networks.

We could decide to learn to play an instrument, giving you opportunities to entertain and take part in music sessions. Almost veryone loves a good session. We can learn the basics of another language and then travel to another country to practice it. This will impress at a job or college interview, perhaps even on a date. We might study up on history, learning great lessons from the past. We could research innovative technologies being developed to see where we are headed in the future. The scope for learning is, especially online, is endless.

I have recently learned, mainly through Youtube videos, how to make Youtube videos. I researched lighting systems and how to set them up, cameras and the angles to shoot footage from to make it more personal and interesting. I learned about recording audio through external microphones and how to put them all together in the editing process. Through friends of mine and a little more Youtube research I learned a little about music production and how I can use an app on my phone to create backing tracks for videos, meditation and my own songs. I've had this app for ages. Without the knowledge of how to use it, it was useless to me. The result is that I can now share more health information with those that would benefit from it. I can also share other projects I have been working on in a way that would have been impossible previously.

The biggest plus was that I found it all so interesting. Exploring the possibilities and then finding ways to use it is a fantastic process. It's extremely empowering. It has shown me that modern technology is nothing to be feared and that knowledge certainly is no load. It has made my life easier and given me new avenues to explore. It's added to my enthusiasm each morning. There is so much I would like to, and now am able to do it. It's all good.

I can happily spend hours researching and learning new things but, as I realised when learning to play guitar and relearning the Irish language, little and often is best. Twenty to thirty minutes a day, every day, is far better than two or three hours, once a week. It drip-feeds information to the brain and allows us to stay fully focused and interested while we learn. It also gives us a habit of learning that may stay with us after our goal is achieved and inspire us to apply it to other areas as you gain confidence in your ability to learn whatever you need to.

PATIENCE

This truly is an age of instant gratification. We get few opportunities to practice patience and so it is often left underdeveloped. Most of us have everything we need and much of what we want available to us 24/7. Food, clothing, entertainment, information and travel are all within reach whenever we want them. In my parents' lifetime alone, we have gone from small corner shops to 24-hour supermarkets, from local radio and limited availability of books to practically unlimited access to movies and programs on-line. Bulky encyclopaedias that seemed to hold the worlds knowledge can't hold a candle to the information we can access with the touch of a button on the small smartphone devices we carry in our pockets.

We've progressed from local transport, primarily by foot, bicycle, horses and carts, to travelling almost anywhere on this planet within a day or two. We also have worldwide online shopping with 'next day delivery' of most products. As a result, we tend to apply that instant expectation to all areas of our lives. We've all heard that 'Patience is a virtue'. Such a virtue is a fantastic addition to a healthy mind. As in nature, some endeavours take time to bear fruit and are all the more enjoyable because of the wait.

Delayed gratification is a pleasure in itself. I remember the excitement of waiting for Christmas or birthdays when we didn't get gifts every other week. These things meant more because we had less. I've seen footage of the shoe-box Christmas presents that are made in Irish schools and sent to schools in third world countries. The reactions of those kids to the small gifts they receive is a joy to behold. You can be sure that the wait for those boxes for weeks sparked excitement and fired their imaginations. I never allowed my kids to get toys, even small ones, within a month of their birthdays or Christmas so that same anticipation could build in them. The same can apply to us when we look forward to a holiday, a birthday, Christmas, or maybe even that treat we promised ourselves at the weekend.

The joy of working towards a goal and eventually seeing it reach its fruition, through commitment and effort, is far sweeter than any success that comes easily or quickly. Waiting for a great movie to be released, a birthday to come around to get that present we've wanted or wondering if the postman will bring the results of an exam builds a sense of anticipation and excitement that whets our appetite for life. If we practice patience rather than instant gratification, we get to enjoy a feel-good dopamine increase while we wait. If we then use positive thinking and gratitude, we get a great big feel-good release as a reward.

Patience also gives us the mental endurance required to follow through with our long-term plans. I've often seen gym clients give up on their fitness goals after only a few short weeks because they wanted major results straight away with very little effort. If it were that easy, everyone would be super-fit! Health, like many of the most important things in life, takes time, consistency and effort and should be looked at as a life-long goal.

GRATITUDE

The feel-good factor that comes from gratitude is about as good as any we will ever encounter. It makes us feel lucky, successful, cared for and contented. We often can't see the woods for the trees. Once we become aware of all we have received thus far in life, our minds open to receiving even more. We can be so busy looking for something that we don't realise we already have it, like running around the house looking for the keys or phone that are already in our hands! Taking stock of all that we have, every now and again, helps to remind us of what we've got to be grateful for.

Robert Sapolsky's excellent book "Behave", discusses the effect of gratitude vs expectation. His example shows how expectation and reward affects primates, which is similar to how it works in humans. Sapolsky explains how monkeys were taught to press a button for a reward. If pressed ten times, they would get a raisin. Initially, the 'winning' of a raisin for their button-pressing effort caused a large natural release of dopamine in the brain. Dopamine is one of the 'feel-good chemicals' our brain produces. This caused the monkey to feel very good.

With each reward, the release of dopamine reduced as the monkey came to expect a raisin each time. This still created some feel-good-factor but not as much as the first time, until it was rewarded with two raisins for the same 10 pushes. The excitement or perhaps surprise of getting extra raisin caused another large release of dopamine. This was accompanied by an equivalent rise in feel-good factor. When only one raisin was 'won' the next time, the dopamine release was even lower still.

Why the difference? Expectation and anticipation! Nothing was expected initially so the first raisin created a 'woohoo' moment. Once one raisin was expected, there was some satisfaction when it arrived but not exactly a woohoo. When only one was expected and two arrived, there was another woohoo! When two raisins were then expected and only one arrived, it dropped to disappointment.

If we humans can manage our expectations and view all our victories, even the little ones, as wins, we can hack our dopamine production to enjoy more feel-good-factor. By reminding ourselves of all that we can be grateful for, for all the gifts each day brings, we can stimulate those sweet sensations. The beauty is that there are loads of gifts to pick from daily and they're right under our noses.

REASONS TO BE GRATEFUL

Ireland has gone through the 'Celtic Tiger boom' and also the 'bust'. Both have taught us lessons. We have seen the downside of affluent lifestyles where entitlement issues arise. Getting everything too easily often leads to expecting everything easily. From this viewpoint, the best we can hope for is satisfaction, and that's only if we get all we want, when we want it and with ease. What if we were to expect little and then view everything we get as a bonus? That viewpoint would give us "Woo-hoo" moments constantly! We'd spend much of our time with dopamine-soaked brain-tissue, as happy people! All because we choose to not expect that life owes us anything and are grateful for whatever we get.

Try this exercise for an instant realisation of how good we have it:
Start by allowing 10 uninterrupted minutes in a quiet place, sitting or lying in a comfortable position.

Bring your awareness to your feet, by feeling them from the inside, then slowly to your ankles, shins, calves, knees, thighs and hips. Think about how lucky you are to have legs that work. Think about how many steps they've taken in your lifetime, how they allow you to walk, run, jump, dance, climb or kick a ball. Remind yourself of the experiences you have had, the places you've been and all the things you have done because of your legs. Imagine, briefly, what it would be like to not have legs that work and ask what you would give to have them back. How grateful would you be to somebody that restored use of your legs to you? How would it feel to suddenly have them back? Wouldn't you literally jump for joy, dance, run and go to all the places you could not previously? Remember that we don't need to lose our legs to appreciate and enjoy them! If you don't have use of your legs, perhaps you can be grateful instead for all the people that have helped you go where you need to, designed and engineered machinery to allow you to be mobile, created laws to give you equal access to areas, where possible and more. There are always reasons to be grateful. Find them.

Take your awareness now to your mid-section. Marvel at how your digestive system can take the food you eat and use it to create muscles, bones, hair, skin etc. Think of how our lungs use oxygen from the air, how the heart can pump it to every cell in the body, nourishing them, while other organs can purify the body by removing waste. Think about how our reproductive systems can create new life from the tiniest of our own cells. If any of these aren't working so well for you, be grateful for the huge effort others are making to help find you cures. Also be thankful for the many ways we can now support these bodily systems through healthcare and technology.

Take your awareness now to your shoulders and arms. Acknowledge how they've allowed you to carry so much throughout your life. Think of the handshakes, hugs, embraces, rounds of applause and encouraging 'pats on the back' as you held loved ones, greeted friends, inspired and supported others. Remember all the work your arms and hands have done, that afforded you a roof over your head, food in your belly and clothes on your back. Think of all you've created with your hands such as art, music, writing, delicious meals etc., and how much pleasure it gave to you or others. Again, if your arms and hands are not available to you, think of the support you received from others and the opportunity you gave them to be kind, caring and helpful.

Now bring your attention to your neck and throat. Take some time to think of how your voice has benefited you throughout your life. Remember how you have communicated with those around you to ask questions or to teach. Your voice allowed you to seek help or to offer it to another. It let you speak up for your own rights or for those around you. Your voice is a valuable gift. Think of how you made a positive difference when you gave a kind word or some reassurance, told a joke or sang a song. Allow yourself to feel grateful for the gift of a voice.

Take your focus to your face and head. Dwell on your features. Your mouth that has spoken so many words, tasted so many foods and kissed those you loved. Your nose that has enjoyed a vast array of scents, from the sweetest perfumes and foods to the aromas of nature. Smells that have triggered memories that transport you instantly to places you've been and people with whom you've shared your precious time. Your eyes that have been treated to so many stunning landscapes and skies, man-made creations, works of art and gained knowledge from books. How lucky are you to have gazed upon the faces, and connected with the eyes, of many other beautiful people?

Become aware of your entire face, a face that makes you one of a kind among billions! Think of how you share similarities with your ancestors and all humans yet are different enough to be unique among the masses. Embrace that which makes you special. Your face may have features that allow you to stand out in a crowd so that you are noticed and remembered, or it may allow you to quietly go about your business. There are advantages to both. Your face might have lines, earned from expressing a multitude of emotions over a lifetime of experiences. It could have wrinkles that show you are lucky enough to have lived a long and interesting life. Your face may be fresh and new, a blank canvas waiting for the inscriptions of the story of your life. Regardless, your face is adored by those that care for you and they love to see it approach. It is yours to wear with pride.

opening the mind

Go deeper inside now, into your brain. Think of its amazing ability to hold such a vast store of knowledge and memories, images, music, and ideas. Its ability to learn and modify ideas to suit your needs, allowing you to overcome challenges. Acknowledge how your mind can create almost anything through imagination and can figure out ways to turn much of that inspiration into reality. Wonder at the brain's ability to regulate so many system in the body, subconsciously, without needing us to be aware of all of its doings.

Our bodies are magnificent specimens of biomechanics. We should be grateful that we are given a body to live our lives through.

Take your attention now outside your body, taking a moment to fully appreciate each one as you go through this list. The clothing you wear to bring you warmth, colour and a style of your own. Your home that provides you with protection from the elements and a place to feel secure, to unwind. Your own personal sanctuary. Your furniture that gives comfort and support, from the table around which your favourite people may gather to the bed where you rest, recharge and dream. The electronic devices that provide information, entertainment and communication, allowing you to instantly connect with the rest of the world. The equipment and kitchen appliances that reduce your workload, so you have more time and energy to enjoy other activities.

Be grateful for the readily available food, from all over the planet that provides you with nourishment and flavours to tantalise your taste buds. The machines that provide you with transport to take you about your day-to-day activities, both locally and further afield to the far corners of the earth. Think of where all the materials used to create these came from – the stone, wood, metals and plastics that were mined, farmed, harvested or created. Imagine all the people that were involved in delivering these items to your door. The contents of your home will have come, in whole or part, from all over this planet and will have required the effort, ingenuity and energy of countless millions of people to reach you in their current state.

Yes, millions of people of all colours, races and faiths have worked to fulfil your desires. Acknowledge and be thankful for the world-wide network that we are all connected to and benefit from.

Focus now, on the people in your life, currently and in your past. Those who loved you and those who gave you the opportunity to give your love. Those who guided and taught you. Those on whom you could count to be there for you when needed and those who challenged you to become more than you were at that point in time. Those you wish were still in your life but are privileged to possess memories of. Say a quiet thank you for the love, wisdom, support and even the tough lessons people gave you that helped to shape the person you are today.

See how you already have the most important things in life and would not trade them for anything. Look for even more reasons, in your daily life, that prove you are being provided and cared for.

Allow yourself some time to rest in your grateful, contented state. Remind yourself that you are truly lucky for all the gifts you have right now, in this moment.

Mind Matters

Chapter 11

A Positive Mind

"The positive thinker sees the invisible, feels the intangible and achieves the impossible", Winston Churchill

SILVER LININGS

Maybe there actually is a silver lining to every cloud, one we can see clearly if we take the time to look?

Irish people are no strangers to clouds and rain. That's why we rarely appreciate them! In fact, we often refer to a wet day as "miserable". As an island sitting on the edge of the Atlantic Ocean, we get our fair share of wet weather. Unusually, as I write this section we are going through a heatwave, the hottest on record since 1976. It's been officially tagged as a drought and it looks to continue. In contrast, last winter was the wettest I have ever experienced. We had rain almost every day for 6 months, at least it seemed that way. Everybody from farmers to sportspeople were praying for the rain to stop, and for us to get a 'real' summer. This year, after a few weeks of 'real' summer, and with everything and everyone dried out or burnt, we're praying for rain again!

The silver lining from all the rain we usually get is lush growth. They don't call it the "Emerald Isle" for nothing. We may not notice it enough, but tourists are amazed by the shades of green when travelling around our beautiful country. Our beef is second to none as our cattle is fed some of the best grass on the planet. We have rivers, streams and natural springs that never run dry. The reality is we are very lucky. While we can be sure of rain we can also depend on Ireland's lack of extreme weathers. A storm for us is the 'tail-end' of a hurricane that has wreaked havoc elsewhere and has almost run out of gas by the time it reaches us.

I recall one particularly showery day, I went hiking in the hills overlooking my hometown. I sat for a while having reached the top to appreciate the stunning view. I could see for miles. The patchwork of greens across the land, created by the different crops and forested areas. The shades accentuated further by the light and shadow from the sun and heavy rainclouds scattered above. It was as beautiful as any painting, even more so as it was

119

alive and moving. As I watched the heavy rainclouds drift along, one started to shower the land below. It looked like a heavy downpour. I could imagine people beneath it, cursing the rain and pointing out to one another how miserable it was. I thought to myself, "if only they could see what I could?" From a higher, wider perspective, they would marvel at nature's sprinkler system that gave life and colour to the land, and our people. From this point of view, they too would be so grateful, not frustrated. I'm often reminded of the beauty of that scene when it rains and so it never bothers me.

When it snows, our hilltops get a beautiful sprinkling of white for a few days, but it rarely settles elsewhere to cause more than a day of disruption. We got heavy snow this year too, the most we've had for thirty years, but it only lasted two days. The biggest problem we had was the shortage of bread when people stocked up as if we would need to hibernate for months. Most of us got to a day off work to play in the snow. Neighbours talked while the kids played. Kids talked while the parents played. Silver linings everywhere.

Trusting that life will work out for us can save a world of worry. I have had many situations in my life where I wanted things to go a certain way. Looking back now, I'm so glad that life didn't happen 'my way' because it worked out well, often for the better. A well-paid factory job I applied for would have fixed my financial concerns at the time. It also would have been far less satisfying mentally and financially than the career I found since. I would have been bored in that factory job, and certainly unfulfilled. When I didn't get the job, I thought I was unlucky! I'm now grateful that life gave me the space and opportunity to do something else. The relationship that ended, that left me more heartbroken than I would have expected, freed me to enjoy new relationships, new experiences and taught me so much about myself and other people. It also showed me that it's possible to get over such loss and be happy again. We can save ourselves a lot of heartache by trusting that life happens for us and not to us.

Positivity is only partly about hoping for the best to happen, although it is certainly good to be open to positive outcomes. Positivity is more to do with looking for and trusting in the reason behind all that happens i.e. seeking the cloud's silver lining. We may have to look deeply to find that good reason or indeed think outside the box, but it's there, somewhere. Even if we can't find the benefit of a challenging situation immediately, a positive attitude allows us to trust that in time and with patience, the reason will become apparent. I regularly remind my clinic clients that an injury can be the best thing ever if it teaches us to understand and then look after our bodies better. The grief that comes from the loss of a loved one may encourage us to appreciate those that are still in our lives. Failure to reach a goal might drive us to put in extra effort towards greater development of our knowledge and skills. Our past failures and subsequent successes can inspire others to get back on their feet and to keep going after a fall. Heartache often inspires creation of the most beautiful stories and songs. The expression of vulnerability can lead to more openness and trust. The ending of any chapter of our lives can signify the beginning of a new one.

Cultivate an attitude of, 'Everything IS ok right now, as it is' rather than, 'Everything will be ok at some future point in time when something changes' for a greater sense of wellbeing.

POSITIVE AFFIRMATIONS

I have found that belief is a very powerful thing.

To use positive affirmations is to reaffirm or repeatedly say a positive phrase until we genuinely believe it. This makes such phrases part of our 'programming', faith or belief system.

The human mindset is programmable and prone to believing what it is told or thinks repeatedly. Our minds won't necessarily change the first time we hear a new idea, especially if it goes against our previous belief. However, if we are told something enough times, by those we trust, we tend take it on board as fact. This doesn't make us stupid or foolish, in fact it has been of significant use to us in the past. This ability to get on board with other's belief systems has been an important part of humanity's survival. It was our ability to work together that allowed us to become the dominant species on the planet. Unlike creatures such as bees and ants, that are genetically programmed to work for the good of the colony, humans have the option of doing our own thing. To work together, all involved need to have a common goal or belief. Great leaders, or rather the most powerful ones, are those that inspire the masses to believe in them and their plan. This ability has led to the rise of empires, the building of incredible structures like the great wall of China, that can be seen from space with the naked eye, as well as terrible acts of genocide such as the holocaust. These were only possible because people believed that such acts were necessary for a 'greater good'.

We only need to look at advertising to see such programming at work today. Most images will show attractive, happy-looking people using whatever product or service the advertiser is trying to sell. The underlying message is simple, "You can be a happy person if you use our product or service". The insinuation is also simple "You are not really happy enough without it". Advertising is aimed at every age group, male and female to push that, "I'm not good enough" button which is as good as any cash dispenser. We will spend any amount available to feel good enough. Of course, what we believe will make us good enough varies significantly from person to person. Positive affirmations are now essential to counteract the barrage of advertising that tells us daily that we're not already good enough.

ORIGIN OF BELIEFS

Our programming doesn't begin with advertising however, it usually starts with our parents, guardians and family. Idle comments such as "Be a good boy and eat your food", suggesting you're not good if you don't eat everything. Obesity issues anyone? "Sit down quietly like a good girl", suggesting it's bad to speak or express yourself. Is it any surprise people develop issues with verbalising thoughts, feelings or rights? "You made such a mess, you're so bad". Sure, the mess is inconvenient, but does that really make a child a bad person? What if they then fully embrace that role and live it out for the remainder of their lives? "Billy down the street is so great at school and sports" suggesting that others are less than good-enough in comparison. "Why can't you be more like your brother, sister, cousin, neighbour?

These phrases are common in every household and family and are not intended to cause any harm. They're meant to teach social behaviour or simply to point out how well somebody is doing. We do as children, however, pick these up as beliefs and rules that demonstrate our value and can carry them through our lives in a counter-productive way. We will then need to reprogram those limiting beliefs if we are ever to break free from them.

THE SELF-PROGRAMMER

There is one form of programming that I believe is more powerful than all the advertising, religious doctrine and words of others combined. That is our own internal voice. We all have one, that voice inside that talks and thinks constantly. Unfortunately, this voice isn't always as friendly as we would like it to be. Sometimes it's not friendly at all. This constant chatter is often critical and doubtful, reinforcing the, "I'm not good enough" belief. While our yearning to work towards becoming 'good enough' has its benefits and often leads to achievements, innovation and exploration, it can also be counterproductive. It can be extremely limiting, preventing us from doing what we want to, for fear that we will recieve similar judgement from others. Even if we do put ourselves out there and succeed, the achievement rarely convinces us we are good enough and were all along. It often leads to setting another new goal that we hope will make us feel good once we achieve it.

BREAKING FREE

To escape old 'I'm not good enough' programming, we need to develop the realisation that we are innately good enough, regardless of what we do or don't achieve. We can still remain open to the experiences of further growth and development by embracing life and using our talents. Wouldn't it be great to honestly say "Yeah, I'm great as I am. I like me. I'm happy in my own skin. I'm going to do lots with my great self and enjoy it all!". Changing from, "I'm not good enough" to, "I am good enough" is not as simple as flipping a switch, especially if we have spent years believing the former. This is where positive affirmations are powerful. Reaffirming a positive belief helps us to overwrite the negative belief and overpower it so it has little or no effect.

I remember a time, having already done a lot of work on myself through meditation, self-reflection and self-awareness, when I realised that I was still overly tough on myself. Regardless of success in several areas of my life, it still seemed as though nothing I did was ever truly good-enough. I gave lots of time and attention to my children and made a conscious effort to be aware of how I parented them. I was even called "Super-dad" by a school principal Still, whenever I was less than the perfect parent, through tiredness or stress, it would really bother me. At work, I would always remember the patients I couldn't heal, despite having a high success rate in general. I ate healthily and exercised regularly but still felt I should be more muscled, leaner, stronger and faster. I expected more from myself in many ways. I was aware of these thoughts and feelings, and how unrealistic they were but realised that awareness was still only the first step toward conquering them.

Logic told me I was doing well-enough in all major life-areas, therefore it was an 'I'm not good-enough' issue. I needed to convince myself otherwise. I had to get to the root of the belief that made everything not quite good enough. I wanted to dig it out and replace it with something else, so I sat and looked inward to address my 'monkey mind'. I decided to use positive affirmations to overwrite the old, negative programming and remind myself that I was already good enough.

I would reiterate the fact that I do the best I can in every situation, and that's good enough for nobody can do more. I acknowledged that a very high success-rate is good enough as nobody scores 100% all the time. I reminded myself that I love my kids and make a concerted effort to show that but that I'm also human, prone to tiredness like anybody else, and that's good enough too. All of these were logical statements and perfectly sensible, and yet I noticed there was a resistance to believing them. The old programming was ingrained in me, like a song stuck in your head that doesn't go away. It was as if my 'monkey mind' was going "yeah, yeah, keep telling yourself that, you're just not good enough and all these nice little phrases aren't going to change that!"

So, I consciously dug my heels in. I know this may sound crazy, talking to myself as if I had two separate minds but that's how the conscious mind and subconscious mind can be! I told my negative belief, "I AM GOOD ENOUGH!", "If you say I'm not, I'll say I am twice", "If you say I'm not twice, I'll say I am ten times", "If you say I'm not ten times, I'll say I am one hundred times and a thousand times, a million.... And a billion!!". "I will keep saying it again, and again and again until the positive voice becomes the dominant one". I felt a little surge of belief when I did this. I'm even getting a shiver as I write it. That is the power of affirmations.

To add even more power to my self-belief, I imagined that my doubts were the tip of an iceberg, visible on the surface but small in comparison with what lay beneath. My self-belief was the remainder of the iceberg, huge, serene and crystal clear, calmly floating unseen below the surface. At a glance, my self-doubts seemed to cover everything, but they were nothing compared to the magnitude of the self-belief which was the foundation of who I was. To top it off, I then imagined that my body was made of the purest diamond while my confidence issues were merely a spattering of mud that could be simply rinsed away. Rinsed clear or not, I was still unshakeable, unbreakable and fine just as I was.

I continued to re-affirm statements such as these until I felt the change take hold and become part of me. Over time it became normal to feel like I was indeed good-enough. I found it easier to put my failures or flaws into perspective, giving them only the attention they deserved. Here again, the old-fashioned scales of positivity and negativity apply. When we stop filling the negative side and, instead fill the positive, it will start to tip towards positivity. At some point it will break even and then tip in the positive direction. Once we continue to feed the positive, the occasional doubt will have no great or lasting effect. The sheer weight and power of our positive thoughts and beliefs can counter even major challenges. Self-belief becomes our norm.

CREATE AFFIRMATIONS
      Creating your own positive affirmations is quite simple. Find the thought that you know is unhelpful or limiting. Find an opposing thought that you want to make part of your own belief system or programming and repeat it with conviction. How you word it is irrelevant. Some like to use phrases in other languages such as Sanskrit, believing them to be more powerful. For me, it's the belief itself that has the power. The words simply allow us to focus that intention. Keep it simple, clear and concise.

Here are some examples you may like you use;

I am strong...
I am stable...
I am capable...
I am brave...
I am loving...
I am lovable...
I am honest...
I am open-minded...
I am intelligent...
I am important...
I am healthy...
I am lucky...
I am creative...
All is ok...

      Say these and others of your own making as often as you need to. Say them quietly, loudly, shout them, write them, draw them, wear them.

Most importantly, believe in them.

Go to www.highestpotential.ie or the highest potential Youtube channel for guided affirmations, meditations and mindfulness exercises and more.

Always seek advice from a doctor or health professional before considering adjusting medications if on a mental health program.

a positive mind

PART 4

Body Matters

Body Matters

Chapter 12

Developing Physical Fitness

"Fitness is like a relationship. You can't cheat and expect it to work"

This chapter on developing fitness is focused on the fitness that promotes wellbeing rather than the fitness that promotes athletic performance. While the two are not necessarily exclusive, it is common for people to sacrifice wellbeing in the pursuit of success. I hope to give you a better understanding of how your body works so you can make more conscious choices in how you maintain it. This can help you to achieve greater physical wellbeing and opportunities to enjoy your body now and in the future.

ANY BODY BUT YOU

In my experience, a great many of us don't particularly like our bodies. Some of us hate our bodies. I would imagine only a small percentage could genuinely say we love our bodies, top to toe, "flaws" and all. This is a pity since we will never own or operate any piece of equipment as fantastic as the body we inhabit. In my time as a fitness instructor, I have seen clients punish themselves with exercises they don't like just to change a body they like even less. I have seen clients commit vast amounts of time, energy and expense, trying to achieve their idea of a perfect body. For some this desired physique is bigger and stronger, for others it's smaller and thinner. There are also those who body-sculpt to intentionally shape their physiques. I have seen many damage their health in the pursuit of these ideals, through steroids, starvation and excessive training regimes. Why? Because the suffering of intense workouts, muscle aches and deprivation, is preferable to living in a body they don't like or appreciate.

SELF-CARELESS

In my years as a Neuromuscular therapist and fitness instructor, I have seen many people suffer injuries through neglect of their own physical well-being. The causes are many. Too little or too much exercise, posture, poor nutrition, no stretching, stress, too much physical labour, unsupportive mattresses or chairs or ignoring minor injuries until they become chronic. I believe that there is a root cause that underpins all activity or non-action that leads to many injuries or illnesses i.e., a lack of self-care.

LOVE YOUR BODY

Throughout the following chapters on physical fitness, and in your lifestyle and exercise habits from this moment on, I ask you to set an intention to love, respect and take care of your body! It deserves this respect. You deserve this care.

A positive attitude and an open mind contribute hugely to our overall state of health as our mental state has a direct effect on our physical body. However, the body needs direct attention and care to be in tip-top condition. Physical health affects our mental state much as the mind affects our body, hence the common phrase "healthy body, healthy mind". Physical exercise can help us to work off pent-up stress, build confidence, sleep more soundly and produce more "feel-good hormones".

Our physical fitness determines how well we move and interact with the world around us. Everything we do in life is done in and through our bodies. Our bodies literally must last us a lifetime. This is obvious, but we often forget it until later in life when we have taken it for granted and have already done some harm. Luckily for us, we have some say in our physical wellbeing at any age through developing healthier habits. All the effort and energy we invest in cultivating our physical fitness is returned to us tenfold.

Improving your physical fitness and your physique won't make you a better, more valuable or more worthwhile person. You're already Stardust, a miracle of cosmic evolution, remember? Still, fitness does help us to live fuller lives in many practical ways. Life, being the challenging experience that it is, is easier to handle with a body that works well. There are places that a fitter body can comfortably go. Some goals are more achievable by an individual with more energy and vitality. Humans with our genetically predisposed attraction to healthier looking bodies, will generally react more favourably to someone with a healthy glow, good-posture and even proportions. Why not strengthen your hand as you play the game of life?

WHAT IS FITNESS?

I would define fitness as "the ability to perform a task successfully". Ideally, it means doing so with relative ease and comfort, although even if it takes all our effort, but we are successful, we are still said to be fit for the task. Fitness is specific to that which we want to achieve. A weightlifters' goal is to lift heavy loads, an endurance athlete aims to cover great distances and a sprinter wants to run short distances at maximum speed. Each one is fit, but in very different ways. The fitness requirements of gymnasts differ to that of cyclists, tennis and rugby players.

For some non-athletes, our fitness goal is simply to get out of bed, wash and dress, go to work and perform typical daily activities with comfort and ease. For others fitness means pitting their bodies against others in competition for medals. It is our lifestyle, our hobbies and our goals which determine the level of fitness and the forms of fitness, we require to succeed. The starting point for improving your fitness is to decide what kind of fitness you would like to have.

To make fitness development easier, it's helpful to understand our potential for fitness, what it means to be fit and how to achieve it.

OUR POTENTIAL FOR FITNESS

The human body is extremely adaptive i.e. it adapts to the stresses it encounters by changing itself to handle these more efficiently. What we do with our bodies regularly tells our bodies how fit we need to be. If we engage in regular physical activity, the body uses nutrients from our food to make the body fitter through muscle development, increasing our blood cell count, improving neural pathways etc. This will help us to handle the workload more easily.

This, like many human traits, is part of our primitive biological survival mechanism. When regularly traveling long distances on foot, our bodies develop the associated muscles to make us better walkers. The exercise would also stimulate development of our heart muscle to pump blood more efficiently and produce more red blood cells to carry extra oxygen to where it's needed. If we regularly climbed trees for food or safety, the body would develop strength in the climbing muscles of the arms, back and legs, along with some core muscles to help us climb more easily.

It appears that we can improve our fitness at any age by taking up exercise, unless we are already at our peak fitness levels, so it's never too late to start. Physical fitness training can offset many of the conditions we often attribute solely to the aging process. With a little time and effort, we can maintain a healthy level of strength, stamina, flexibility and vitality.

USE IT OR LOSE IT

In this section we'll discuss why we seem to have to work hard to gain fitness only to lose it so quickly when we stop. Rather than using this knowledge as an excuse to avoid exercise, I would hope you use it as motivation to make exercise a part of your routine for life! In doing so you will benefit from that extra fitness right to the end.

We lose fitness, if unused, to save energy and nutrient resources. Our bodies have the amazing ability to downgrade when our full fitness isn't required. Imagine the body as a factory where extra workers are hired and trained in, and new machinery is powered up when there's lots of work to be done. Likewise, workers are laid-off and machinery is powered down when the workload reduces.

In the body, our muscles and cardiovascular system will maintain a "skeleton crew", i.e. the bare minimum needed to manage the workload to be performed. If we lead an inactive life, the body downgrades itself so we can only expect our 'workers and equipment' to be able to handle that lower level of activity. We will then struggle to keep up if the workload increases a little and fail if what we ask of our bodies suddenly increases a lot.

UPGRADING OUR FITNESS

If we want to handle a heavier workload or more activity i.e. get fitter, it takes some time and consistent effort to upskill our bodies. We do this by progressively increasing the workload by small amounts. This extra work must be specific to the goal we wish to achieve. This means that if we want our bodies to be stronger, we must use our strength by consistently lifting or moving objects heavier than we currently lift. We can also increase strength by moving our own body through more difficult movements and positions as is the case with body resistance exercises such as push-ups, chin-ups and lunges. If we want the body to be more flexible, we must stretch it through the many movements it is already designed to perform. Again, we should increase the range of our flexibility slowly, bringing our muscles to positions where we feel a stretch that is comfortable rather than painful. By easing through the tension, we can make our soft tissues more elastic and in time, we will see that we can stretch further with more ease.

If we want more stamina or endurance, we must engage in endurance exercises that require more oxygen to be brought to our working muscles. These will increase our heart and breathing rate and stimulate physiological changes within us to make us more aerobically efficient. All these changes and gains revert to our baseline level should we return to a sedentary lifestyle.

Exercising the body can genuinely feel good while we exercise it. Initially the discomfort level can often outweigh the visible benefits, especially if we push too hard, too soon. The breathlessness, dizziness, muscle burn during exercise and muscle aches in the following days put many off exercise before ever seeing the results. Within weeks this changes as the body develops and the discomfort lessens. By week four of a typical training program, most of us are feeling far better. By week eight the improvements are easily visible, the exercise habit is formed, and the feel-good-factor is high. Getting to week eight is a major milestone. The keys to reaching that stage are finding an exercise form that's enjoyable, committing to the program and having adequate patience to follow through as we "upskill" our bodies. The effort is absolutely worth it, and our bodies certainly deserve it.

SHAPING UP

Firstly, the root message of this book is to remind you that we are fundamentally good enough regardless of shape, size, colour or perceived success. Getting 'in shape' won't make us more valuable or worthwhile human beings. I 've never seen a headstone inscribed with, "Had amazing arms, glutes or bodyfat levels" or, "Fondly remembered for their marathon running time". These generally don't sit on top of any list of important attributes, especially not for the people who care about us! A phrase I read once comes to mind. It said, "People won't remember you for what you did or said, they'll remember how you made them feel". I think we can safely apply, "People won't remember you for what you had" too.

Secondly, we must be realistic about basing our expectations on what we see in advertising and media. Images of super-toned people are taken at their absolute fittest. There are many 'tricks of the trade' used to enhance these images even further. Photos are taken during or immediately after exercise to take advantage of 'the pump' as working muscles fill with blood, becoming fuller and more toned looking. This extra blood is diverted from the gut, so the waist looks smaller while the arms or legs look stronger! The fitness model is likely to be flexing their muscles while perfectly posed. This is an art in itself. They may not have eaten for hours or at all that day to keep their waistline small. Lighting angles and tanned and oiled skin are used to make muscles look more defined.

Then of course there's the photoshopping. Digital wizardry can let photographers do almost anything! Many of the 'before and after' photos, used to advertise nutritional supplements and exercise equipment, are taken within an hour of each other. The before pic is taken with poor lighting, relaxed muscles, paler skin and poor posture. The after pic is taken using the tricks of the trade. How can we expect to look like the fitness model in the photograph when the model doesn't even look like that? Never, ever compare yourself to the people in these images. Also, if you are considering buying whatever fitness product the advertisement is selling, remember that the model, who doesn't look that good all the time, was probably in training long before they even heard of the supplement or fitness equipment they're helping to sell. Rather than aiming for the "perfect" body, remember that a healthy body that works is an achievable and excellent goal.

Thirdly, our body-types are as individual as we are. What it means to be 'in good-shape' will vary from one person to the next. Be kind to yourself and realistic in your expectations. In both sports-science terms and in ayurvedic medicine there are three distinct body-types. Each of us can be any combination of these three categories. The three main body types, in scientific terms, are Endomorphs - large, heavy build, Ectomorphs - lean, slim build, and Mesomorphs - medium, muscular build. In Ayurveda, those predisposed to a Kapha dosha have an earth build i.e. large and soft. Those with a more Vata type build have the quality of air i.e. light, slim. Pitta dominant bodies have the qualities of fire and are muscular, competitive or sporty in nature. Acknowledging our own natural body-type to get it fit and healthy is more important than striving for a body type that is more natural for another.

Lastly, feeling good is more important than looking good but the two can go hand in hand. Taking care of our bodies through healthy living choices will naturally give us a healthier look as our skin becomes clearer, posture improves, muscles tone up and body fat levels balance. Wellbeing shines through in how we look, feel and perform.

PRACTICAL BENEFITS OF GETTING IN SHAPE
So, while we are good enough regardless, there are practical advantages to looking fit and healthy. Due to our evolutionary drives to survive and reproduce, we react differently to people's presentation and first impressions can indeed last. We are drawn to certain physical characteristics when we wish to find a mate or identify weakness. This is why people will almost al-

ways comment when they see a very positive change in someone's physical appearance. We notice and admire such things.

In primitive terms, a healthy look may indicate somebody that will be capable of providing food and protection with strong genes to pass on to our kids, so they have a better chance of survival. In more modern terms we may read, from their physique, that they have discipline, drive, commitment and higher energy levels. We might also guess that they enjoy active hobbies and possess enough self-love to take care of themselves. If single, why not improve the odds of landing a catch? If already in a relationship, it may help to keep the fires of passion burning. "They look too good naked!" is a complaint I've never heard! Wellness often brings with it an easy confidence which can be attractive and pleasant to be around. Being a generally nice person, helps too. Aesthetic beauty loses its appeal very quickly if there's none underneath.

How we look or carry ourselves can sometimes be the difference between being treated with due respect or treated poorly. It's estimated that 75% of in-person communication is non-verbal. We instinctually observe posture and gait, skin and hair condition, odour, muscle tone and body language to assess each other. This creates our impressions of people and influences how we deal with them daily, whether at work, in social circles or romantically. In an equal world we would all be loved and respected as we are. In the reality of the world we live in and the evolutionary forces that shaped us, we judge, and we are judged. Luckily, we get to choose how to play the game by shaping our Stardust in ways that are advantageous.

OBESITY

With obesity levels increasing rapidly in western culture, we can't ignore this issue while discussing health. Obesity is defined by the WHO (World Health Organisation) as abnormal or excessive fat accumulation that presents a risk to health. Obesity is considered a major risk factor for diabetes, cardiovascular disease and cancer. Being skinny isn't necessarily a sign of good health, nor is carrying bodyfat a definitive sign of poor health but obesity is generally an indicator of imbalance in the body and lifestyle.

Many of my past gym clients, having lost extra bodyfat, admitted that they didn't feel good about themselves previously. They had pretended they were fine with their physiques, denying that it bothered them. They hid their bodies with layers of clothing and avoided situations where they might be seen. Many also practiced self-shaming in front of a mirror. Embarrassment from owning an old run-down car or a home in need of repairs is uncomfortable. Living in a body you dislike and can't immediately escape causes stress for many people. This is worth addressing for mental and emotional well-being alone. There are certainly some cases where metabolic disorders and other diseases cause weight gain and fluid retention, and these would need to be addressed by a specialist.

In general, when we are physically active with a balanced diet, most of the energy we consume is used by our muscles to fuel our movement and bodily functions. When we are inactive, the unused carbohydrates and fats will go to our fat stores instead. We'll only 'burn-off' the stored fat when our activity levels increase, and our muscles use more fuel than we consume. Again, this comes from our bodies' survival mechanisms that would save some energy as fat when food was plentiful and use it when food was scarce. These mechanisms haven't yet adapted to the fact that human societies increasingly have access to more food than we need but can survive without moving very much at all. The volume of food we eat is only one part of the puzzle. What and how we eat are also factors. Refer to the "Food and Nutrition" chapter for more on this.

3 PILLARS OF FITNESS

Now that we have a clearer understanding of what fitness is and the potential we possess to develop and maintain higher levels of fitness, we can discuss what I would consider to be the three main aspects of physical fitness. These are flexibility, strength and stamina, and are all areas over which we have much control. Improved levels of each of these three forms of fitness will afford us more opportunities in where we can go and what we can do with our bodies. Developing them will also affect our physical appearance through muscle tone and posture while strengthening our sense of physical wellbeing.

When developing fitness, your training program must be geared towards that end. There are plenty of fitness professionals to lead you down the correct path. Do some research, ask around and invest your time in a good one, then follow their advice.

Go to www.highestpotential.ie for more links and advice on developing physical fitness.

We'll start with flexibility in the next chapter as it is the most obvious aspect of fitness that we are born with but tend to lose as we age as most of us don't develop or maintain it. Even for active or sporty individuals, flexibility is often neglected unless involved in activities such as dancing, gymnastics or martial arts.

Body Matters

Chapter 13

Flexibility

"Notice that the stiffest tree is easily cracked, while the bamboo survives by bending with the wind", Bruce Lee

FLEXIBILITY, OUR PRIMARY FITNESS?

Flexibility is one of the major aspects of fitness that we are born with in abundance. Being flexible makes the birth a little easier on our mothers and ourselves by making us squishier and less breakable. That protective benefit never changes i.e. a flexible, elastic body is less likely to become damaged when stretched. In dynamic activities, elasticity of the body is involved in power generation as our soft-tissues stretch, tighten and then recoil. Examples of these are jumping, sprinting and many gymnastic movements. In normal daily life a loss of elasticity often results in injuries when performing even the simplest tasks. Many of us carry tension in our bodies that restricts us greatly, wrongly attributing it to age or simply "never having been flexible". Those that cannot remember ever being flexible probably lost that natural flexibility at an early age and remained inflexible since by never working to regain it.

There are some muscles in the body that are more prone to becoming short and tight. This is mainly due to people in western cultures tendency to spend too much time sitting, standing with poor posture, and sleeping on poor quality mattresses. I have found through my clinic work that the hip flexors at the front of the hips, spinal muscles of the lower back, upper back and neck, hamstrings at the back of the thighs and gluteal muscles of the backside or rear end tend to be the most problematic. These certainly account for the vast of proportion of imbalances my clients need treated to relieve back pain, neck pain, sciatica etc. As such I recommend that everyone should pay these muscles regular attention.

SEIZED UP

In my late twenties I found myself "seizing up". I was working as a physical therapist, running a home, parenting and going to the gym regularly. My gym program didn't involve much flexibility work though I knew of its importance and so, my muscles got progressively stiffer and tighter. I found that when demonstrating flexibility exercises to my clinic clients to aid in their rehabilitation, I struggled to perform the movements myself. I often hid my discomfort while showing these basic stretches.

I was aware from my earlier years of practicing karate that a higher level of flexibility was possible for me. I figured that I had it before and could have it back again. I also knew that I should be stretching regularly but I put it on the long finger, focusing instead on high-intensity strength and cardiovascular training. This ended when I strained my back while squatting a weight almost twice my bodyweight. I didn't feel too bad immediately after and cut my gym session short but the next morning I could barely get out of bed. The pain was intense and my movement severely limited. For all my supposed fitness, I felt 100 years old and moved like it too. I couldn't pick up my kids, who were only five and six years old at the time and struggled to slowly get myself out of an armchair or car. Even that was at the limits of my pain threshold.

GERONIMO

At one point, during the two weeks I was in the most discomfort, I lay on the ground with my daughter Roma to do a jigsaw puzzle. It was easier to lie out straight than sit and get stuck in an armchair. My son Luca, who was 5 at the time, got the idea to climb up onto the back of the couch. He then proceeded to do a cannonball jump off the couch, while shouting "Geronimo" or rather, "Gerrrooonnimoooooooh" directly onto my lower back.

I can now admire his agility and accuracy and see how funny it must have looked as he propelled himself towards me, sticking his landing perfectly. At the time I didn't appreciate the pain that seared through me on impact nor the thought that I could be paralysed! After I roared with pain and it started to subside, I tried wiggling my toes. They moved. Thankfully, so did everything else and there wasn't any damage done. I was forced to rest from work and gym training for a few weeks. I also reassessed my fitness levels. "How fit are you when you can't do the basics without pain?", I asked myself. Knowing that I was out of balance and this was the proverbial 'kick in the arse' I needed to change that. I decided to take the lesson, learn from it and regain my flexibility by stretching daily.

LOOSENING OUT

At first every stretch was uncomfortable. I couldn't reach anywhere near my toes with my legs straight. Many other movements were difficult, but I persisted. The improvements came slowly but surely. Within four months of regular stretching, my flexibility was almost back to where it was in my martial arts days as a teenager. I felt the benefit in every move I made. I could get in and out of the car with comfort, I could pull on socks easily, I could show my clinic clients how to stretch without hiding a grimace! I've maintained much of that flexibility since as I now see it as an essential aspect of fitness.

I'd like to add that I'm not super flexible, but this extra mobility has proven to be useful in my rugby coaching when demonstrating exercise techniques and body-positions. It also helped when I went on hiking trips, tried a surfing holiday and when I took up yoga. I simply couldn't have done these, at least not with ease, in my stiff and aching state. I'm sure I wouldn't have even tried. Mostly, flexibility gives me easy movement and comfort in my own body. I've certainly been converted to the benefits of stretching and there's rarely a day when I don't encourage a client to make stretching a regular habit.

Visit www.highestpotential.ie or the highest potential Youtube channel for links to flexibility routines, posture advice and more. Always seek advice from a doctor or health professional before starting an exercise program.

HOW ELASTICITY WORKS

It's good to understand a little of the science behind flexibility to see why some development is helpful if we want to feel well in our bodies. Here we'll discuss how the skeleton is moved and supported by our muscular system which is, in turn, surrounded and supported by a fascial net. This fascia is a connective tissue that you will recognise if you have worked with raw meat and noticed the semi-transparent skin-like sheets that lay over and through it. Meat is muscle after all. Understanding how to maintain the health of our fascia is a key factor in freeing up our bodies so we can move with ease.

Bones are the internal frame of the human body and are unable to move by themselves. Joints are the point where two or more bones meet. Some joints are immovable as they are fused together. Moveable joints like knees, elbows, hips and shoulders are held together by ligaments. These ligaments allow a specific range of movement much like hinges hold a door to its frame. Just as the hinge only allows the door to open and close, your knee ligaments only allow the knee joint to bend and straighten, but not bend sideways or twist. Ligaments can be damaged when the joint is forced through an unnatural movement like bending the knee sideways. The muscular system supports and moves our joints by holding and pulling the bones into various positions. Our joints often have a higher possible range of movement than our muscular system will allow due to myofascial tension.

Muscles work in opposing pairs or groups to pull our bones in the direction we choose. When one muscle is shortening or pulling to create movement in one direction, another is lengthening or stretching to allow that movement to occur. Imagine two people on either side of a door holding a handle each - one to pull it open and one to pull it closed. As neither can let go of their handle, one must stretch while the other pulls, if the door is to move. Our muscles must do the same to allow a bone or joint to move - one must relax and lengthen while the other shortens.

This pulling and relaxing occurs all over the body. If a muscle is excessively shortened by tightness, we call it dysfunctional. Several issues can arise from a muscular dysfunction. The opposing muscle(s) will have to pull harder and waste precious energy. The associated joint may be restricted i.e. it will no longer move through its normal range. The dysfunctional muscle may impinge underlying nerves causing referred pain from a trapped nerve.

139

The dysfunctional muscle will pull more on its tendon and tendon attachment causing inflamed tendons and swelling around the joint i.e. tendonitis. Fascial restriction is one of the most common root causes of muscular dysfunction, stiffness and pain.

FASCIA

Muscles and muscle fibres are surrounded and supported by a connective tissue called fascia. A tissue that has come under the spotlight in recent years, its significance is only truly beginning to be understood. Now we see that fascia is the connective tissue that holds most of the body together and is considered by some to be an organ in its own right, possibly the largest organ in the body. To get a sense of the fascia in your body, think of an orange. Imagine the inside layer of the orange-peel is fascia. If we peel off the skin, we see the edible part of the fruit. The thin layer of skin surrounding this part of the orange is also fascia. If we separate the segments of the orange, the skin surrounding the segments is like fascia too. If we split an orange segment open, we will see small pockets of juice. The skin that separates the juice pockets is also comparable to fascia. The material that separates but also holds together all the parts of the orange are similar to fascia in our bodies.

Within the body we have layers upon layers of fascia surrounding our muscles, tendons, organs, bones and blood vessels but also woven into them. Without fascia, we would fall apart inside. The term "net" is often used when discussing fascia for good reason. Imagine your body is surrounded by a net that wraps around every muscle, joint and even your organs. A tight net will feel uncomfortable whereas a flexible and stretchy net feels good – like a perfectly fitting suit.

Understanding our fascia is worthwhile as its health impacts our general health in many ways. When dysfunctional, fascia can restrict our muscle and joint movement as if we were encased in layers of tight spider web strands. These strands can tear with force if we stretch beyond their range. Nerve endings may tear with them and we will then feel pain. When functional, fascia supports our muscles and joints, giving them strength but also easy movement. Unhealthy fascia can stick muscles or organs to other body parts that should slide past each other. These are sometimes referred to as adhesions. I often compare adhesions to superglue between the fingers, preventing them from moving independently. These glued parts can now pull on each other during movement, causing discomfort when there should be none.

Areas of myofascial restriction where the muscle and fascia are contracted (often referred to as knots) can cause nerve impingement, reduced blood flow and pain. Releasing these restrictions will often restore normal healthy function. Soft-tissue restriction can also pull or hold our bones in unhealthy positions affecting our skeletal alignment and posture. The strands of our fascial web are growing all the time to support us in postures that we hold often and to help shorten muscles that we contract regularly. They're a bit like the guy lines we use around a tent to make it more stable. This should have a beneficial effect but if we sit a lot, we can eventually find that our fascia

140

works to hold us in a sitting position but makes it difficult for us to stand up straight again.

CAUGHT IN A WEB

Imagine sitting all day and having strands of spider web laid all over your body. If you get up and stretch fully the next day, you would break many of these strands. Stretch fully every day for years and you will continue to break them, so they never hold you back. But what if you don't stretch fully each day? What if you mostly sat and then just moved a little? How many days and how many strands would it take for you to find you could no longer break free? This is the case for many of us. We often sit with poor posture, forgetting to stretch our hips and spines until we find we have no choice but to sit that way, even struggling to stand up straight. We may forget to reach between our own shoulder-blades and then find we need a stick to scratch an itch. We really should be able to reach any part of our own bodies.

If we do not bend our hips and back fully on a regular basis, we eventually find we cannot reach our own feet to pull on socks with ease. This applies to squatting, reaching over our heads and any movement you can think of. As time passes, we stiffen and find movements becoming more difficult.We then tend to avoid such movements to prevent discomfort. Over time this reduces our ability to move even more until we struggle to climb a stairs, get out of a chair or brush our own hair. We become immobile and lose much of our independence, some becoming virtual prisoners in our own bodies.

Luckily, we have some choice in this and the phrase, "A rolling stone gathers no moss" is appropriate in this case. We can choose to stretch our bodies regularly, through all its movements, to break away strands of fascia that might otherwise stick our tissues together and cause us to stiffen up.

TOO LATE TO STRETCH?

"What if I've already seized up?", you might ask. Well, if many layers of fascia have already tightened around your muscles and joints, stretching through Yoga, Pilates or any other form of exercise will help but may not be enough to release them fully. There may be too many fascial strands binding your muscles in a short and tight state. You will then need some external aid.

Neuromuscular Therapy, of which I am a practitioner, aims to restore movement by manually releasing fascia restrictions through deep-tissue massage, trigger point therapy and various other hands-on techniques. After 15 years of practice, I'm less surprised by the positive results clients' experience, but still impressed, nonetheless. Drastic improvements occur weekly with conditions such as back pain, sciatica, headaches, weak ankles and general aches, pains and stiffness. If more people understood the benefits of myofascial release, they could save themselves a great deal of discomfort. I would also recommend daily stretching exercises to support treatment and create positive changes in the body. Seek out a practitioner to work on you if stretching alone isn't sufficient or you want to boost your progress.

ISSUES IN OUR TISSUES

While it is only in the initial stages of scientific research so there is no hard evidence that I'm aware of, many bodywork therapists including myself believe that our myofascial (muscular and fascial system) hold emotional trauma. It seems as if the fascial system carries information much like the nervous system. These signals are altered by chronic pain and injury. We often use the phrase "issues in our tissues" meaning mental or emotional issues that create problems in the physical body. I have seen many clients with muscular tightness that would normally be associated with intense physical activity, yet they don't engage in such hard labour.

Almost without fail, there are accompanying signs of stress expressed in their tone of voice, body language, posture or a negative or anxious mindset. Very often, during treatments, clients will discuss painful, challenging and traumatic life-events that are weighing heavy on their minds and hearts. This suggests that working on the physical trauma triggers the emotional trauma in the same way that a smell can trigger a memory and the feelings connected to it. I've lost count of the number of times a client has said afterwards, "I don't know why I told you all that!" or "I should pay you for the counselling too!".

A prime example of this physical holding of emotions occurred with a client that attended my clinic several years ago. A fit, active and healthy lady with an excellent quality of life, her only justification for an ongoing back problem was a car accident which occurred over ten years previously. Upon assessment, we found there was significant tension in the musculature running from her pelvis, both sides of her spine, to her neck and out to her shoulders. I explained that it generally took between three and five sessions to release such tension and we got to work.

It was challenging work, for me too, as the tension stored in my client's back was incredibly strong. I can remember my hands aching after our sessions, but it seemed to be beneficial, so we continued. After our third session, there was some progress but not as much as I would have liked so I suggested that perhaps there was some stored stress that counselling or psychotherapy could help release. My client explained that although another practitioner had recommended the same, she herself was sure that all was ok in that department and would continue with physical treatment.

After five sessions there was progress but not enough for my liking, so we decided that taking a break from her exercise routine might help to give her body the chance to improve between treatments. This helped a little, in fact she lost several pounds that she had been working hard in the gym to shift. Her body had been in "stressed mode" and was storing body fat as a result. Some of this weight could also be attributed to inflammation caused by exercising an already strained body. It still wasn't enough to restore her body to full health, so she decided to try another physical therapist to see if she could get to the end of it. She thanked me for all I had done, and I wished her well. I also asked her to inform me, if she found a cure, so that I may incorporate such treatment into my own practice. If I couldn't, I would still have somewhere to send future cases such as hers.

Approximately two years later, I bumped into her outside a shop near my clinic. I could see she was in good health. I said, "You're looking very well, how are you". She replied, "I am very well, thank you". "What did you do?" I asked. Laughing, she said, "I went to a counsellor!". "Ah, did you now" I said and laughed too. She went on to explain that she released more tension in two sessions with the counsellor than we did in all of our deep-tissue massage sessions. I wasn't surprised. I could feel the resistance in her body. It would ease a little in each session but mostly come back within the week. It turned out there was an ongoing family issue that was challenging for her. It was playing over and over in her mind and her body was reacting to it, but she didn't realise it was a problem. Identifying the stress associated with this issue allowed her to minimise its effect so it no longer created such intense physical tension. Perhaps she also addressed the situation with family members so that it was dealt with fully and no longer an issue.

Before we went our separate ways, she said that she would like to book in for a treatment with me out of curiosity – to see how her muscles were at that stage. Two weeks later, during our appointment, there was a significant improvement in her muscular tension levels. At one point, as I massaged her upper-back area, there was what I can only describe as a "clunk". One of her thoracic vertebrae, which must have been held out of its natural alignment for years, suddenly shifted back into position. I asked if she was ok and she responded with a positive sigh, "that has wanted to move for years!". To the best of my knowledge, her back has been in good health since and she went on to become a yoga instructor.

HOLISTIC COMBINATION

That experience truly highlighted for me the importance of a multi-disciplinary and holistic approach to health and wellbeing. In this case the physical treatment had some benefit, as did the mental and emotional treatment but it was the combination that got the best result. It's worth mentioning that this particular client also had a healthy, balanced diet and was a regular exerciser. These helped her greatly to manage her condition and regain a higher quality of health after.

Change in the bodies' condition can take time and effort to restore full movement once more. Full movement, that is, if years of tightness and extra joint compression haven't resulted in some permanent structural damage. Even so, improvements can still be made and are generally sufficient to return to wellbeing and a better quality of life.

I would highly recommend that we all engage in full-body movement programs, performed at least three days per week, at a comfortable intensity. Starting young is worthwhile but is not essential. This is one of the reasons I love yoga so much. With such variety of movement in routines and so many modifications for each posture / asana, there is a form suitable for everybody. Another reason is that yoga strives to work on the mental and emotional states while working on the physical body. It is the most holistic form of exercise I have encountered yet, followed closely by tai chi. This is not surprising

143

to me as they have been developed over hundreds and thousands of years. A weekly class will help to bring positive change, but daily practice is far better. If attending a daily class isn't an option, you could can still practice regularly by learning routines at a class to use at home, or following book, online or Youtube routines. Where there's a will, there's a way!

BEYOND PAID AND STIFFNESS

I prefer the word elasticity over flexibility when referring to a muscles ability to stretch. A healthy level of elasticity is very important for injury prevention but even more important for your physical performance. A higher level of elasticity promotes easy movement, dynamic power and resistance to injury. The term "bounce" has recently become common in rugby to describe when a player side-steps quickly to avoid a tackle or create space in the defence and it fits perfectly. This "bounce" is a gift in most field sports. Recovery times can increase as there are fewer microtears during intense training and with easier lymphatic flow, metabolic waste products can be processed more efficiently.

Breaking down dense myofascial restrictions through soft-tissue release can be an uncomfortable process but is often necessary to regain easy movement or pain relief and so, it is definitely worth it. Regular full-body stretching sessions are your cheapest and least painful method, so add these to your daily/weekly routine for the best results. Keep in mind that stretching should be comfortable. Your muscles will tense if you overstretch to prevent tearing. Be aware that it takes more than 5-10 seconds of stretching each muscle to get results. Even slight discomfort can cause the soft-tissue to contract and tighten. This is the opposite of what we want to achieve when stretching. Holding a gentler stretch for 1-2 mins per muscle or muscle group tends to be more effective. It is also more enjoyable, so we will be more likely to want to practice.

Be patient and allow months of regular practice to see significant improvements in your freedom of movement.

flexibility

Body Matters

Chapter 14

Strength

"Where there is no struggle, there is no strength", Oprah Winfrey

In this section on developing physical strength, my aim is to again show you that we all have the capacity and potential to be stronger. Genetically, some have the potential to become stronger than others. As with many of our physical and mental traits, it is in using our strength that we develop it to reach that potential. Like our other abilities, strength allows us to experience many things that would be unavailable to us without it.

STRENGTH, OUR SECONDARY FITNESS

Strength is the second major component of fitness we must develop as infants. At birth, we do have some natural strength for example our hand grip which is likely a throwback to far earlier times when, as primates, we needed to hold on to our mother's backs. We also have a powerful kick, thought to help develop stronger bones and joints while still in the womb and probably to help push us out of the birth canal. We certainly lack the strength and coordination to hold ourselves upright or to walk, as many other creatures do within hours. It takes a lot of practice and effort to develop such strength as can be seen from the effort babies put into trying to move in the early months. We start with moving our legs and arms, arching our backs and trying to lift our heads. We then progress to rolling onto our bellies, sitting upright, crawling, climbing and standing. Once we have developed enough strength, balance and coordination to move from one leg to the other, we can progress to walking, running and jumping. Having worked so hard to develop these, many of us revert back again due to sedentary lifestyles and a lack of strength building activities. It seems to me a pity to lose much of our strength well before the natural aging process should take it from us.

STRENGTH IN EVERYDAY LIFE

Strength is important to our everyday lives as it allows us to move and hold ourselves in our ideal postures. That includes standing, walking and working. Strength protects our joints and bones when we lift heavy objects, carry children or work in our gardens. Strength gives us the power to engage in high-intensity activities through sport or hobbies such as hiking. Strength in our muscles protects us by absorbing much of the impact when we fall. This reduces the likelihood of breaking bones, tearing tissues and dislocating joints. Developing strength in our muscles also creates a firmer muscle tone which gives us a more athletic, fitter appearance.

STRONG BODY, STRONG MIND

The mind-body and body-mind connection can benefit from developing strength too. Creating strength in the body can give us more mental and emotional strength and stability. We often feel emotionally stronger from knowing that we are physically strong and this knowledge boosts self-confidence. It also proves to us that we can achieve goals through our discipline and effort. We can then trust in this ability to reach other goals in future. Our muscle tone is a key factor in getting in shape, along with posture and bodyfat levels. Since muscle strength can help with posture, active muscle tissue burns fat as a fuel and muscle gives us shape, the confidence from owning such a body transfers into other areas of our lives where making impressions count.

SELF DEVELOPMENT

Having improved my own stamina fitness, increased my energy levels and lost my "puppy fat" at the tender age of 13, I soon decided to continue looking at ways I could develop my own body. I could see that "fit" people looked more muscular and so I made a stronger physique my goal. I bought some Joe Weider free-weight dumbbells, which came with an exercise chart showing the muscles they would develop. The exercises were difficult to begin with, but I believed in the "no pain, no gain" theory and after the initial soreness, I enjoyed the effort. The "burn" sensation as I reached muscular fatigue and the muscle aches over the next few days told me it must be working!

As I grew stronger, my two small dumbbells became too light to challenge me, so I put them both into an old gear bag and lifted them together. I outgrew that too and bought some more free-weights, but my bedroom space was limited, so I decided to go to a gym. Gym training wasn't all that popular in my hometown of Clonmel in the mid 90's. There was a small but successful powerlifting club that I felt was a bit out of my league and a small gym attached to the local swimming pool that I was too young to attend.

Luckily for me, only minutes from my house was a backyard shed, converted into a gym by two brothers and their friends that charged a small weekly fee to cover maintenance costs. I remember the first time I went in there. It looked to me like a 'Rocky' gym with rusty iron weights, machines and mirrors. It had barbells, dumbbells, benches, cable pulley-machines, chin-up and dip bars, an exercise bike and a punch-bag in the corner. The equipment was old but very functional and the mirrors were everywhere to check your technique and have a quick pose when nobody was looking. Between the mirrors were posters and calendars of the bodybuilders you might aspire to look like.

There was no official gym instructor, but the members were quick to offer help, encouragement and advice. A few of the gym users were huge and judging by their size, I imagine, chemically enhanced. Steroids were not as widely available then as they are now, but they could be found if you asked the right people. Most simply ate well and trained hard. This was my approach also as health was still my priority. I believed that using hormone altering drugs could do more harm than good. I also felt it would lessen my sense of accomplishment from any gains I made, if drugs were responsible for some of it. I used protein powders regularly to supplement my diet as I simply couldn't eat enough fish, eggs or meat to match my training intensity. I'm sure they helped but my interest in using supplements has waned since, and now that my exercise levels are reduced, I opt for real food only.

MUSCLES FROM BRUSSELS

I began practicing Karate at 15 and continued with gym training 3 times per week, hoping I'd end up looking and moving like the Hollywood action star Jean Claude Van Damme, aka "the muscles from Brussels". I never did get that muscular. I don't have the genetics for it, but I did get more muscled than I would have been otherwise and far stronger! The extra training contributed greatly to my Karate performance. With several years of strength development, I was still quite light in build but unexpectedly strong which gave me an advantage in sparring competitions. Our strongest muscle fibres are also our fastest which I'm sure improved my reaction times. Essentially, I was "Strength and conditioning" my body at a time when few Irish amateur athletes did so. My strength gains also reinforced the understanding that we can develop ourselves by investing a little time and effort.

HOW STRENGTH WORKS

Understanding a little of the physiology of how our muscles work makes it easier to accept the need for regular strength-specific exercise. This knowledge will also clarify why strength is built over time and maintained consistently afterwards. You will find links to videos to help you with your strength training program on www.highestpotential.ie and highest potential YouTube channel. You will also find that there are many excellent instructors and fitness facilities to aid you in your goals. My primary goal here is to encourage you to see the benefit of strength training, set a goal and find your way to achieve it.

I would define strength as "the amount of force our muscles can generate to move the body or another object or the capacity to withstand a great force or pressure". Strength is our ability to lift ourselves, to lift or move other objects or to bear weight or pressure safely. Our strength, aka the force we generate, occurs through contraction (shortening) of the muscle fibres that pull on their tendons which are attached to the bones, thus creating movement of the skeleton. When people talk about "pulling a muscle", they mean straining the muscle. Pulling is what muscles are supposed to do! We move ourselves because a muscle or group of muscles pulls some part of our body

149

in the way we want them to. That applies to standing, walking, jumping, chewing, blinking and every other movement you can think of.

To be truly strong is to have enough strength to move the way we want to, with relative ease and without causing any harm or injury. To a weak body, common movements are impossible or may cause injury. To a strong body, such movements and are well within our comfort range. Strength allows us to perform in ways that weakness prevents.

3 FIBRES, 3 STRENGTHS

I'll start with a little muscle fibre anatomy, followed by an analogy that I hope will give you a practical sense of how muscles work. It should also help you to understand why variety in exercise routines or daily activity is necessary for us to enjoy all-round functional fitness. Functional fitness is fitness that allows us to function day-to-day and in our relative sports or hobbies. While functional fitness will improve our physiques, its main goal is to give us greater use of our bodies.

Skeletal muscles, the ones we use to move our bones, are made of many tiny fibres. We all have a mixture of three main types of muscle fibres. The proportion we have of each type is as individual as we are, and our body types and genetic make-up decides what percentage of each we are born with. This explains why some of us are naturally very strong, some are naturally high in stamina and others lie somewhere in between.

Type 1 muscle fibres are thinner than the others and lower in strength but with a higher capacity for stamina. These are excellent endurance muscle fibres as they can generate a low level of power repeatedly, before tiring out. We use these fibres for the lighter physical tasks and low intensity exercise. Light and lean marathon runners would naturally have a high proportion of these Type 1 fibres.

Type 2a muscle fibres, are thicker in size, have a medium capacity for strength and stamina. They can generate a higher force than Type 1's but will fatigue sooner. We use these muscle fibres for more strenuous physical tasks and mid-range intensity exercises that tire us out more quickly. A muscled but lean rower is likely to have a higher proportion of Type 2a fibres.

Type 2b muscle fibres are the thickest in size, highest in strength but lowest in stamina. They can generate a lot of power for a short period of time before reaching fatigue. This means they can work at a very high intensity but only for a few seconds before they become exhausted and must rest. We use these for the most physically demanding tasks. Big, stocky powerlifters or heavily muscled sprinters have a higher percentage of these.

MUSCLE FACTORY

One analogy I like to use to explain how our 3 types of muscle fibres operate within the body is to imagine 3 types of workers in a factory. The 1st worker types have a very light build and are low in strength but have great stamina. Worker Type 1's can handle all the lighter jobs, working away without much need for rest for most of the day. If the factory's workload only requires Worker Type 1's, that's all that will get involved and the rest lie dormant. All the other workers Type 2a's and 2b's are available but will remain idle until they're called upon. A practical example of how we often use only a fraction of our strength can be seen when picking up an egg. If we were to use all the strength our hand can summon by recruiting all our muscle fibres, we would crush the egg by over-squeezing. By engaging a small percentage of our smaller, weaker fibres we can squeeze the egg with just enough force to pick it up, without breaking it.

Worker Type 2a has a bigger build and is quite a bit stronger than Type 1. Worker Type 2a is capable of handling heavier tasks when needed but won't get involved in the light tasks that the Type1 workers can handle alone. The medium Type 2a workers will only get stuck in when the factory's workload increases, and the lighter Type 1 workers need help. Likewise, in muscle terms, our Type 2a muscle fibres only get involved when we are working at an intensity that is higher than the Type 1 fibres can handle alone. Examples of this are times when we lift heavier objects or run faster.

Worker Type 2b's are very big and strong. These will only get involved when the job is too difficult for both the Type 1 and 2a workers combined. Worker Type 2b's are suited to lift extremely heavy objects and sprint explosively but will get tired very quickly from all that effort. Their recovery time is slower than the others and will need to be rested for longer periods before they are ready to work hard again.

EFFICIENCY
If most of the jobs in the factory are very low intensity and only require some of our Worker Type 1's, only these few will become more efficient, but the rest will become less so. This means that we could have most of our strong and medium workers inactive and dormant but also maybe half of our light workers. It's like having a huge workforce available but only a small percentage are actually geared up to do some work. This equates to a sedentary lifestyle where we only do the most basic activities but drive everywhere and sit lot. If we do a lot of low intensity work such as walking, and light physical movement, then most of our Type 1 workers will be fit and active as they are working regularly.

If the factory's workload increases to a point where all our Type 1's are working hard and the stronger type 2a's have to step up and help out, they will do so. However, if they haven't worked for some time, it will take a while for these workers to get up to speed again. Some patience and consistency will be required. They have been redundant and are out of practice, so they will need to be retrained. This is the case with our Type 2a muscle fibres. If we haven't engaged in moderate intensity activities, in recent times, our Type 2's will be slow to get going. This is part of the "use it or lose it" principle. If we push ourselves a little by taking on more physically demanding activities, our Type 2's will start to wake up again. With patience, time and training, they will become efficient and valuable workers once more, improving the overall efficiency and productivity of the body.

It is only when the factory has times of peak demand that the biggest and strongest Type 2b workers play their part. Remember that they cannot work all day as they fatigue easily but when the pressure comes on and there's fast and heavy work to do, these workers are the experts. In the body these Type 2b fibres help when there's heavy lifting to do or speed work. This could be the lifting of a heavy wheelbarrow or buckets in the garden or carrying heavy shopping bags or luggage. It could mean sprinting to catch a bus or a child that's darted off. It could even be the opening of a tight jar lid. Any situation that requires a high level of effort calls in the big guns. Again, if they've been laid off for extended periods, they will be unfit to perform. They won't be of much use initially and will need to be trained in again if they are to be ready for action when we call on them.

PEAK PRODUCTION

So, to stay with this analogy, in an ideal world, if we wanted our factory to be fully efficient and productive, how would we do it? We would develop our workers to do exactly what we need of them. We would give them regular work and training that allows them to hone their skills. We would feed them with healthy foods. We would take care of them with healthcare plans, massage, physical therapy and give them adequate rest between shifts. As our workers become more skilled and capable, we could increase the workload so that our factory is even more productive. With such a healthy and well cared for workforce, we could also expect fewer injuries and sick days.

In the body, this super-efficiency can be seen at the highest levels of sports. The rest of us mere mortals don't need that level of fitness to go about our day-to-day business with ease, but we can aim higher in our expectations of fitness than many of us currently do. Full-body exercise programs that combine a variety of activities to challenge our various strength and stamina levels should keep all our muscles fibre types active, toned and primed for action.

To sum-up strength fitness, our bodies have the capacity to be efficient and adaptive. Our lifestyle choices and activity habits will decide how much fitness we require and stimulate strength development within the body. For some, our jobs or our hobbies will involve a lot of activity that will keep our bodies highly efficient. If this is not the case, we must find activities to develop strength so it's available to us when we need it.

Exercises that work our type 1 muscle fibres (the lightweights);
Low intensity activities that we can do repeatedly for several minutes or more.

Examples of which include;
Walking, jogging, distance cycling, distance rowing.

Exercise that works our type 2a fibres (the middleweights);
Medium intensity activities that we can perform or sustain for 1- 5 minutes before fatigue sets in.

Examples of which include;
Steep hill-walks, stair climbing, rowing, cycling, running-sprints, weight training 8 - 20 repetitions.
Exercises that works our type 2b fibres (the heavyweights);
Maximum intensity activities that we can perform for 1 to 20 seconds before fatigue sets in.

Examples of which include;
20 - 100m running sprints, short distance cycling / rowing sprints, weight training 1 - 8 repetitions.

Go to www.highestpotential.ie or the highest potential Youtube channel for links to full-body strength programs and more.

Always seek advice from a doctor or health professional before starting an exercise program.

Body Matters

Chapter 15

Stamina

"Grit is that 'extra something' that separates the most successful people from the rest. It's the passion, perseverance and stamina that we must channel in order to stick with our dreams until they become a reality", Travis Bradberry

It is stamina that helps us to keep going when we need to rather than giving in or giving up. We rely on higher levels of stamina when we climb great mountains, run marathons or cycle vast distances. We also use stamina when working physically demanding jobs or perhaps are on the go all day looking after a family and home. When our lives and our goals demand that we keep pushing on, stamina is our greatest resource. Working on this can also improve our heart and circulation health, increase energy levels and reduce excess bodyfat.

In this section, I would like to explain the amazing system that allows your body to turn a breath into movement. I use the analogy of our blood's circulatory system as similar to a network of streams and rivers that blood cell "boats" use to carry oxygen and other fuel to all the cells in our body. Understanding this will allow you to appreciate your body even more and give you a greater capacity to develop your own stamina fitness. Before getting into the details of how it works, I'd like to explain why I highly recommend adding some endurance development to your routine.

FAT TO FIT

No offence is intended in my use of "fat" in this section heading. It's a term that I would have used in 1991 to describe myself. When I first ventured into fitness development at 13, stamina was where I saw the greatest improvement. Previously, I would have become breathless quite quickly at soccer training, P.E. (physical education classes) at school, or just playing football on the green outside my house. I still remember being embarrassed one day when a group of us cycled to Loch Mohra, a lake in the hills about 12km from Clonmel. At one point, on a steep climb, I had to stop and get off my bike. I thought and said aloud, "I'm going to die". I could barely catch my breath and felt awful.

155

The others found this funny as they were fitter and better able to handle the effort. The fact that I remember this tells me that this experience played a part in my decision to make a change. Within 6 weeks of starting a daily exercise program, my aerobic fitness had risen dramatically, my energy levels skyrocketed, and I had burned a stone (14 pounds / 6kg) of excess bodyfat while fuelling my efforts. Carrying less bodyweight made it even easier to move. I could now run all the way to the local shop and back with ease. Although I was far from being the most skilled, I could play football at a higher intensity for far longer which made it more enjoyable. It didn't make me a better human being and I know now that there was nothing wrong with having some extra bodyfat, but I felt a lot better.

STAMINA, OUR TERTIARY FITNESS

Endurance is the third of the three main aspects of our fitness we develop naturally as children. I would define stamina or endurance as the ability to perform an action repeatedly, hold a position or posture or withstand pressure for extended periods of time.

High stamina levels are possible when our endurance muscle fibres and cardiovascular system are working efficiently together. We discussed the three types of muscle fibres in the last section and it is the Type 1 fibres we are mostly concerned with in relation to stamina. Because our Type 1 endurance muscle fibres rely heavily on a strong supply of oxygen to create energy for movement, our ability to get oxygen from the air to our muscles is just as important as having active and fit Type 1 muscle fibres.

Like other areas of personal development, the payback from improving stamina is significantly greater than the time and effort we put into it. Higher stamina levels allow us to walk, run or cycle longer distances without becoming breathless, and to play sports, dance or swim comfortably. In our daily life, stamina allows us to work longer in our jobs, home or garden without needing rest. As per usual, our stamina levels are largely determined by the activities we engage in on a regular basis. Unless already at the peak of our stamina development, most of us can improve our levels if we choose to.

BREATH FUELS MOVEMENT

To begin with, we must draw air into our lungs by inhaling. Flexibility of the muscles around the ribs allows for greater ribcage expansion, while strength in the diaphragm and some other inspiration muscles allow for a more powerful inbreath. Together these give us a deeper and fuller breath, so we can draw a greater volume of air into our lungs. Having healthy lungs that aren't damaged by smoking helps as a shallow breath cannot take in as much air. I try not to be a preachy anti-smoker, but I do see smoking as one of the most pointless, unhealthy habits there are. Damaging the organ that takes life-giving oxygen from the air seems ridiculous to me!

Next, we must get oxygen from the air in our lungs into our bloodstream. We have tiny blood vessels called capillaries that wrap around the alveoli in our lungs. Oxygen can pass through the walls of these capillaries from the lungs. This oxygen then attaches to blood cells in our blood stream. I like to picture these blood cells as boats that carry oxygen bubbles from the lungs and away through the bloodstream. The 'streams' that carry these blood cell "boats" have many tubes or waterways (veins and arteries) that run throughout the body. This 'water' (blood) is pumped by the heart much like the water in a radiator heating system needs a pump to move it through the pipes and radiators.

The heart has four pumping chambers. Of the larger two chambers, one pumps blood to the lungs to pick up oxygen in a loop that leads back to the other heart chamber. The second, stronger chamber pumps this blood which is now carrying oxygen to the rest the body. When these blood cell "boats" reach a muscle cell that needs it, the oxygen moves from the blood cell to the muscle cell. The muscle cell uses this oxygen, with some fuel in the form of carbohydrates or fats to create energy for movement. I like to compare this to a combustion engine that uses diesel and oxygen to ignite. The energy released then creates movement within the engine itself that then propels the car. If you think your car engine is an impressive feat of engineering, I would like to remind you that it is child's play compared to what's going on in your own body!

At the same time, carbon dioxide (a by-product of the muscle's energy production) moves from the muscle cell to the blood cell "boat" to be carried back to the lungs. This carbon dioxide moves from the blood cell to the lungs and is breathed out. We breathe in again and the cycle continues over and over. We breathe in air, take the oxygen from it to nourish our cells and we breathe out the carbon dioxide that is waste to our bodies. This process continues throughout our lives. Interestingly, the carbon dioxide "waste" that we and other creatures exhale, is "breathed" in by plants and trees who then "exhale" oxygen in an even greater world-wide breath cycle that allows us all to live.

The average person takes about 16 breaths per minute which is roughly 23,000 breaths per day or close to 8.5 million breaths per year. Pretty amazing isn't it? Even more amazing is the fact that, at rest, the average person's heart beats roughly 70 times per minute, over 100,000 times per day or over 36.5 million times per year! Of course, those figures would be dwarfed by the number of times red blood cells pick up some oxygen and deliver it to working muscle cells. See how even "average" human bodies are truly magnificent and worth taking care of? Does that make you want to look after your heart and lungs?

UPGRADING OUR STAMINA

When we perform activities that require more stamina such as walking, jogging, cycling, swimming and dancing, we adapt internally to become more efficient at carrying and delivering oxygen. Our bodies upgrade our oxygen delivery system a.k.a. our Cardiovascular System, by strengthening the heart muscle to pump a higher volume of blood each time the heart beats. Our body also grows extra red-blood cells, so we have more oxygen -carrying "boats". Our bodies can even develop new blood vessels or improve existing ones to give us more or bigger streams and rivers for those boats to travel through. The result is that those with extra red blood cells, improved blood vessels and a stronger heartbeat can absorb and deliver more than twice the oxygen inhaled compared to their unfit counterparts. This explains why fitter individuals have a lower resting heart rate. An efficient Cardiovascular System means the heart can beat more slowly when the body is at rest and still supply the whole bodies' oxygen needs.

HEART-BREAK

Level	Per min	Per hour	Per day	Per year	80 years
Unfit	90	5,400	129,600	47,304,000	3,784,320,000
Average	70	4,200	100,800	36,792,000	2,943,360,000
Fit	50	3,000	72,000	26,280,000	2,102,400,000
Very fit	40	2,400	57,000	21,024,000	1,681,920,000

Getting aerobically fitter actually gives our heart a break of sorts. By making it more efficient, it takes less effort for the heart to get it's work done. If we look at the chart above, we can see there is a significant difference in the number of times the heart of a fit person will need to beat compared to an unfit individual. If we could reduce the workload on a mechanical pump, we could safely assume that it should last longer before wearing out. We often talk about 'wear and tear' of our skeletal muscles and joints and we accept that, but what about the wear and tear or stress on the heart? Shouldn't it be spared when possible?

An unfit person's heart rate, at rest, works at around 90 beats per minute or over 3.75 billion beats over an eighty-year lifespan. Super-fit people can maintain a resting heart rate of 40 beats per minute or 1.7 billion beats over the same lifespan. That's a difference of 2 billion heart beats! Miguel Indurain, a five-time tour de France winner was recorded as having a resting heart rate of 28 beats per minute which means his heart only needed to beat once every two seconds. As most of us are not at rest all day, every day, our actual number will be a bit higher depending on our activities. However, a lower resting heart rate is reflected in a lower general heart rate. While engaging in the same activity or work, the fitter persons heart rate is likely to be far lower than the unfit persons.

Upgrading the body from unfit to average or average to fit could save your heart over 10 million beats per year. If your heart could thank you for that, I'm sure it would! Much of the rest of your body would also be pleased with your newfound fitness levels as your balanced exercise program raises your energy levels, tones your muscles, reduces excess bodyfat levels, improves circulation and increases feel-good factor through serotonin production. You may also get a longevity boost. Heart rates in mammals tend to be inversely proportionate to their average lifespan i.e. a higher heart rate usually means a shorter life. Lowering your heart rate could give you extra years to enjoy. When physically fit, active and energetic, those extra years should give you quality along with quantity.

WHAT TO EXPECT?

In my experience of endurance fitness training, there is a "hump" that most people need to get past to see very noticeable improvements in their aerobic fitness. This hump is often passed as early as 6-8 weeks into training. Almost everybody experiences great progress by the 12th week, once a balanced exercise program is followed consistently and combined with a balanced nutritional program.

There are various approaches to deciding how intense exercise should be. Some believe in "no pain, no gain", some like to wear heart-rate monitors and increase or decrease the intensity to work at a specific heart rate. If you have a pre-existing heart condition, I would certainly recommend using a heart-rate-monitor. I personally prefer to listen to my body and as such, I have been a fan of the R.P.E. scale for many years. This stands for Rate of Perceived Exertion. To use this scale, you simply apply a number, out of ten, to rate the level of exertion or effort you experience while exercising.

How to rate your exertion level;

1	At rest with no exertion beyond the effort of breathing
2	Resting but with slight effort such as sitting upright
3	Light, very easy movement
4	Active but could comfortably sustain for hours
5	More active, noticing increased heartrate and breathing rate
6	Very active, sustainable, can hold a short conversation
7	Challenging activity but could sustain for 30 mins plus
8	High intensity activity, difficulty speaking more than a few words
9	Almost maximum effort, sustainable for maybe 15-30 seconds
10	Maximum effort possible, exhausted within 10 seconds

The best thing about using this scale is that it is personalised and requires no equipment or instructor to monitor. Jogging at 8km per hour for example, could be rated a 5 by an experienced and fit runner but an 8 to an unfit beginner. Aiming to exercise at an effort rating of 6 or 7 will stimulate your body enough to improve its cardiovascular fitness without overstressing the system. To reach this 6 or 7, the unfit beginner may need to walk briskly initially, rather than jog as jogging could be too intense.

As the beginner gets fitter the brisk walk will become easier, lowering to a 5 on the scale. Then, some jogging would need to be introduced gradually to reach that R.P.E. rating of 6 or 7. Using this scale promotes steady improvement within a manageable comfort range. When we peak and fitness gains level off, using this scale allows us to maintain what we have developed.

This scale also allows us to modify our exercise according to how we feel on the day. If we are feeling a little tired, we will naturally do a little less to reach our 6 or 7. If feeling more energetic, we will naturally do a little more. This, I feel, is far more beneficial than sticking to a set distance, speed or intensity no matter what the body is telling us.

STARTING OUT

Consult a doctor before beginning any exercise program if you have any health concerns. In the earlier stages of fitness development, advice and instruction should be sought to get the best results and remain safe. It took me years to learn the shortcuts to getting results. There is no easy route to fitness but there are certainly ways to train and eat smarter. Professional advice can allow you to benefit from your instructor's years of experience, using their motivation and encouragement to get you through the tougher times and over any humps you encounter. In time, as you learn about your body and develop good habits, you will need less support from professionals and can develop your own training programs and nutritional plans to suit your needs.

A very simple way to begin developing stamina without equipment or cost, is to commit to 30 mins per day of walking. If fitness levels are very low this can be divided into 2 x 15 min walks, 3 x 10 or even 6 x 5 mins. If extremely unfit, 1 min walks to a front gate or around the house will bring about positive change. The key thing is that you aim to reach a 6 or 7 on the R.P.E. scale.

When physically capable, start to introduce a slow jog for 10 - 30 seconds out of every 5 mins. Slowly, week by week, increase that jog time to 40 seconds, then 50, 60 etc., staying within your 6/7 R.P.E. Always listen to your body and stop if you feel pain, discomfort or dizziness. You should find, over time, that you will spend more of your time running than walking. Eventually you should be jogging the entire 30 mins. You could seek out a local running club for advice and motivation as many have programs aimed solely at beginners. If running is not your thing, you may stick to walking, but as your fitness improves, challenge yourself with a faster pace and hilly routes to stay exercising at a 6/7 R.P.E. You could also join a hill-walking club for company and guidance.

This approach of consistency, listening to your body and gradual improvement should be applied to any form of exercise you begin i.e., swimming, cycling, dancing, aerobics, yoga, gym training etc. I would highly recommend combining several forms of exercise to develop all-round fitness, more social contact and to keep your exercise program interesting.

Visit www.highestpotential.ie or the highest potential channel on Youtube for videos on stamina development and more.

Always seek advice from a doctor or health professional before starting any exercise program.

stamina

PART 5

Emotion Matters

Emotion Matters

Chapter 16

Emotions

"One of the reasons I was so unhappy for years was because I never embraced my emotions and I was trying to stay in control", Demi Lovato

THE PURPOSE OF EMOTIONS
      I believe that the meaning of life is to experience life in whatever form it presents itself, and that emotions are an integral part of the human experience. Emotions bring colour and flavour to an experience that would otherwise simply amount to facts and details. A stunning sunset is just a mixture of colours without the feeling of wonder and awe that accompany it. A pet dog, without the feeling of companionship and caring, is simply another creature that requires feeding and attention, and in some cases, protects you and your property. Looking upon the face of your new-born child would not be so magical without the overwhelming sense of love that flows through the parent. Winning a final, or achieving a great goal is just another event, if not for the feelings of accomplishment and the sweet taste of victory.

EMOTIONAL GUIDE
      I also believe that emotions serve to help guide us towards our life's purpose and realising our full potential. Winning at life is more about feeling like we're winning life than reaching any specific goal. Our thoughts provoke feelings that tell us if that thought is productive and beneficial, just as our physical sensations tell us if our physical actions are helping or hurting us. Our feelings are our greatest guide, not always to reality, but rather a guide to how we are perceiving our reality. As such, our feelings must be acknowledged and respected. They must be felt and used to address our mental state and life choices.
      Sometimes it is the feelings of loss that show us how much we valued what we had, teaching us appreciation for what remains. The value of any person or thing is based on our perception of its worth but it is the emotional value we place upon it that makes it truly meaningful to us. Our greatest and most transformational life experiences are measured by how we felt in relation to a situation rather than the facts of the event. Without the emotional

165

element of our experiences, our lives would become quite robotic in nature and rather tasteless. I'm not sure that music or art of any form would exist if not for our need to be stimulated emotionally.

Several years ago, though I enjoyed good health and was satisfied with my life in many ways, I was discontented. My life had become routine, my timetable almost identical each week, divided between work and family life. I had ideas and plans for books, workshops, music, rugby coaching and more but I wasn't doing very much to bring them into my reality. My conscious mind was focused on the day-to-day necessities but something deeper inside me wanted more. Perhaps it knew I was destined for more even when I consciously didn't. This feeling only changed when I fully started to pursue my dreams. Previously, I would wake up feeling like I should be more grateful but thinking, "Here we go again, another day another dollar". Now I wake up looking forward to what the day will bring thinking, "how much will I get done today?". There is a zest for life, for learning, for growth and development and for the new experiences I will encounter as I go. I trust my intuition now and other subtle feelings that poke me to say, "Hey, this isn't your way" or "Hey, this is good, do it more!"

It's interesting to me that we can so easily disregard or distrust our gut feelings in favour of a thought when our thoughts can be totally fabricated by the imagination, sometimes with no sound basis. If we felt tightness around our waist we would expect, and most likely check, to see if our clothes are too tight yet a tightness in the gut or uneasy feeling can be left unaddressed. How often do we say, in hindsight, "I had a feeling that..." but never gave it enough credit? Logic and good sense certainly should be involved in decision making but emotions deserve a seat at the table, perhaps even at the head of it! It is also quite interesting that the citizens of developed countries spend much energy and resources on home-comforts to feel more contented but only a fraction of that to feel emotionally at ease.

Our physical sensations of touch and temperature are triggered by external sources. We feel emotions just as we feel the physical sensations of hot, cold or pressure on our skin, yet we do not have the obvious stimulus of a warm fire, cold-water or the touch of another's hand to explain them. We feel certain emotions in specific areas of our bodies such as love in our hearts or anxiety in our guts. We can feel emotional pain without a physical cut or bruise in sight. Beautiful moments can make our spines tingle and sad moments make our eyes leak. Emotions affect our physical world.

Physical feelings can also tell us what's going on inside us. An internal pain indicates that there's injury or dysfunction that we cannot see. A feeling of tightness can show us there's a restriction or blockage within our tissues and tiredness tells us we need rest. Physical feelings serve the purpose of telling us that we're doing well, when feeling good, or not so good when unwell, to perhaps take more care of ourselves. To acknowledge and address such feelings is a great step towards improving well-being in the body. The same holds true for emotions as the wide range of feelings we experience serve to identify emotional ease or dis-ease. It is important to remember once more that our physical, mental and emotional selves are all part of the one entity that we call a human being. These can be separated by words and terminology but not in any meaningful way. Each part is linked to the others.

RANGE OF EMOTIONS

According to the Greater Good Science Centre, based at the University of California, Berkeley there are 27 distinct emotions, all interconnected with varying intensities. This is in contrast to a previously held belief that we had 6 primary emotions of happiness, sadness, anger, fear, surprise and disgust. Our emotional health is quite complicated. Identifying exactly how we feel and putting a word on it can be challenging. Allowing ourselves to fully feel our uncomfortable emotions takes bravery. It's sometimes easier, but only in the short-term, to distract ourselves from the brunt of difficult emotions with work, tv and hobbies or to numb them with medication. Long-term, unresolved emotional issues and their root causes can be damaging to our physical, mental and emotional state and those around us.

Once we've identified them, we'll want to heal our emotional issues so that we can live in a more balanced emotional state. One difficulty encountered with working on our emotions is that while their effects on the physical body can be seen through muscle tension, high blood-pressure or perhaps self-harming, treating emotional disharmony is not as simple as splinting a broken bone or stitching a wound. To get to the root of emotions we often need to look elsewhere in the body. We must observe our surroundings or lifestyle, perhaps our sleeping patterns, diets, relationships, hormonal systems, or commonly, to the thought patterns of the mind.

EMOTIONAL HEALTH

To help develop physical wellbeing we have fitness centres and gyms, classes and health-food shops on main streets with big signs and lots of advertising. We have nutritionists, doctors, hospitals and weekly physical education in schools. None of these are hidden, in fact many people now happily reveal their fitness habits through social media with selfies and updates on their workouts and results. This is possible because we fully accept the need for guidance and good practice when caring for our physical health. We see no reason to hide it.

Thankfully mental health awareness is increasing too with counselling and psychotherapy, school programs and mental health services becoming more widely accepted. However, attending a psychotherapist or counsellor still tends to be kept more private, which suggests there is still some stigma and shame around requiring such services. I still haven't come across Facebook posts proudly checking in "at the psychologists" or Instagram selfies captioned "on the therapy couch working hard on my issues". When a time comes where we can speak of emotional and mental health in the same breath as physical health, we will have accepted the reality of what it is to be human. We're on the right track though and, in time, I hope mental health training is deemed as normal as going to the gym.

HIDING IN PLAIN VIEW

Despite our progress we are still inclined to hide our emotions with smiles and poker faces. I did it myself for years and nobody, even among my closest family and friends knew what was going on behind the façade. Centres, courses and practitioners dealing with emotions do exist but they are often only used when in people are in serious distress much like our accident and emergency services for extreme physical injury. Why are we comfortable to talk openly about our physical aches and pains but not that we feel like crying or are numb inside? The "I'm in hospital, pay me attention" pics are common on social media but where are the "I'm hanging by a thread and need help" posts?

I would suggest it's because we don't really want to "air our dirty laundry" publicly. Even using the term "dirty laundry" when referring to unpleasant experiences or emotions says a lot and shows how we expect judgement and criticism rather than compassion and support. A physical fall would spur anybody within sight to rush to our aid. Wearing plaster casts or bandages to support healing of a physical injury inspires others to help us do that which we can't manage. Yet emotional instability is sometimes met with disapproval or fear. We prefer others and ourselves to be calm, collected and emotionally balanced at all times yet we don't expect to go through an entire lifetime in perfect physical health. We accept that if we don't care for our physical health, we will get sick or injured. Shouldn't we apply this same logic to our emotional health?

THE MASKS WE WEAR

Ever-present, whether we acknowledge or talk about them, we feel emotions, expressing or repressing them daily. Sometimes we completely numb them if they overwhelm us. If the level of anti-depressants being prescribed world-wide is an accurate measure, we are numbing unpleasant emotions more and more. This suggests that more of us are feeling bad than ever before. If a symptom of depression were broken legs, I believe we'd see crutches and wheelchairs everywhere we go. We'd also see limping and shuffling from those with lower level emotional dis-ease.

Unfortunately, the symptoms of emotional distress are less obvious until they reach extreme levels. It takes keen observation, training or experience to see it and even then, it's not always so simple. We learn to pretend to be ok from a young age, to hide our feelings because we believe that feeling down, angry or lonely is somehow wrong. Emotions are often masked and left undiscussed, particularly amongst men, yet their effect on the individual affects every area of their life and all those in their circle. Thus, a large part of this chapter is aimed at exploring what emotions are, where they come from and how they affect us. Armed with more understanding, we can then work on our emotional fitness.

It seems that women are generally better at discussing their emotional states than men. At least that is my experience from personal relationships and from the conversations I have had with clients over the years. Women, when struggling emotionally can stand tall and strong in public for sure, but often have close friends and family to confide in to get support. Men can have close family and friends to confide in but are less likely to use this support network. This may very well come from a distant time in our evolution where displays of power and strength were necessary for survival while showing vulnerability could mean our end.

ACTING LIKE APES

In apes, male power-struggles for the top spot in the hierarchy are often won by the one that looks and sounds the strongest. They beat their chests, roar and jump around breaking branches and throwing objects to scare their rival and show who is king. This approach often avoids any direct physical conflict, thus saving them life-threatening injuries, while guaranteeing that they mate and carry on their seed. This doesn't seem so very different from how men today can sometimes react when feeling threatened, stressed or vulnerable. I personally have found that showing vulnerability to another male is difficult and something I would have avoided if possible. Consuming alcohol may reduce inhibitions enough to talk but that can lead to a whole other set of problems.

Showing vulnerability to women can present its own issues for men, especially if we are in or want to begin a relationship with them. Since evolution encourages us to mate with fitter partners to pass on strong genes to our kids, men have an instinctive drive to appear strong to women to attract them. Showing vulnerability doesn't fit in with that, so men are more likely to say nothing about what's bothering us. Instead, we might retreat to "man-caves" to avoid being seen or to our jobs to show we are still strong, worthy men. Sometimes we may revert right back to shouting and breaking things. Unfortunately, the most vulnerable among us fall deepest and may lash out at partners and children.

Teaching men that showing vulnerability in a safe environment shows true strength, that we can rise above our primal conditioning, could do much good for mankind. Teaching everybody this actually - men, women and children alike. I remember how difficult it was for me to do that on a weekend workshop I took part in several years ago with thirteen other people in the room. I knew I needed to talk but there was a resistance I couldn't explain despite much meditation and contemplation. I now know that there was still a sense of shame around it but having shown that vulnerability, I have seen how empowering it is.

Being strong enough to say, "I have weaknesses" allows them to be treated in the same way that revealing a physical injury does. Once healed, greater strength is restored as is greater self-confidence. True confidence is not so much about looking amazing or appearing successful to the world – that's a trick used by apes. True human confidence is about being ok with ourselves, all of it, warts and all. I believe that greater emotional health comes from accepting the variety of emotions, acknowledging their purpose and learning to balance them to use them to our benefit.

EMOTIONAL PHYSIOLOGY

Emotions are generated for the most part in the limbic system, which, for simplicity's sake, we'll refer to as the "feeling brain". The "feeling brain" receives information from our primal reptilian brain aka "survival brain" and our pre-frontal cortex, which we'll refer to as our "thinking or imagination brain". In short, our feeling brain creates emotions based on the information it receives from our survival brain and our thinking brain. For example, when we see a dangerous animal our survival brain tells our feeling brain to feel terror or if we imagine losing a loved one, our imagination brain tells our feeling brain to feel grief. It's important to remember that our imagination brain generates thoughts, images and scenarios, that are not always based on reality. We can imagine any kind of situation, beautiful and calming or horrible and terrifying. Real or not, the emotional brain can still react with a full emotional response as if this imagined situation where happening for real.

The brain absorbs massive amounts of information from the body and from external sources through sight, sound, smell, touch and taste. It must filter this information for the conscious mind to focus on what needs to be addressed or we would be completely overwhelmed. For example, in a busy restaurant we filter the other voices and sounds of cutlery, music etc., to focus on the conversation with our dinner guest. During our conversation with that person we hear the words but also the tone of voice, watch body language and facial expression. Although probably unaware of it, we also smell pheromones that give us more information. Some would suggest that we can pick up on the vibes or energy fields of other people and put all these together to assess the situation. Energy fields or not, all this information combined can give us a deeper sense or feeling around a situation that may not fit with what our dinner guest is saying. Life experience and dealing with people helps us to hone these perceptive skills as we recognise patterns and learn to acknowledge and trust our "gut" feelings. Filtering out our own preconceived, biased ideas that might interfere with how we assess others is important too.

PRIMAL EMOTIONS

Our emotional state is heavily influenced by our primal instincts to survive. When we are in immediate danger, our sympathetic nervous system switches on to help us fight for our lives, fly from harm or sometimes freeze and do nothing while we wait for the threat to pass. It also makes our posture and facial expressions more menacing to deter a possible threat from attacking us. Dogs bare teeth and arch their backs. We're not so very different. Would this alone be enough to save us, if we didn't also feel some fear or rage towards our aggressor? Would we react to ensure our survival if we felt relaxed, comfortable and at ease when threatened? Probably not, until the aggressor attacks and the physical pain forces us to fight or flee, though it may be too late at that stage. Just as physical pain helps protect us from further damage, some unpleasant emotions are protective.

If, however, we know that we are safe from harm because that threat is fenced in, our reactions will be reduced accordingly, replaced perhaps by one of humour or excitement. Otherwise we could never bring our children to the zoo or watch wild animal documentaries on television. While the external stimulus of seeing a dangerous animal triggers an emotional response, our internal filtering and processing of the information through logic and trust plays a large part in how we feel. Knowing that we are safe allows us to feel safe. How we read a situation can determine how it affects us emotionally.

War zones aside, most of us rarely come across genuine life-threatening danger since we have created societies and adapted environments to minimize risk. We have built protective housing, developed road safety rules, health and safety procedures and we keep dangerous animals away from our living spaces. We have socially accepted rules and laws to keep us safe from other people which the majority adhere to. There are also policing services for those who are at risk from other harmful people, if we are brave enough to ask for help. In such societies, logic should tell us that we are quite safe from immediate harm.

Despite our relative safety, many of us experience daily perceived threats as our lifestyles, sense of self-worth, property, goals and belief systems become threatened by the fear of change. The idea of somebody breaking into our homes and stealing our possessions can be enough to trigger anxiety. The mere thought of people from other countries and cultures coming to ours, taking our jobs and bringing 'false-gods', temples and beliefs can trigger hatred, but only if we already think like that. Our sense of self-worth can be threatened daily by media images of seemingly perfect people with seemingly perfect lives, if we believe the images are real. Advertising has used this threat for years to sell us products, with the underlying message that buying their product or service can make us more perfect, valuable or worthy too.

Nowadays, we have become both consumer and promoters as we advertise our own 'perfect' lives on social media to convince others that we too are good enough. Then, once we have shown our best selves, we rely on likes, retweets and the number of 'friends' or followers gained to validate that we are indeed worthy. We have countless videos on social media of people, posing in gyms, doing make-up tutorials or taking crazy physical risks to get millions of views, likes and followers. Success in the modern world is quickly becoming more about who clicks our like button or wants to be like us than about living a contented and fulfilled life, making the world a better place or achieving life goals.

To keep our survival brain and fight or flight system at a level where the emotions it sparks are calmer and genuinely helpful to us, we can learn to apply logic and a clearer perspective to our thoughts. Only then can we rationally identify genuine risks vs perceived threats and see what will truly support our wellbeing needs. With more balance, clarity and understanding we can feel and then act, accordingly.

THE EMOTION TRAIN (THE LOC-EMOTIVE)

In Cognitive Behavioural Therapy or CBT, the process through which we think, feel and act is worked with to change unhelpful patterns of behaviour and emotion. Awareness of our 'triggers', i.e. the thoughts that spark an emotion, which we then act on are the starting point. By identifying these triggers, we can use techniques to modify their effect and change the resulting emotion and behaviour which follows. As habitual creatures, we can work towards developing habits of positive thinking, calmness, compassion and contentment through awareness and practice.

Many of our unpleasant emotions are triggered without us being fully aware of the thoughts that cause them. We often don't see how we live our lives based on these emotions. All three parts of our brain are working together simultaneously. Because of this, the mind is often the driver, fuel and passenger of what I like to think of as our "emotional train" all at once. An external situation or internal thought is like a ticket for an emotional train that's going in a certain direction, let's say to Anxiety-ville. We use our ticket to jump on board this emotional train.

As we sit in the anxiety train feeling anxious, the "feeling brain" encourages the "imagination brain" to replay the initial trigger and possibly to imagine more reasons to justify going further into anxiety. These thoughts fuel the engine and we stay on board. Maybe that's why they call it a "train of thought"? As the passenger, we often get "carried away with ourselves" then wonder how we ended up way down in Anxiety-ville, living anxiously and surrounded by other anxious people telling us that there is indeed lots to be anxious about! If we go there too hard and too fast, we can go "off the rails" and become a train wreck.

Then there's also the habitual side of us where we take a route so regularly that we do so on autopilot. Just as our commute to work becomes so familiar that we can arrive there with no memory of the journey, we can get on our emotional trains without noticing any of the process. We can even become so accustomed to our Anxiety-ville trips that we go there when there's no real need, like taking our work route, on our day off, just because we usually do. If Anxiety-ville becomes our home or base, we don't even need a trigger or ticket to go there. We wake up there, spend our day there and sleep, if we can fall asleep, in anxiety.

This emotional and behavioural rail system can apply equally to all other unpleasant states and actions. Anger-ville, Stress-ville, Doubt-ville, Sad-ville, Lonely-ville, Victim-ville, Dissappointment-ville etc. We don't just land there out of the blue. Much of the time we choose, on some level, to go there. Major life challenges can send us there temporarily, despite our best efforts, but if we keep going back there it's usually because WE keep going back there! Accepting this responsibility without self-blame can empower us to start choosing our direction more wisely.

CHANGE DIRECTION

What if we were to take a different approach when handed a ticket? We could choose to see it as a multi-pass for many routes. When presented with a ticket that we might have habitually used for anxiety, anger, frustration, disappointment etc., we could sit with it for a few moments instead, noticing its effect. Rather than allowing our "survival brain" to automatically take control, we can take time to look at the departure screen and use our conscious thinking brain to decide where we want to go. We could sit, breathe and encourage calmness and positivity to empower our reaction and direction. It doesn't take long to pass through the instant reaction phase. Counting to ten or taking a few deep breaths can make all the difference.

Instead of Anxiety-ville we could take more responsibility and control, choosing instead to go to Safe-ville, somewhere that we feel secure – internally or to a trusted person or place. Instead of Anger-ville we could look for somewhere like Calm-ville. Instead of Disappointment-ville we could go into Trust-ville i.e. trusting that all is ok even if not working out as we had hoped. We can look for the routes that take us to happiness, contentment, peace, joy and all the emotional states that make life more bearable and enjoyable.

These journeys may require that we look inside ourselves to find our peaceful and happier places, if we know how. If we don't have such tools, we will need to seek others to show us the way. There are many counsellors, psychologists, therapists and meditation teachers trained to do that very thing. We could, of course, waste the ticket by rolling it up and throwing it away, but that costs us the opportunity to develop healthier ways of dealing with unpleasant situations and emotions. I believe that these tickets come our way for our benefit and each one should be used accordingly.

If we're already in an uneasy place or living with unhelpful habitual thoughts, feelings and actions, these tickets can be opportunities to leave and find a nicer state to live in. They can take us away, bit by bit, trip by trip, perhaps starting with shorter visits, like a well-earned holiday break, until eventually we settle in and stay exactly where we want to be.

FIGHT OR LIGHT?
I had three situations within two years that showed the difference my own emotional state affected how I reacted to potential physical threats. In the first, I was at an outdoor music gig where several acts were performing. One of the acts was anything but mellow. They started their set and the crowd got stirred-up by it. I've heard music described as 'how emotions sound' and I believe music is one way to bring up the emotions that reside deep within us. This certainly seemed to be the case with the fast-paced, intense beats and lyrics blasting through the speakers as fights were starting to break out around me.

I'm not suggesting the music alone caused these fights, but I do think the combination of alcohol, possibly drugs, and the stimulating effect of the music ignited and released the anger and frustration some of these guys held. I could feel it rising in me too due to an unresolved area of my life that was bothering me at the time. I know now that when we try to ignore our issues, they sit there underneath waiting to be resolved. I wasn't so aware back then. As my friends and I watched the scuffles and scraps that were flaring around us, I turned to one of my friends and said, "I feel like a fight too". I said it as a joke but maybe I was only half-joking?

CAREFUL WHAT YOU WISH FOR

Within half an hour my request was granted as I walked to find the toilets. A large, aggressive looking guy bumped into me growling "Mind your f***ing drink". He blamed me for spilling my drink on him. I didn't and told him he was mistaken, but he wasn't interested. He was angry and he wanted to take it out on someone smaller than him. I don't remember what exactly sparked the physical fight. He came at me and I reacted by sweeping his legs, pinning him to the ground and punching him several times, as my self-defence karate training from years before came flooding back. Within seconds, some nearby spectators intervened and separated us.

As we stood there a nervous steward came and asked me to leave the venue. It was a fair request and I would have left since I was fighting after all. Before I could answer, a couple standing right behind me stepped forward and told the steward, "He's not to blame, the other guy started it. We saw it all!". Pointing at the other man, they said, "He was causing trouble and got what he asked for". In a sense, I got what I asked for too having told my friend earlier that I'd like a fight! I was glad they spoke up, not because I got to stay for the rest of the concert but because I would have questioned and second-guessed my part in the row afterwards. They saved me a lot of guilt, not all as I still reacted in a way I would prefer not to, but at least I knew it wasn't all me.

While it certainly was an act of self-defence, there was also anger in me and I'm sure I vented some of it in those seconds. Not my proudest moment and something I hope to never repeat but like all experiences, it happened, and for a good reason. When analysing a situation like that, I feel it is more productive to focus more on the reason than the wrong and what good can come from it. I believe there was some benefit for both of us in this situation. The other guy obviously had his own issues but perhaps had a habit of taking them out on people he saw as an easy target. He was a bully only this time he learned that bullying can backfire. Our encounter might have curbed his enthusiasm for starting fights. Maybe he even decided to look at himself and his issues!

I learned a powerful lesson too. I didn't feel good afterwards. There was no sense of righteousness or that he got what he deserved. It bothered me that I lost my temper and that I had even half-wanted a fight. It demonstrated that I needed a healthier release for my frustration, or this would happen again. Ideally, I needed to find a way to accept or resolve my personal issue so it would cause no frustration. Stress and frustration often erupt from us and harm others or we internalise it and harm ourselves. I started working on my issues soon after this through regular meditation, self-reflection, letting go of the things I couldn't control and choosing to trust. Trusting that life happens for us, rather than to us, is a big one for me.

SELF-DEFENCE

The second situation several months later, occurred when a friend of mine was attacked by two guys while we waited for a cab after a night out. I had been talking further up the street and, as I followed on to catch up with my friends, I saw one getting knocked to the ground. The two aggressors looked as if that wasn't enough for them and were going to continue the fight. I stepped in between them and said something along the lines of "Ok lads, you've won the fight, we're done here, just leave it at that". They didn't agree and the first one came at me.

I was in a much calmer state after months of daily meditations and had no interest in fighting, but my friend needed some help, so I stood my ground. Once the first crossed into my personal space, my self-defence karate experience kicked in again and I threw a jab. It isn't a very powerful punch but it's fast and sharp and he dropped to the ground. When the second guy came at me, I shifted slightly into a more defensive stance by offsetting my feet and raised my hands up to protect myself. Without moving off the spot, I again struck when he came close enough to hit me. I remember him going backwards a few yards before he too fell.

Still, I didn't want to fight and had no anger, so I stayed where I was, watching him and his comrade while scanning around us to see if there were any more coming. The first guy stayed down but as the second got to his feet, three gardai arrived and pulled him into a police van, then picked up his buddy. I waited for my turn, thinking I would surely get arrested too. I wasn't arrested as the guards had seen what happened and knew it was purely self-defence on my part. I found out afterwards that both attackers were known for making nuisances of themselves and starting fights.

The point of these two stories is that there are times when anger and force may be necessary to protect our right to safety. The level of anger reached, and the resulting amount of force used will depend on our state of mind. In the first situation, I got a little carried away and felt some guilt after. I already had simmering frustration before the fight began and vented it. In the second, I was fully in control of my actions as there was no simmering frustration to be triggered. I used minimal harm, having already tried to resolve it with words and felt no guilt after. Peaceful solutions are ideal, just not always an option. Turning the other cheek can be effective when words or insults are being thrown but offering a cheek to be punched shows a disregard for our own well-being. If we are unable to defend ourselves, we must seek support from those that can.

THE STRENGTH OF WORDS

The third situation occurred around midday on a Saturday as I drove in a busy part of town near my home. I passed an altercation between a man and a woman by the side of the road and saw them physically pushing and pulling each other by the open car door. Since it could have potentially been an abduction, my first instinct was to stop and try to help. I didn't want to hear a report on the news the next day that somebody was missing or hurt, and nobody intervened! As I got out of my car, I noticed another man standing within yards of the couple watching this unfold. I figured he was with the male involved in the scuffle or he would surely have helped the girl. I saw there was a young child in the car and thought this may be an access changeover. I know myself how difficult these situations can be for all involved, so I had compassion for them both. I guessed too that if I physically tried to stop the argument, I would have added fuel to a fire that was already raging.

Instead I chose a calm demeanour and posture, showing open hands. I took care with my words not to blame anybody for what was taking place or to present myself as a threat. I didn't know why they were arguing. Men are often blamed but aren't always at fault, so I didn't judge or assume. I just knew it had potential to get worse. While I didn't blame him, I did direct my words towards him as there was an obvious size and strength difference and a greater risk that she would be hurt. I said "You need to stop. No good will come from this" to which he responded "This is none of your f'ing business". I said, "You're right it's not my business but you have to stop before you do some harm!".

By this time, I could see that she was baiting him by goading, and he was taking the bait. My next comment to him struck a chord when I said, "You're not going to feel good about this in the morning". That had an effect as he froze on the spot, looked me straight in the eye and asked with a quiver in his voice, "Do you think I feel good now?". I replied, "I know you don't, but you can save yourself feeling far worse tomorrow by stopping now". He stopped, got into his car with his buddy, and left. She went into her home and it was over.

I could have gone to her door to see if she was ok but decided my part was done. She was out of harm's way and so I got back into my car. Another benefit of developing a clearer mind from meditation and contemplation is that we think more rationally and quickly. I had halted traffic on both sides of the road by stopping my car on one side and standing on the other so I'd have more observers and support should it be required.

As I drove away, I wondered why, out of ten or more cars that had stopped, not one other person got out to help. Was it the fear of getting hurt? Maybe the fear of getting involved in another's business? No time? Or just didn't care? Had I driven on too, what would have happened? I'm not suggesting that we all should recklessly endanger ourselves while trying to be do-gooders. I'm saying that if we do find ourselves in such situations, a calm state is more helpful.

What was the major difference between these three situations? My emotional state resulting from my habits in the previous months! In the first, neither one of us was mindful enough about our issues and vented our frustrations out on each other with unnecessary harm. In the second case, when I was mindful enough, the harm was limited to a reasonable force necessary for protection. The last situation shows where a calm, balanced state can be shared to bring a quick and easier resolution. Nothing could be done about what had already transpired but who knows what some calm and logical intervention prevented.

We can only really work on our own mindset, emotional state and behaviour, but this work can affect others. We can share calmness, logic and compassion. Choosing to deal with our issues so that we can feel more balanced is also choosing to help others to feel better. What we do with our stardust affects the stardust of those around us!

As with physical and mental fitness, we can work on ourselves to develop more emotional flexibility, strength and stamina. This extra fitness can bring us more ease internally and help us to minimise the harmful effects of other emotional stimuli. Rugby players develop physical fitness to tackle others with more efficiency, but they can also tolerate tackles with reduced risk of injury. Likewise, emotional fitness lets us take bigger hits and bounce-back more easily from the occasional hard-knock that life deals us.

For more on emotional health and wellbeing visit www.highestpotential.ie

Chapter 17

In Love or in Fear?

"The choice that frees or imprisons us is the choice of love or fear. Love liberates. Fear imprisons.", Gary Zukav

It has been suggested by various spiritual teachings that our emotions and the actions resulting from them stem from a root state of either love or fear. This, I believe is aligned with being at ease or dis-ease. This philosophy also ties in nicely for me with how our nervous system works i.e. Sympathetic (stress) mode or Parasympathetic (peaceful) mode. With such a range of emotions that flow into one another, it can sometimes be difficult to identify exactly what we are feeling, and why. Simplifying it to "do I feel at ease, secure, peaceful and loving?" or "do I feel uneasy, stressed or unloving?" can at least indicate on which side of the fence we are sitting.

Fear causes the body to release Cortisol, often known as our "stress hormone", to switch us into survival mode. Obvious fear-based emotions that would have aided our ancestors in times of threat include anger which can spur us to lash out at an aggressor or terror which can make us run away or hide from danger. The benefits of other fear-based emotions are a little less apparent, but we will discuss them too, to see how we may use them to bring about positive change and personal growth. Fear can nudge us towards love if we are brave enough to work with it.

THE IMPORTANCE OF LOVE

Most of our pleasant feelings come from a root state of love in its various forms of expression. Love causes the body to release oxytocin, sometimes referred to as a, "cuddle hormone". Oxytocin is involved in maternal behaviour, lactation, labour, social bonding, male reproduction and orgasm. It has the added benefit of counteracting the damaging effects of the hormone, often associated with fear and anxiety, i.e. cortisol. Of the love-based emotions, an obvious one is romantic love, especially in the early-stages when all is new, exciting and full of potential. Then there is the love of a parent for their child and the child for its parent and siblings etc. We also have the love of friends that are dear to us, those we know and accept unconditionally. We

179

can compassionately love strangers and animals or joyously love our jobs, hobbies and our lives.

Love, I would suggest, is even more important than fear in modern times. Where fear helps us to get through immediate danger, love underlies our long-term survival and success as a species. It allows us to bond with others, bring new life into the world and then care for our children until they can continue the cycle. Love allows us to work together as communities to overcome challenges. Love prompts us to care for our sick until they are well-enough to contribute again to society. In a sense, even in a loving state, we're all still trying to survive but in a far more pleasant and productive way! Given that humanity has already overcome so many of the natural risks to our survival into old age, we are now freer to use love as our main survival tool, if we choose to.

Other pleasant states that come from a loving perspective that are worth cultivating include;

Contentment

Loving our lot and our lives as they are. There is no set amount of material wealth i.e. money, property or possessions that brings automatic contentment. Nor is there a perfect life-situation i.e. fame, success or relationship status, that guarantees it. I'm almost certain that instagram followers won't guarantee it. Contentment instead, depends on our personal perspective. It comes from being grateful for what life has already given us. Choosing a mindset of gratitude can bring contentment in even humble situations.

Tranquillity

Loving and accepting the world, as it is, while trusting that all is as it should be, brings a feeling of peace. If we were to love our neighbours whether next door, across the road or across our borders, we would not want to fight with them. If they feel the same, they will not want to fight with us, and we would all enjoy the tranquillity of peace-time. A loving intent induces an urge to connect with others rather than harm. Two neighbouring countries whose leaders operate from a compassionate mindset would want to work together. They would focus on trading, sharing ideas and technologies and appreciating one another's traditions and customs. They might even provide support when needed. This could allow both societies to flourish, enjoying the best of what both have to offer. The coming together of different societies would promote interracial relationships resulting in greater genetic diversity, another very important factor in our species survival.

Similarly, self-acceptance brings tranquillity as it reduces internal conflict. To be completely at ease with ourselves, flaws'n'all, is a beautiful state of being. In fact, such a relationship means that we stop seeing them as flaws but rather characteristics that make us uniquely us. Self-love allows us to be our own best friend, to be self-motivated and to develop self-belief. Peace starts with us individually and can spread to those around us if we let it.

Joy

The love and appreciation of what we are doing or experiencing in the moment brings pleasure. When we are completely present in doing something that expresses who we are and what we love to do, we experience joy. It excites and exhilarates and can be seen most often in children when they jump for joy, clap their hands and smile from ear to ear. Sports, music, art and family occasions can bring about the same reaction from adults. We cheer, clap, punch the air in victory and hug each other as joy courses through our veins.

When carried away by music we sway and dance, transported to an alternate state of bliss. Dancers, singers, artists, bakers, athletes, craftspeople and gardeners, professional or otherwise can all know joy when loving what they do. Joy can also come from doing nothing if we are fully present and undistracted by thoughts of what else we could or should be doing. A key requirement for experiencing more joy is granting ourselves permission to do that which causes us to feel it.

Freedom

The love of being and expressing who we are brings freedom to show ourselves to the world. Freedom to simply be is such a valuable commodity. It is one of our innate rights and one that feels wonderful when we accept and embrace it. I remember a scene from the movie Robin Hood – Prince of thieves, that remained with me since I saw it at 13 years old. Morgan Freeman's Moorish character Azeem is asked by a young English girl, on seeing a black man for the first time, "Did God paint you?". He responded, "Did God paint me?", then laughed and said, "For certain!". "Why?" she quizzed. "Because Allah loves wonderous variety!" he replied.

How much nicer would our world be if we all accepted that "Allah, God, creation, evolution, or indeed, Stardust" loves wonderous variety? What if each one of us chose to love this wonderous variety? We'd look for the beauty in our differences and encourage self-expression. Rather than hiding our talents or opinions for fear of judgement and reprisal, we'd all be free to share them. The innovation, art, culture, foods, music and stories that would come from a society like that would be mind-blowing. The freedom we'd all enjoy to shine would be exquisite.

Compassion

The love we have for the well-being and non-suffering of others brings a sense of warmth and connection. When we wish others well in thought or action, we show them compassion. Their best-interest is important to us, as is our own. This doesn't need to be completely altruistic as compassion serves us too. Our surroundings, our social interactions and life in general improves if those around us are also well. "Love thy neighbour as thyself" is an old idea that never becomes outdated. Compassion comes naturally to most of us unless we close our hearts through fear or judgement. Compassion lets us view life from others perspective, to imagine how they might feel if they are suffering. We see that natural tendency in children who get upset or excited when watching television shows, as they identify with the characters. To tap into our compassion, we only need to take a break from thinking solely about ourselves and wish others well.

Gentleness

This comes from loving ourselves and others enough to grant patience, softness and tenderness. Through gentleness we handle people with care, physically and emotionally, reminding them that they are safe with us. That sense of safety is essential when bringing somebody out of fight or flight mode and to ourselves if suffering with anxiety or stress. Gentleness and patience come easier to us when dealing with a small child that is upset or angry, but we can sometimes forget this with older children and adults. Our need for safety when in fight mode never changes. Gentleness rather than self-judgement helps us balanced our state of mind and emotions.

Kindness

The love of others that allows us to share what we possess to improve their lives. Kindness should be applied to ourselves as much as anybody else. This love may be shared through time, attention, advice, acceptance, well-wishes, money or materials, all of which can be incredibly valuable to those in need. We benefit from the feelings that come from knowing we make a positive difference in the world.

Forgiveness

This requires more than simply turning the other cheek or choosing to take a higher moral stance when we have been wronged. Forgiveness means loving enough to be understanding and compassionate when we or others fall short of our expectations. Love helps us try to look at the situation from a perspective where we can understand the reasons why we or others acted, reacted or made mistakes. At times when we cannot get our heads around the reason, we may simply choose to love regardless.

Determination

The root of our determination may be self-love as we work towards making our own dreams, or ideal life, a reality. It may be love for those close to us or the world in general that ignites our determination to make the world a nicer place for them. I believe determination also involves loving and trusting in our skills and talents enough to believe that we can use them to achieve our goals. If those goals also come from a place of love, there is cohesion as the destination and the vehicle by which we get there are aligned.

Commitment

Loving a person, situation or plan enough to stay with it even when the going gets tough. All significant relationships and journeys present obstacles or detours in some form or another. At each challenge we are presented with opportunities i.e., to get over them, around them or stop and turn back. Commitment lets us stay with it and find our way if at all possible. If we must turn back or let go, love lets us do so with kindness and gratitude for what the journey gave us and fond memories of those who walked with us.

THE BENEFIT OF RESOLVING FEARS

World peace is, to me and I'm sure to most, a beautiful idea. Despite the existence of many sages, prophets, gurus, teachers and wise or holy-people, past and present, we still have wars. There is sure to be a war raging somewhere in the world, at any given time. Why? Because these are started by fearful people, not the truly powerful, confident or righteous. Those who fear that other cultures are not living appropriately may attempt to take over and teach the natives to live "correctly". Leaders who are afraid of not having enough resources to ensure survival or abundance invade other countries to obtain theirs. Those that fear invasion may start a war to strike first. The borders we see on maps are man-made notions of who owns the land. No human can truly own the Earth or any part of it, so these ideas and boundaries, based on belief, will change as surely as everything else in the universe does. Fear of other cultures' influence on our own can be a catalyst for war but is division by skin colour any more logical than classification by eye colour? Is a war against another's religious belief any less ridiculous than one based on music preferences?

We can engage in conflict at a personal level with unnecessary skirmishes and internal battles that we project onto others. Remember that when we are in fight or flight mode, we view the world as something to fight against or fly away from. The "dog-eat-dog" business world involves corporate wars, head-hunting and the race to climb the corporate ladder. My clients' accounts of the all too common, "survival of the fittest" approach to success make me wonder if the salary, promotion or perceived esteem are worth it. Surely knowing a goal was achieved through lying, cheating or stepping on somebody takes the shine off success? Neighbours fight over land-boundaries, hedges and even leaves blowing into a garden often because of a fear that their rights are being disrespected.

Wouldn't a positive relationship with our neighbours offer practical benefits that outweigh the sacrifice of a little ground or the sweeping of leaves? Families can become divided through sibling rivalry and inheritance disputes. These are the people we have shared our most formative years with and could be our closest allies if we choose. Peace starts with us, but I do believe it is a two-way street. If we can choose to be at peace with whatever is going on around us, we become less distracted by fears and more peaceful inside. Then the fight in us subsides, reason is restored, and we can see there is no need to fear.

The following is a list of common fear-based feelings and some exercises we can use to help resolve them;

Guilt

The fear of having done wrong or made mistakes, can sit in us indefinitely unless resolved. We are at a complex stage of our human evolution where we have the capacity for great love and potential to imagine and create our own utopia but at the same time, we are animals capable of beastly behaviour. It's no wonder we find ourselves so mixed up at times! We are still learning how to balance the best of our loving human spirit with our animalistic fear side, so we must make allowances for our own primal instincts or lack of experience.

I believe everybody does the best we can with who, what and where we are at that point in time. This does not mean that we always act and react in our ideal way but when feeling guilty about times we messed up, we can choose to use those experiences as lessons to make more positive choices in our lives. If we believe that every experience has purpose, we need see none as failure. It's important to remember that it's only a mistake if we don't learn from it. Knowledge comes from books, but true wisdom comes from experience. So much wisdom can be gained from making mistakes. Focusing most of our energy on the present and what we can do now, lets us use it more efficiently. Accepting and learning from our past to do better in future is paramount to letting go of guilt and turning it to our benefit.

The opposite of guilt is innocence. By tapping into a time when we had nothing but innocence, we can help to alleviate feelings of guilt. Try this exercise. Sit quietly and comfortably. Imagine yourself as a new-born child, when you knew nothing of the concepts of right or wrong. There were no immediate expectations on you, you simply were what you were. As you developed movement and emotional expression, you started to explore your world to learn more about it. You laughed when happy, cried when upset, fed when hungry and slept when tired. You were innocent, and you learned and grew. As you got a little older, you explored further. Sometimes you made a mess and broke things that were valuable to others. These breakages were only problems if there was an attachment to the object or to cleanliness. You were only a child, still figuring out how to move your body and interact with the world. You were not bad.

You had no body-image issues, it didn't matter how you looked. This was only an issue if others had attachments to height, weight or appearance. As you grew a little older still, you started school and sports. You learned to play and interact with others. Sometimes you dropped the ball or left in a goal. Sometimes you lost. It didn't matter as it was only a game, unless somebody had an attachment to winning and taught you to attach your self-worth to it. It didn't matter what your schoolmates had or didn't have, unless somebody had an attachment to material possessions. If you hurt someone, you said sorry, made up and moved on. You forgave easily too, unless you or they held a grudge. If you lied, it was for fear of judgement. Even if it was to get what you wanted, that is quite normal behaviour in intelligent children. There is only guilt where there is judgement. Let go of judgement and enjoy the beauty of innocence.

Shame

The fear of not being good enough in the eyes of others, can be brought about by comparisons with others or our expectations of how we should be. Shame is generally attached to a fear of others seeing our perceived flaws with the view that they will judge us harshly. Here's the thing - almost everyone has parts we would like to change if we could. This includes the most famous, talented and most aesthetically beautiful people in the world. If everyone is 'flawed' then maybe we're all just perfectly imperfect! If this shame is connected to our own poor hygiene or self-care, we can choose to use this shame positively as motivation to achieve more in our lives or to take care of ourselves better. Preferably, our primary motivation for self-care would be love for our bodies and a wish to live a fulfilling life while using our natural gifts. If you carry shame as the result of someone else's judgement, remember that critical people are so inclined because they judge themselves so harshly. Their criticism may never have been about you to begin with. Certainly, how they delivered their criticism was about them and not you.

Acceptance of ourselves as we are along with our past experiences are key factors in resolving feelings of shame. Try this exercise. Imagine yourself in the company of somebody whose opinion you value and trust. This can be a real person in your life, past or present, or your own spiritual God. Imagine you are in your most revealing state, physically, mentally and emotionally. Fully exposed with nothing to hide behind. Allow yourself to relax, letting it all 'hang-out' so to speak. The person or deity you have chosen has full access to everything you have ever done or thought, down to the most intimate detail. They can see your curves, bumps, wrinkles, blemishes, lines and cracks. They see you in your strongest moments and in your weakest. They see your brightest, most loving ideas and your deepest and darkest fear-filled thoughts, the ones you would never act on or speak out loud. They see everything that you ever kept to yourself for fear of judgement and still they love you for it. All of it, every act, thought and every inch of you. They love you not despite the flaws but because of them as they make you uniquely you and are part of your story. Allow yourself to be seen and loved completely and unconditionally. Now imagine you are in front of a mirror, looking closely at yourself and loving yourself the same way. This kind of self-love and acceptance negates shame. This may take time and practice, but I have found it gets easier with each attempt.

Loneliness

The fear of being alone or getting rejected should we try to connect with others. Alone time is wonderful and hugely beneficial if we are happy with and by ourselves. It gives us freedom to do as we choose - to read, write, rest, play, sing, create, plan, meditate or to just enjoy silence, totally undisturbed. Being alone can be difficult however, spending time with our own thoughts and feelings, if they are unpleasant. Sometimes we need the company of others and their distractions so that we don't have to face our own feelings and thoughts. Bringing more peace to our minds and balancing our emotions can let us see time alone as a gift. Using some of this time to just sit and be can make it more pleasant. Choosing to use some of that time to increase our feel-good-factor makes it very valuable and productive. We could put on some music that we love, watch a movie, listen to comedians, do some art or take up a new hobby. We can educate ourselves. There are lessons on Youtube for almost anything we want to learn, I use them constantly myself and have learned so much from them. Explore the possibilities and see where they take you.

We often define our identity based on our relationship to others. We are parent, child, sibling, husband, wife or friend. We are teacher or student, employer, employee or customer. We are teammate or coach. These are all relative identities and rely on the presence of others to be true. But who or what are we when we are alone? What is our purpose, our raison d'être when there is nobody else present to connect with? Is there any point in my writing this book without you to read it? Many parents experience this 'empty nest syndrome' when their children leave the family home. Suddenly their identity as mother or father dissolves and they must create a new one to fill the gap. Those parents who maintain a sense of self and a portion of their parenting life that didn't involve their children should fare much better and even enjoy the extra freedom and space of the empty nest. A positive sense of self or one that doesn't rely on an attachment to a specific role can bring more ease to a lonely heart.

I wonder if our increased use of social media reflects a sort of collective loneliness. Having rented four different houses in twelve years I notice that many neighbours politely pass each other daily but make no real connection. Busy working lives often mean long days and commutes, so we choose to relax, undisturbed when we get home rather than calling around to neighbours. Television has become our company and we connect to others through our phones with texts and likes, sharing images of our lives, or at least the best bits, without letting others into them. We're more digitally connected than we have ever been but it's more virtual than reality.

We must accept that humans are fundamentally social creatures. We thrive with regular affection and social contact. It's good for our long-term wellbeing and our survival. It is rated higher in an ongoing Harvard study on longevity than healthy eating and exercise. Some time alone can be very beneficial, but we work best in communities with each contributing our own talents and gifts to the overall group. We are often surrounded by people, yet we can be lonely amid a crowd if we do not make meaningful connections or feel like we don't belong. The fear of rejection can make us shy about attempting to connect with others.

On a recent trip to London, I was reminded of this while commuting on the underground rail system. It was strange to see so many people living together, travelling together and physically touching while sitting side by side, yet there wasn't a word spoken. Aside from the occasional passing glance, most eyes were fixed on phone screens or closed to shut their surroundings out completely. You might say it's pointless to make a connection with somebody you may never see again but I believe a connection, however short, is still meaningful. I enjoyed a lengthy conversation with an Indian man, that was also on a short visit to London, on the train from Stanstead airport. Like me, he hadn't been conditioned to non-connection and as a hotelier, it was normal for him to strike up conversations with strangers. We discussed family, work and life in general, gaining insights into each other's lives. We then parted way, possibly to never meet again, but that is irrelevant.

We can make new friends at any stage of our lives. I know I certainly have in recent years through hobbies and work. Doing what we love is one of the best ways to make new connections. We will meet like-minded people with whom we can connect through our shared interest. There are so many groups and clubs to suit all interests where friends can be made. Online connections help but actual contact is better. Expect that once people get to know you, they will like you and vice-versa. Let new friendships develop over time. To help them become long-lasting and strong, remember that to have a good friend, it helps to be a good friend. If our spiritual or religious belief includes a sense that we are all part of and connected to something greater than ourselves, we can tap into that. If this is the case, then we are never truly alone.

Jealousy
This is wanting what someone else has for fear of not being or having enough already. Once upon a time that may have meant wanting essentials such as food and shelter or a position in the hierarchy that improved our chance of survival and reproduction. That jealously and the effort it sparked to acquire more may have aided our survival then. Now, jealousy is most often related to the status symbols we desire so that we can feel that we are as good as them, stemming from a fear of not being good-enough already. Whether it's the new car, good job, fit body, confident attitude, great relationship or financial situation the root fear is the same – I'm not as good as them or they are luckier than I.

We can forget to see that they may have worked hard to achieve their fitness or material wealth and that they might have a great relationship because they are good partners. That too requires work. Luck may have very little to do with it. I find that if we are genuinely happy for others to have abundance, it becomes easier to believe that we deserve abundance too. When we adopt such an attitude, we are more likely to open the door to plenty, make an effort to improve our life situation and less likely to sabotage our own success.

Disappointment
This is simply wanting a different result to the reality that has unfolded, stemming from a fear that life isn't ok just as it is. If we become attached to a specific outcome, our contentment is at risk. When we trust that there is purpose and benefit to every outcome, we can be happier regardless. We can look forward instead to seeing how a result may be to our advantage. I have personally seen that so many times throughout my life. This applies to even minor events like a slight detour that makes me bump into somebody

I needed to meet or a delay that gets me somewhere at the ideal time. Now, when my plans go astray, I mostly find myself saying "Okay, I know this is for my benefit, let's see why!". If we can use disappointment as motivation for future success, it becomes a positive. Doing so while also trusting in divine timing takes off the pressure we put ourselves under also.

Worry

This is the imagining of a future we don't want or one we fear we can't handle. We don't worry about that which we believe we can handle with ease. To counter this, we must be realistic about the possibility of our worries becoming reality. If it is very unlikely, then we can replace that worry with a more positive thought – one that is less likely to occur. We can daydream and fantasize about our dream outcomes. This comes easily to us as kids, but we often drop that as we get older, probably having been told to 'get real' or get our heads out of the clouds. People use vision boards to keep their minds focused on working towards their dreams. Why not fill our heads with dreams and let them stew until we find ways to make them real?

If our worry is realistically likely to happen, we can trust that we will find a way to manage it. Talk to people that have experienced something similar and get their advice. Seek support beforehand to help when things get tough. Build our own resources so that we have something to use when the time comes. Better yet, come up with a plan to achieve a best-case-scenario.

Grief

This is sadness from the loss of someone or something we care deeply about. Death of a loved one may spark a fear of the afterlife or lack thereof upon realisation that we are all mortal and will die too. If we firmly believe that the spirit continues in a heavenly afterlife or returns to live another life, we would not grieve for their sake, only for those left behind. Sure, we have no measurable scientific proof yet, but neither can we disprove an after-life. We are free to take whatever side we like.

The end of a relationship can be cause for grief too, not just for the loss of the person but also for the life we had expected with them. One moment, we can find ourselves on what we believe is our life-course and then suddenly adrift with no idea where to go next. Grief is a natural stage of loss but can be more destructive and long-lasting if we become gripped by the fear that life can never be enjoyable again. If we have confidence in our potential to be okay, even without our lost loved one, life can go on and still include joy, contentment and happiness.

I recently had a conversation with a client that lost his wife on the birth of their third child. His other children were three and eighteen months at the time. Of course, this was tragic, and he suffered greatly. However, he was supported by his own family, and his in-laws who lived locally. He continued to live life and worked a full-time job. He also socialised occasionally. Within three years he met another lady whom he refers to as 'a fantastic human being'. She became his wife, bore him four more children and became mother in every meaningful way to all seven of his children. His new wife, having lost her own mother quite young, developed a very close relationship with his mother-in-law, who of course had lost her daughter. This new relationship helped to fill the hole that was left in both women's lives. Because they were open to moving forward, the husband, wife, children and grandparents were able to live happy lives despite the tragedy.

I believe if we look at them a little more closely, most of our unpleasant emotions can be rooted in fear, fight or flight, sympathetic mode. To reduce the power that fearful thoughts and beliefs have over us, we can try to rationalise them and make the fears somehow ok in our minds. I can equate this to my karate training where I learned to defend myself against punches although I accept this is a controlled and safe environment. Getting punched on occasion while at training, and being alright after, reduced the fear of being hit in future. In a sparring session or competition, where there was potential to get hit, one of two things were going to happen. I would get hit or I wouldn't get hit. I would block or avoid the punch as I had been trained to do or I would mistime my block and get punched. If hit, I would have found this unpleasant initially, but the discomfort would lessen, and I would heal again. I would also learn to block more efficiently next time. This understanding allowed my fear levels to reduce to a point where I could function logically and enjoy facing off against an opponent in competition. The enjoyment far outweighed the risk and occasional pain.

We can apply this to other fear-based unpleasant emotions. If we make it ok, in our minds, for others to have the things we do not, there is no jealousy. If we make it ok to have made mistakes, there is no guilt. If we make it ok to spend quality time alone or to reach out to others, there is no loneliness. If we accept the unknown future and embrace its mystery, there is no worry about what will come to pass. If we acknowledge that our innate value is separate to our material wealth or social standing, there may be no greed and so on.

Chapter 18

Developing Emotional Fitness

"The key to success is to keep growing in all areas of life - mental, emotional, spiritual as well as physical", Julius Erving

Emotions bring colour and flavour to our experience of life. We all feel them. Some can be light and barely perceptible and others deep, powerful and at times, all consuming. Have you ever really thought about what emotions are, where they come from or why we have them? Have you ever thought about how we can use them to our advantage rather than living life at their mercy? What about choosing to act rather than react, or to embrace rather than suppress? Now that we understand how emotions arise within us, we can accept that there are ways to work on our emotional fitness. We can see that more emotional balance is possible, just as it is with the body and mind, through practice.

EMOTIONAL FLEXIBILITY
Flexibility in all aspects of health implies range. Physical flexibility is the ability to move our joints through greater ranges of movement with comfort. Mental flexibility is the ability to accept and understand a greater range of ideas while stretching our minds beyond what we already know into the realms of creativity and possibility. Emotional flexibility, I believe, is the ability to feel and embrace each of the complete range of emotions possible when we need to. Emotional flexibility allows us to do this without getting stuck in any one or harmed by our emotional experience. There are no "bad" emotions or good emotions for they all serve to add to our experience of life. Emotions indicate how we are perceiving a situation and instigate a physiological response to react accordingly.

This is not to say that emotions are neutral or equal in our experience of them, as there are certainly pleasant and unpleasant emotions ranging from mild to extreme. We have emotions that feel wonderful, making life seem great in that moment. There are emotions that feel awful, making life seem terrible, again in that moment. How we view life affects our emotions and how we feel affects how we view life. This cycle of cause and effect can

191

let us spiral down into the depths of depression if consistently unpleasant. It can also raise us to the realms of peace, contentment and joy if we choose to guide our emotional fitness in that direction.

The aim of this section on developing our emotional health is not to strive for wonderful feelings all the time. Prescribed and recreational drug use has taught us that is not practical or healthy. Why, you may ask, am I now professing the importance of embracing unpleasant emotional states, having already touted the importance of feeling good? It's because unpleasant emotions give us a fuller experience of life. They give us contrast. How would we know a good day without a bad one, light without dark? They show us that some change is needed in order to return to feeling well again. Unpleasant feelings push us to assess our life situation and our thought processes. In knowing where we are emotionally, we can choose to stay or to go elsewhere. We can develop a plan to bring change, then we can put that plan into action.

Loneliness can bring about connections to others, should we acknowledge its unpleasantness and seek change. Anger can motivate us to speak our truth and defend our rights. Frustration can breed awareness of an unfulfilled life and encourage new beginnings. Loss can bring appreciation of what we still have. Unpleasant emotions can make life far more interesting, perhaps even inspiring great works. Exquisitely powerful stories, musical pieces and works of art have come to be through the experience of sadness, grief and loss. We could equate emotions to the musical notes on a piano. Were we to only use the white keys, wouldn't we be limited in the songs we could play? If we play only one note, a melody becomes impossible. But if we include all the notes within our range, allowing them to shift, change and flow harmoniously, we can create something wonderful.

To develop emotional flexibility, we must feel. This requires us to come out of our heads and into our bodies, into our gut and often into our hearts. We must challenge ourselves to go into those emotions that are outside of our comfort range or our norm. This can mean summoning up the courage to delve into unpleasant emotions. Sometimes it takes a push to give ourselves permission to feel good. Allowing feelings of joy can be as difficult for some as pain is for others. I have seen many people struggle with embracing positive emotions, myself included, when a held belief tells us we're not deserving of it. How many of us search for somebody to love us yet struggle to love ourselves? We give compliments easily yet bat away any that might make us feel good about ourselves or suggest that we might like ourselves.

A RANGE OF EMOTIONS

To begin developing a greater range of emotional flexibility, it's important to start slowly, as we would with our muscles. We must only go to the edge of our comfortable emotional range and stretch into it, otherwise we might snap! Growth and healing in the physical body requires time. Emotional wellbeing deserves the same level of patience. A study by Alan S. Cowen and Dacher Keltner, PhD from the University of California, Berkeley and published in 2017, identified 27 distinct categories of emotions.

They are, in alphabetical order, admiration, adoration, aesthetic appreciation, amusement, anxiety, awe, awkwardness, boredom, calmness, confusion, craving, disgust, empathetic pain, entrancement, envy, fear, horror, interest, joy, nostalgia, romance, sadness, satisfaction, sexual desire, sympathy and triumph. I find it interesting that love or compassion aren't on the list, but I believe they do underlie many of the others. Equally, anger and frustration are unmentioned yet quite common. Perhaps the study may not have included situations where these feelings were triggered. Perhaps we all have our own favourite words that we would use to describe how we feel and the subjects or scientists didn't use these terms.

Where you would begin stretching depends on the emotions you don't feel regularly or tend to avoid. These are the emotions that I would suggest are currently out of range for you. As an exercise to begin stretching your emotional range, write out the list of emotions on piece of paper. You could use the list above but add other words that you feel describe important emotions for you. I would suggest including words such as loving or compassionate, safe or secure, grounded or solid, easy and content to the list. These are states in which our nervous system operates in parasympathetic or peaceful mode. We want a range of emotional flexibility that easily encompasses this mode and these feelings. This will help us to make our default mode a peaceful one i.e. the one we go to sleep in, wake up in and return to unless there is a genuine threat, or by choice if we are thrill-seekers who choose exhillerating experiences. I would also add words such as anger, frustration, spite, disappointment, hopelessness and loneliness as these need to be acknowledged first to then be addressed and their frequency or power lessened.

Beside each emotional state, note how often you feel it e.g. always, several times a day, daily, several times a week, weekly, monthly, rarely or never. Then write a brief note of the most recent situation that sparked this emotion. Remember it may be a real-life situation, a dream you woke from or a scenario you imagined but the feeling is still legitimate. Lastly, rate the power of this emotion with 1 being barely noticeable and 10 being overwhelming e.g.;

Emotion	Regularity	Recent situation	Rating
Admiration	Weekly	I admired a friend for their ability to balance a busy work and family life	8
Anger	Monthly	I was annoyed by another driver for misusing lanes on a roundabout	4

Through this exercise, you will get a visual sense of the emotions that are well developed, one's you are able to feel with ease. You will see the ones that you spend too much time in and are possibly over-developed, reaching excessively elevated levels in minor situations e.g. road rage caused by another driver not using indicators correctly. You will also see those emotions which could be tapped into more often to add more flavour to your experience of life. Dipping into our unpleasant emotions helps us to work through old, repressed experiences and to let go of the baggage that weighs us down. Giving ourselves permission to feel pleasant emotions can open us up to seeking a life that supports our needs, is interesting, exciting and fulfilling.

If you find that you spend more time in unpleasant emotions or you regularly feel a way that is harmful, I would certainly recommend attending a counsellor. Likewise, if you feel emotionally numb or not feeling very much at all about anything. Using counselling is like hiring a fitness instructor to take you safely through your program towards better health. Your counsellor will work with you, confidentially and non-judgementally to restore balance.

If not quite ready to work with a professional, there are several useful options. We can tap into memories of times when we did feel an emotion that we now struggle to feel. By picturing the environment, the people and the situation we can return to that state and sit with it for a while, noticing the sensations and feeling it fully.

EMOTIONAL STRETCHES

We may seek out new experiences that will encourage such emotions. Here are some ways we could safely stretch our emotional muscles;

If we needed to feel and release anger or frustration, we could take up a martial arts or boxing class and work through it on the pads or punch bag. I found Karate particularly helpful during my mid-late teens when, as a teenager, lots of people annoyed me! A few minutes of pad or bag work was great to vent my frustrations in a controlled and safe way. This applies to other intense physical sports and activities that allow the body to "hit" something or use up any excessive heat that's simmering under our surface. Examples include rugby, weightlifting, tennis and running. Dancing, with its expressive nature, can be helpful too.

If we need calmness, joining a meditation class and spending time with people that feel it easily can allow us to learn their way. There are various forms of meditative practice and it may take a little searching to find a class or group that fits our particular needs and wants. I would suggest starting local and find out if any classes offer "tasting sessions" to try it out without requiring any major commitment.

If we want more love in our lives, we can start with some easier ways to feel love. We have less resistance to loving someone or something that shows us affection without any judgement. Consider getting a pet. As "man's best friend", dogs are very affectionate, loyal and likely to give lots of love in return. That combined with the cuteness factor of babies should make your puppy quite lovable! Kittens, bunnies, pot-bellied pigs, horses and I'm sure a whole host of other pets give us easy opportunities to feel love. If owning one isn't an option, we could volunteer to help at an animal shelter, walk a neighbour's dog or visit pet shops. As our capacity to love grows, we can aim to feel more kindness, gentleness and compassion towards ourselves and those around us. To "Love thy neighbour as thyself" is only useful if we're good at loving ourselves. Maybe instead, we should treat everyone as we would our beloved pets! Simple acts of kindness, in fact, even just mentally wishing people well opens the heart to loving more. Remember, it is feeling love for others that brings us the greatest benefit, rather than searching to be loved and will often attract those that are happy to love us right back.

If we have experienced loss but are unable to go into our grief or sadness so that we may come out the other side, there are ways to ease us into it. We could read stories or watch movies with storylines that include loss. Identifying with the character can bring us into that state and allow us to connect with our own stories. Then we may feel our own pain so that we can process it fully. Life is about experience and feelings are an integral part of this. I believe we must feel an experience fully or we tend to get stuck there or repeat it, in a loop of sorts, unable to move on to the next experience. I have personally found that the fear of strong, unpleasant emotions is far worse than the reality. Joining groups where others are also grieving can give us the opportunity to talk about our experience. This also reminds us that while we may have lost somebody very dear to us, we are not alone.

Joy and amusement can be brought back into our lives quite easily. There are more hours of stand-up comedy footage and programs available free online than any of us could ever need. Listen to it while driving or doing housework. Replace serious soaps, programmes and news with light-hearted comedy that lets us look on the bright side or at least just laugh at the irony of life. This will also help us to take ourselves less seriously. We can spend more time with the people that make us laugh, play with our kids and be silly.

For more awe, entrancement and confusion, we can seek out the entertainment of magic acts and programs on the world's greatest mysteries. There is so much we don't yet understand, and we get a strange form of pleasure from being bewildered and astounded. It brings a childlike sense of magic. If we can enjoy these mysteries, perhaps we can embrace the mystery of how our futures will unfold, looking forward to the unveiling of what is to come.

To feel triumph, we must challenge ourselves beyond what lies within our comfort zone. We must set meaningful goals that we cannot currently achieve but can work towards. These will test our abilities and our resolve. They will require that we make sacrifices. They will ask us to believe in ourselves and the possibility of success. Triumph will be the reward for our efforts and will serve to inspire us to set and reach new goals.

For sexual desire we can allow our minds to fantasize, to wander where they may. Fantasies are our own private thoughts and within that safe zone, we can do whatever we like. We can explore our own bodies to see what feels good. This is a natural and healthy part of our development into adulthood. When mature enough, we can then seek out another consenting adult to share in that experience. In Ireland, strict religious dogma for generations has led to sexual repression. We are emerging from it but there is still much shame carried by Irish people around our bodies and the pleasures of the flesh compared to many of our European counterparts. Embracing our freedom and right to express our sexuality is important and I would suggest, necessary for emotional wellbeing. As with any form of repression, the liberation that follows has the potential to be equally extreme, much like the pendulum that when pulled one way then swings in the opposite direction. A release of sexual expression may need to be tempered with self-care, self-respect and patience to encourage positive and meaningful sexual experiences. Shallow connections tend to leave us feeling empty and dissatisfied while intimate lovemaking creates strong bonds and beautiful memories.

For more admiration, adoration and aesthetic appreciation, we can draw up a list of the people we would like to be or want to be like. These are people with qualities that inspire us or are simply pleasing to behold. They give us pleasure because we focus on their beauty, qualities, abilities or their achievements, looking beyond their flaws. I believe this is an essential element of love. With practice, we can then begin to look at ourselves and others with the same intent, finding there are opportunities to admire, adore and appreciate all around us, especially in the mirror.

For anxiety and awkwardness, we can tap into recollections of times we felt that way, especially our earliest memories as these can often stay with us and have the greatest impact through our lives. Many people carry fears of the dark, water or spiders for example due, in-part, to the in-built instinctual fears they excite, but also from frightening childhood experiences of these. We can imagine the scenario and how it felt in that moment, fully feeling it yet knowing that time has passed, and we survived it. We could use this opportunity to do some inner-child work where we, as our wiser and stronger selves guide our younger selves through the memory. We can remind our young selves that they are safe, explaining how this experience can and will make them more resilient. We can modify the experience in our memories to see it as a gift rather than a reason to feel victimised or vulnerable.

For boredom, we can simply give ourselves a break, from everything. Life has become so busy that we rarely do nothing. We can turn off our electronic devices, drop everything briefly and just sit or lie down. We can tell ourselves that, in this moment, absolutely everything that needs to be done, is done! There is a profound sense of relief in this momentary pause with no anticipation, plans, to-do lists or effort. We can just be. Sometimes the ideal answer to "What to do with Stardust?" is absolutely nothing at all!

For craving and satisfaction, we can practice abstinence, choosing to forego some form of pleasure, for a time, allowing an appetite to build in us. They say, "hunger makes great sauce", i.e. food tastes more delicious with an appetite. This could mean that rather than impulse buying something we desire, which internet shopping has made ridiculously easy, we would wait for a birthday, holiday or a treat for when we have achieved a goal. Satisfaction levels increase significantly having gone a little hungry before enjoying our feast. We can also apply this to our relationships if passion has been replaced by disinterest. Forbidden fruit always looks riper and juicier.

You might ask what the benefit of feeling disgust is, as I did. Disgust's primary evolutionary benefit is to protect us from disease. We are particularly disgusted by the idea of eating rotten foods, touching an oozing infection or getting close to somebody with bad body odour due to poor hygiene. Before humans ever understood anything about bacteria or the transmission of disease by organisms that we cannot see, we instinctively knew to avoid such things, in the interest of survival and health. If we have become complacent about maintaining a healthy personal level of hygiene or towards our living space or environment, we should allow ourselves to feel a little disgust so that we clean up our act. This will improve our own health, surroundings and allow others to happily enter our personal space should we want them to.

Empathetic pain and sympathy come from imagining what it would be like to walk in another's shoes. Reading biographies or watching documentaries with true-life stories about suffering are more likely to stir an emotional response than a story we know to be fiction. We may find it easier initially to connect with characters that bear similarities to us. I find that where there are great distances or time differences between their stories and ours, we can sometimes be less sympathetic to their suffering. We don't always see that people all over the world, from all cultures and all generations are or were essentially the same. In the words of William Shakespeare from the Merchant of Venice, "I am a Jew. Hath not a Jew eyes? Hath not a Jew hands, organs, dimensions, senses, affections, passions; fed with the same food, hurt with the same weapons, subject to the same diseases, healed by the same means, warmed and cooled by the same winter and summer as a Christian is? If you prick us, do we not bleed? If you tickle us, do we not laugh? If you poison us, do we not die?". Identifying with the pain of others can bring out our more caring, compassionate and softer sides, willing us to help those who suffer.

Feeling envy, by looking at others that have achieved something we haven't, can show us what we subconsciously place value in. I've noticed myself, in the past, feeling envy towards those in happy marriages and relationships. This tells me that a strong and loving long-term relationship is something I would like in my life. I also believe that people and experiences come into our lives at the right time. The solution was to work on simply being happier, using that time to achieve what may have been more difficult when committing time to a relationship. With this, I chose to keep myself open to such a relationship, should it come along. I have also noticed myself feeling envy towards the owners of new cars. In Ireland, the registration number plate includes the year of registration so it's plain to see how new a car is. On contemplation of this envy, I realised it came from my belief that a new car is a symbol of financial success and business success which I mistakenly equated to personal success. My resolution came from identifying the areas of my life in which I wanted to succeed. I saw that I was happy with most and could work on others. The importance of owning a new car moved further down my list of priorities after that. Whatever we envy, we can use the feeling to make positive changes to our lives or perspectives.

Intentionally stimulating fear and horror, in small doses, can be beneficial for us if done in a safe environment where we can enjoy the experience. Horror movies, books or fun ghost train experiences can boost neurotransmitters temporarily to make our brains more focused and alert. Short-term fear can increase our adrenaline levels and stimulate white blood cell production for a stronger immune system. It's important to remember to return to ease shortly afterwards. Allowing the feeling of fear temporarily but then calming can remind us, in difficult real-life situations, that this too shall pass. Reducing our fear of fear can help minimise the effect of irrational fears such as public speaking or exposing ourselves to judgement.

With such incredible access to information, entertainment and education, finding a way to feel interested has never been so easy. There are interesting things everywhere! We can explore the internet and sign up for local courses. We can travel to exotic destinations or just look around us to see what catches our eye, then investigate further. We can talk to people. Everyone has a story and something interesting to say. If we're interested in a topic, we will want to learn more, and study will not seem like work. With enough knowledge and practice we can become experts in our respective fields, sharing our knowledge with others, using it to benefit our world and adding to our sense of fulfilment and purpose.

The good old days, when life was better, and everything was simpler. Sure, much of this belief comes from selective memory but still nostalgia makes us feel good. Long summer days as kids, playing with friends, first loves, first kisses, first cars, trophies won, trips taken, and happy memories made. Nostalgia shows us how great the simple things in life can be. Nostalgia reminds us of what we have achieved already and how lucky we have been. Nostalgia can inspire us to get out there and make new memories. Flick through the old photos, watch old video footage, read old letters and take a leisurely stroll down memory lane. The early stages of a relationship tend to be the most pleasurable as we charm one another with praise, affectionate touches and kisses and other romantic gestures. We can delve into the nostalgia and those early-day memories to feel more romantic and act on that feeling by randomly surprising our partner with some token of our affection.

Music is a powerful medium for stimulating emotion. With apps like Spotify, Youtube music and more, we can access music from all genres though a smartphone, tablet or laptop. We're talking classical symphonies, hard rock, pop, indie, music for meditation and everything in between. Full albums, individual singles and concerts from world-famous artists and emerging musicians. There are playlists that other users create so we don't have to go searching song by song. Find the songs or playlists you need and let them stir the emotions you need to feel, then try a different playlist to experience more flavours.

We can also use guided meditations in local classes, online or on Cd's that take us through visualisations to our desired state. Such practices can bring us into a deeper state of awareness, to access feelings that lie under the surface. Go to www.highestpotential.ie for videos, links and more on this.

I hope that you will see that all emotions can be of immense positive benefit to us if felt, acknowledged and accepted. With a complete range of emotions available, we have more opportunities to feel how we want to feel, gaining more control of our emotional state.

EMOTIONAL STRENGTH

Emotional strength, I would suggest, is the ability to dive into our most powerful feelings, to feel them fully without shying away. Emotional strength also helps us to stay more stable when circumstances might otherwise throw us off balance. Although there aren't any scientifically proven bodily locations for them, it's as if our bodies are vessels that contains our emotions. For all intents and purposes, they reside within our whole being, triggered by the brain or hormonal system and felt throughout the body. In the words of Marty Pellow of Wet Wet Wet's love song, originally by the Troggs, "I feel it in my fingers, I feel it in my toes".

In many spiritual teachings, emotions are linked with the element of water. In general terms, we talk about emotions welling up in us, anger spilling over, bursting with joy. We speak of waves of emotion washing over us or being drowned in sorrow. I'm sure it's not a coincidence that so many of the terms we use to describe emotions are often fluid-based and I will continue with that theme in this section. Water is a powerful element, wearing down even the hardest of stones over time while also necessary to create life. Like water, emotional strength can allow us to break through the toughest barriers while supporting the life we want to grow.

In my mid-thirties I found myself at a roadblock with my journey towards balance. I had experienced complete bliss several years earlier but found I was still subject to the common day-to-day stresses that I had briefly let go of to experience that heavenly state. I understood that this was a normal part of our human experience, but still felt that I could let go of more unnecessary stress, if I could just work through the issues that were in my way. I had been meditating regularly and had learned a lot about myself through non-judgemental self-reflection. I was feeling much better in general, but I noticed still that when I would sit and take my awareness inward, a blockage to complete ease remained. I could comfortably relax my legs, hips, abdomen and most of my torso but when it came to my throat there was a resistance. It felt as if I was gripping tightly, not that I couldn't breathe or swallow food, but still a constriction.

HOLDING BACK

I was conscious that, while I had done much internal work, I still hadn't spoken to anybody about my past depression or how I had wanted to end my life. Nor had I spoken about the guilt I felt from leaving my kids. As an independent man that prefers to paddle my own canoe, I hadn't really spoken about any issues I had over the years. Typically for me, I would bottle it up, swallow it down and get on with it. Not talking to others indicated shame on my part. I could acknowledge the emotions, the fears and the vulnerability to myself but not to anybody else. I wondered if the gripping in my throat was connected to me holding these inside, like a cork on a bottle.

An opportunity came my way, thanks to a friend of mine, to attend an "awakening of love" weekend retreat. Sounds very hippy, and I guess it was. I've been referred to as a bit of a hippy over the years and am proud to say that I am in some ways. Love was the underlying powerful emotion I could feel during my profound experience and I wanted more in my daily life. I knew that at the very least, I would learn a little more about myself and human nature from the others. At most, I might learn to let my shame grip go.

REMOVE THE BARRIERS

There were several different techniques used over the course of the weekend by our facilitators Samved and Mairead, to help our twelve participants awaken love. More specifically, I would say the techniques worked to remove our barriers to love. Love is natural to us and quite simple really. Removing the barriers can be a little more complicated. One of the first exercises we used on Friday evening, when divided into two groups of six participants, was to stand silently in front of the other five. The purpose was to simply be seen for one full minute.

Some found this difficult, yet I was fine as my class teaching and coaching experience meant I often stood in front of groups. Then we had to speak about why we were at the retreat. This was tough for me as it meant addressing personal issues. I explained that during meditation, I could feel a tightening in my throat and hoped I could learn to let it go. Mairead asked me to explain further. Not a chance! As the initial session of the first evening I wasn't ready, and we still had two days to go. I could already feel emotion rising from my abdomen, through my chest to my throat. Swallowing it back down I said 'jokingly', "Nope. That's all you're getting for now!". It would take some more coaxing to uncork that bottle.

We were advised to keep a journal over the weekend to take notes after each session of our personal thoughts and feelings. We were also recommended to go to bed early, to rest well as Saturday would be a full day. I sat on my bed to meditate, as I often do, to relax my body and calm my mind. Going inward, I could feel the neck tightness but also the sadness that lay beneath. Along with that there was fear of letting that sadness out. I wrote into my journal, "I am terrified of going into it. It feels like there's a river of sadness in me and if I go in, I'll never come out again. It will wash me away forever".

CHOOSING TO FLOAT

I chose to be braver. I closed my eyes and imagined standing on the banks of that river. I stepped into it slowly, walking until I was waist deep. I turned to face the bank and I lay back into the flood. I let it wash over me, surround me. I even let myself inhale, hoping I wouldn't drown and let it carry me where it wanted. I chose to trust that I would be ok, wherever it led. I felt the sadness build in my chest, pressing against my throat like a dam about to burst. It did, and I cried for the first time in a long time. I let it out. Well, I let some of it out. If I had let all the sadness, grief, guilt, shame and disappointment out in one go, it might have washed me away completely. It was a good start though, a breakthrough of sorts, and I went to sleep tired but feeling a little lighter for it.

The next day's coursework may as well have been designed specifically for me. It involved talking and lots of it. In the morning we paired off, sitting face to face. One spoke while the other listened. It was an interesting exercise to note that by just speaking, uninterrupted, what comes out. At times you stop and think "did I just say that? Ah that's interesting!". I've noticed while working on this book that this also happens while writing. It's a form of therapy and a wonderful way to gather my thoughts. I was also interested to notice that listening without offering advice or understanding was quite difficult for me. I would get distracted by memories and scenarios that I could connect with what I had just heard. I would want to offer a kind word or to help fix a problem. I had to consciously pull myself back to focus. Focused or not, a silent presence still helped my workshop partner to speak freely.

Then we were separated into three groups of four people. Again, one spoke, while the others listened. We were given a general topic to speak about such as "the masks we wear" or "the role we play in our families". I waited until last in our group to speak. I found myself talking about a past relationship where I said the other person "made me feel like crap". As soon as I said it, I knew I was playing the victim and said, "Ok, I know nobody makes me feel anything, they're my feelings". I noticed at this point that the other two groups of four people had finished and were silent. This meant that all the other eleven participants were focused on me and both facilitators were now standing with my group. I had gone from not even discussing my personal life with one person to now telling a whole room full!

KILLING ME SOFTLY

Samved stood beside me and asked a simple question, "How did you feel?". I tried to respond but the words wouldn't come out. The answer was mixed in with the emotion and if I let one out the rest would follow. Then he did the worst or best thing he could have done to me in that moment. He knelt beside me on my left, placed his left hand on mine, his right hand on my shoulder and spoke to me in the kindest and yet strongest voice I've ever heard "It's ok, how did you feel?". "You're killing me here" I said half-jokingly. Humour hides a multitude. "How did you feel?" he queried again. I spoke the words, "That I'm just not good-enough" and the floodgates opened.

I cried. Couldn't stop myself. The thirteen others in the room were silent, totally focused on me, as I bawled. The only other time anyone else had seen me cry since childhood was when I was leaving my young son and daughter, broken-hearted. The group gave me a few moments to be upset. They gave me the safe space to show vulnerability. I am still grateful to them all for that. After the retreat, several of the other participants thanked me for revealing what I did. It helped them too. I cried again the following day, in another group exercise where I was lying down, wrapped in a blanket. Years of emotional build-up takes some releasing.

To finish off our weekend, we all sat on chairs in a big circle to talk briefly about our experiences of the retreat. I listened as the others spoke about how wonderful it was, meeting great people, the beautiful energy etc. It came around to my turn. "I'm really glad you all feel wonderful" I said. "I'm exhausted! This weekend has taken so much out of me but it's exactly what I needed so thank you all". It wasn't easy but it was certainly worth it. As I said goodbye to Samved and Mairead, our facilitators, he gave me a hug. "Stop, or you'll have me crying again" I said. "And why not?" he replied. "The greatest injustice done to men is to be told it's not ok to cry". I never forgot that statement and can see the truth in it. It seems to be more acceptable, and certainly more common for a man to be angry or silent than to be upset. No wonder we often lash out or shut off when feeling stressed or down.

I left that retreat feeling better but tired. Had I known the effect, I would have taken a week off work after to rest. It took much strength to go through the fear I had of talking about my repressed emotions. More to face them and to feel them and to be vulnerable in front of others. Like all forms of strength development, it gets easier with practice, but I feel it's essential to mention that too much of the hard and painful work can wear us down. A little work and plenty of rest and nourishment in between is far more effective. I find I'm more comfortable talking about emotions now and addressing my own to others. "What to do with Stardust?" and the personal accounts it contains wouldn't have been written without finding that strength. It may take more strength as friends, family and strangers learn my innermost thoughts, feelings and experiences. Every reader will know what I hid from my nearest and dearest for years. Still I know that strength is in me and believe that some good will come from using it.

To strengthen these emotions they must be used, not just in the easy situations but also in more challenging ways;

Feel

Feel whatever needs to be felt as fully as you need to feel it. Our emotions reside within us therefore can never be greater than we are. They do not have to overwhelm us. We can handle them. If you find yourself going through something similar, use your emotional strength to dip into the river and seek help. It's worth it. Start small and build it as you go. A counsellor will guide you much as a gym instructor would, only giving you what you can handle each session. In time you can become strong enough to bear what you must and cast off the rest. Most likely you will learn that you were strong enough all along.

Live

Remember that challenging life experiences make us stronger once we take time to rest in between. Life gives us plenty of opportunities to develop emotional strength without looking for them. Avoid creating or being drawn into unnecessary drama where possible. Every tough day, when we feel like giving up but pick ourselves up and carry on empowers us. Each time we rise above a situation and choose to act in the manner we want to, as the type of person we want to be, develops our strength.

Trust

Each moment we trust that everything is ok and choose to love rather than fear, makes us more emotionally centred and balanced. That can be difficult to do when we are stuck in unhelpful patterns of behaviour or unhealthy relationships but when we apply trust and love we grow stronger. We use our strength to take responsibility for where we are and to then trust our ability to pull ourselves out of a hole. This effort is important for if we rely solely on others to do this for us, we may fall back in again.

Be brave

Bravery is not acting without fear, bravery is acting despite fear. A mindset of "Better the devil you know than the devil you don't" can encourage us to stay in situations that don't really work for us for fear of something worse should we change. It takes strength to let go of current relationships, jobs or beliefs or patterns of behaviour while trusting that venturing into the unknown may lead us to a better place.

Talk

Share your experiences and thoughts with others to lighten your load. It takes courage and strength to do this, risking the judgement or criticism that we may expect but rarely receive. This allows us to let go of our burdens. With less baggage, we can then use our strength to help carry others when they need our support.

Listen

When we speak, we hear only what we already know, when we listen, we can learn something new. Perhaps there's a reason we have two ears and one mouth! We often only half-listen to what others are telling us. In our heads, we are already rehearsing what we are about to say in response. Or, we are gone off to a world of our own. Being strong enough to set aside the ideas we want to express, or our firmly held beliefs creates the opportunity to be present, non-judgemental and open. New knowledge can help us to understand a challenging situation and other perspectives more clearly, giving us more power to deal with it effectively. The unknown can be unsettling unless we trust our ability to handle the outcome regardless. Understanding what's going on can help us to feel more secure.

Act

Expressing our emotions and our needs strengthens our sense that they are as valid and important as anyone else's. We can first sit with our emotions and thoughts to clarify what we need. Then we can plan how to address them for more positive outcomes rather than simply reacting unconsciously. We can try to do this in a way that causes no offence or hurt to others, so everybody involved comes out shining. When an instant reaction is required, we can use our emotional strength to remain steady and compassionate.

As mentioned earlier, focusing and training the mind has a profound effect on balancing our emotional state. Practicing awareness to become more present and centred can help to restore our emotional stability. Using positive affirmations to reprogram negative thought patterns that create unhelpful fears and doubts, can improve our emotional strength. Developing our physical strength helps us to feel stronger emotionally too. Knowing that we are physically more powerful broadens our range in what we feel we can accomplish and handle in other areas of our lives. Sometimes we need to fight for our rights and strength training can unleash the warrior in us. Refer to the section on developing physical strength and visit highestpotential.ie for more information on this.

EMOTIONAL STAMINA

Emotional stamina grants us the power to keep going if undertaking a particularly emotional journey. This may be difficult but must be followed through if we are to reach our goal. Let's say you decide to start working through some repressed, unpleasant emotions having already summoned up the strength to get in deep. Here's an exercise to help you.

DIP IN

Imagine your emotional self as a pool of water that may look clear and still on the surface, but has a thick layer of mud sitting at the bottom. You decide you want to get rid of some of your 'crap' so you get in there and start reaching down to pull out the dirt. This isn't pleasant and you get your hands dirty, but you manage to scoop some out. A few minutes of clearing out is all your energy levels can handle before you get out again. Your pool now looks a bit darker than it was before, still muddied from all the rooting around, its calm surface now rippled and unsettled. You wonder why you bothered even trying, since it seems worse now, but you know there is less crap in there than there was before. After a while, the surface settles and clears again and you leave it be, to rest until you're ready to do a little more clearing.

GOING UNDER

You go back in a few days or weeks later to do the same again. Each time you find some more dirt to scoop out, muddy the water and emerge a little tired and dirty. But you also notice that you're getting a little fitter, and better at finding and scooping out what needs to be removed. You become less scared and judgemental of what you find. You even start to enjoy observing what's been buried for so long. Self-exploration becomes more interesting as you dive deeper and stay under the surface longer. As you examine the depths of your emotions you start to see beauty in the stones and sediments you find. You realise that much of what lay beneath was in fact pleasant. It wasn't so bad after all.

As the pool becomes clearer, you decide that it looks better and more interesting with some stones and sediment at the bottom. Some bright and shiny, others dark and rough. Rather than aiming for a pure pool, emptied of all but the clearest water, you prefer the depth and layers of your emotions. Much of what lies beneath reminds you of the lessons you've learned, challenges you've overcome and the beauty we all possess. The emotional fitness you've now developed gives you the patience to pick your way through it to decide what stays and what goes. You see that we can be caretakers of our emotional pools to gain more mastery and enjoyment of our emotional state.

STICKING WITH IT

Emotional stamina is also expressed when we commit to life-changing decisions by sticking with our new choice. While we must acknowledge our feelings each day, if they are quite erratic, we may have to overlook those that would prevent us from achieving our goals. For example, if in the initial stages of a new fitness program we don't feel like exercising one day, tapping into our emotional stamina can remind us of why we started and that we will feel better afterwards. In fact, this feeling is generally temporary and passes within minutes of starting to exercise.

If we choose to believe in our right to wellness, we must practice wellness each day. Whether it's positive-thinking, meditation, healthy eating, exercise, beneficial lifestyle habits or nurturing good relationships, ideally a combination of these, we must persist for them to become our norm. A few days or weeks of self-care is helpful, but we can achieve so much more over a year, decade or lifetime. In the beginning it can be easy to fall back into old unhelpful habits, so it takes daily discipline and endurance to pull away from these. Just remember, every step brings us closer to our dream.

Building stamina is simple. It's just not always easy. It's important to move forward one step at a time, one day at a time, at our own pace, ensuring that we rest when we need too. Emotional journeys are challenging but can be enjoyable too. At the journey's end, we get an even greater sense of satisfaction as we triumph through adversity.

COMMON IMBALANCES THAT AFFECT EMOTIONAL STATES;

THIRST

A French study funded by Danone Research and conducted by Forenap, published in 2014, compared the effects of water consumption on emotional states. Two groups were chosen. The HIGH group normally drank at least 2.5 litres of water per day. The LOW group typically drank 1 litre or less per day. Their water volume consumption was reversed in a controlled 3-day experiment and several mood scales were administered at various points. Their conclusion was that reducing the HIGH group member's water intake had a detrimental effect on mood in areas such as calmness, positive thinking and sleep or tiredness levels. Increasing their water intake had beneficial effects for the LOW group members, especially in areas of sleepiness.

This is certainly the case with me. If I am dehydrated due to having taken extra exercise or activity, higher temperatures or because I simply didn't drink enough water, I will feel it in many ways. I find it more difficult to sleep, I'm a little more irritable and feel more stressed even if I have nothing on my mind. When I notice these symptoms, my first go-to cure is a 2-part water to 1-part orange juice mix, ideal for rehydration. My water comes from a natural spring, so it contains minerals and the orange contains some carbohydrates. I will drink at least one pint straight away and more within the next hour. I'm practically guaranteed to feel at ease again within two hours.

HUNGER

More specifically, nutritional deficiency that causes hunger can make us feel out of sorts. Hunger is the body's way of telling us we need the nutrients that come from our food. Many of us, myself included, find that we get 'hangry' or hunger-angry, irritable, unsettled or anxious when running low on energy. This is natural to us from birth. As any parent knows, if a small child is upset, they're almost always hungry, tired, hot, cold or in physical discomfort. Loosening their clothing, wrapping them up or feeding them will often change their mood instantly. If they can be put to sleep, then that's even better. They wake up as their happy little selves again.

As blood-sugar levels drop, our bodies produces cortisol, adrenaline and a chemical called neuropeptide Y which triggers aggression. From a survival standpoint, this "hanger" might have inspired even the most peaceful humans to fight predators to scavenge their food or to hunt, kill and eat other creatures when there wasn't enough nuts, berries and fruit to sustain us. Keep in mind the vegetarian diet would have been unsustainable in many parts of the world, throughout the year, without supermarkets, freezers or preservation techniques. It would have been necessary to supplement diets with calorie dense, high protein and mineral, meats and organs. It was a case of kill or be killed.

It's worth noting that while we may not be hungry for calories, we may still be hungry for nutrients. A highly processed diet or one lacking in variety will eventually result in nutritional deficiencies. Much of the world now lives primarily on bread, grains, cereals or rice. Then, there are the high-protein, no/low carb diets that have become popular in more affluent areas. These diets are nutritionally poor compared to the wide variety of foods our hunter gatherer ancestors enjoyed. As our bodies cannot create all the proteins, hormones, vitamins and minerals we need for optimum health, it stands to reason that a reduction in these could lead to regular 'hanger' or anxiety. Adding more variety to our diet can help to balance our emotions.

TIREDNESS

We all know that we don't feel well when tired. We get irritable and anxious. Late nights out without alcohol can still leave us feeling hungover from tiredness. Getting a consistent sleeping pattern with adequate hours to match our needs is important for wellbeing. I find that getting to bed around 10pm and getting up around 6am to be most beneficial. I will often meditate before falling asleep at 10.30pm and, according to my Fitbit wristwatch, wake for approximately 45 mins per night. This 7 hours of sleep seems to be enough for me to rest and recharge as I wake without need of an alarm. This pattern works far more effectively than say a 12pm to 8am routine. Consistently poor sleeping patterns will result in consistently lower moods so aim to create better habits. If you find you are not tired enough to sleep at 10.30pm, set your alarm to wake you early. You will then be tired enough to sleep earlier. Power-napping for 20-40 minutes during the day can help too if we haven't rested sufficiently overnight.

HORMONES

We're familiar with mood-altering hormonal effect on toddlers when throwing tantrums, teenagers as they pull away from their parents and assert their individuality and males reliving youth during mid-life crisis. Often when we're under the influence of such hormonal states, if we can acknowledge that they are controlling us like puppets on strings, we might have a chance to cut the strings or become the puppeteer too.

Hormones operate in our bodies all day, every day, regulating many systems in the body. As discussed earlier, our thought processes and the habits leading up to each moment play a role in finding ourselves in fight or flight mode, or easy, calm and content. If we're in a highly emotional state, it's helpful to break the cycle to allow hormone levels to rebalance. This might require us to 'count to 10', take the day or maybe a week off. For some, breaking the cycle requires a month off or a total lifestyle change. The degree of change required of course depends on the level of dis-ease we are experiencing and how much of our life has or is currently spent on adding to this dis-ease.

To sum up this chapter, I believe we are both puppets and puppeteers of our emotional state. Developing and practicing methods to pull our own strings can bring more wellness, ease and productivity to our lives. It can allow us to be calm amidst a storm, brave despite fear and to find joy in the mundane. These can certainly enrich our experience of life.

For more on developing emotional health and wellbeing, visit www.highest-potential.ie

PART 6

Spirit Matters

Spirit Matters

Chapter 19

Connecting to Spirit

"Once we believe in ourselves, we can risk curiosity, wonder, spontaneous delight, or any other experience that reveals the human spirit", E.E. Cummings

Whether in a religious context or in terms of human behaviour, when we talk of spirit, we refer to the best in us. Team-spirit invokes a sense of loyalty and determination while a spirited performance is courageous and energetic. Community-spirit suggests togetherness, with all in the community working for the common good. We speak fondly of those with gentle spirits as the kindest and most caring among us. When sunshine brings smiles to our faces and a spring to our step, we say it raises our spirits, suggesting that joy and happiness are attributes visible when the spirit rises to the surface. To enter into the spirit of an occasion is to join wholeheartedly with others, indicating that the spirit is a positive energy of sorts, and can be shared by many. When we say the spirit is willing, but the flesh is weak, we equate the spirit to our best intentions that the body and mind cannot always live up to.

The title of this chapter is a little misleading as I don't believe it is possible to be disconnected from our spirit. At the very least it is part of us, at most it is who we are. I acknowledge that we can become disillusioned and distracted to a point where we cannot see or feel this connection. I view this as shutting our eyes and turning our back to the sun and then believing we are alone in the dark. As such, this chapter is to remind you of your unbreakable connection rather than teaching you to create one. I also don't believe that we can improve upon the spirit as it is already perfect. As such, this chapter will not make your spirit more powerful or pure. Your spirit is already these and more. Nor do I believe we can heal the spirit it as it is invulnerable. As such, this section will not attempt to fix your spirit. We cannot fix that which cannot be broken. I do believe that there are practices that allow us to benefit more from our spiritual connection. We can let go of the distractions and disillusions to enjoy the warmth, energy and vibrancy that comes from turning our attention towards the light. We can remember our always present connection to our spirit and strengthen our belief in it, so it can play a greater part in our lives.

211

If spirit encompasses our ideals, joy, togetherness, kindness, courage and vitality, then surely we must aspire to living a more spiritual life as part of our "What to do with stardust?" plan?

WHAT IS SPIRIT?

Defining the spirit is nearly impossible, as it is immeasurable and open to the interpretation of each of us. As such, every definition is as valid as any other. I will explain what I believe the spirit to be and what I do not believe it to be to give you a sense of what I mean when I talk about connecting with your spirit. I would like to mention that these beliefs are based largely on my own experiences and contemplation rather than religious texts and philosophies, although I'm sure I have been influenced by those to some degree. I respect all religious and spiritual beliefs and hope this fits in with yours.

The spirit is not the body. The physical body is replaced cell by cell throughout our lives and yet we, our consciousness or our spirit remains. The spirit does not appear to be the mind either as we possess a consciousness that listens to the chatter of the mind and watches its imaginings. When we talk to ourselves, inside our heads, who or what is it that listens? When the mind imagines and dreams, who or what is it that watches these stories unfold? The spirit appears to be very much connected to the mind and body, yet it is still something else of itself. Nor does the spirit seem to be the emotions, or at least not the fearful ones. It does seem to be connected to our feel-good emotions but if the spirit or consciousness is the intelligence that is feeling the feelings, then surely it cannot be the feelings themselves?

I believe that the spirit is the consciousness housed within these constructs, experiencing life through these filters. It is the observer of all that we do. If the eyes are indeed the windows to the soul, it is the spirit that looks out through these portals, into the world. It is that timeless part of us that doesn't feel older, despite the passing of years. It is the consciousness, or perhaps the conscience, that chooses how we live and act when we are living through love, clarity and peace. It is that which is undisturbed by the illusions of an unnecessarily fearful mind.

It is that part of us that understands the world from a higher perspective, granting us flashes of insight into what it sees from that viewpoint. It is the spirit that knows we are all connected and never alone, part of something greater than ourselves. The spirit sees that we are all worthy and that we all belong. It feels true, unconditional love. Maybe it is love in its purest form. The spirit is completely accepting of its own skin and the skins of others. Perhaps it chose the skin it would wear before it entered our world. It recognizes that, at a deeper level of existence and experience, all is ok.

I believe these things because I experienced such knowing, as described in Chapter 3 "A life-changing experience", when I briefly set aside the superficial distractions of my dualistic and judgemental mind and connected to my spirit. For me, connecting to our spirit is about reminding our egos to relax, to open our minds to greater perspectives and to become more compassionate and loving towards ourselves and others.

WHAT'S GOD GOT TO DO WITH IT?

Everything and nothing. Gods and religions are human concepts that we create to try to make sense of our existence, our purpose and to give us direction. Typically, our Gods are all-powerful creators and destroyers of life, whose will must be done. Religious organisations often place themselves as the messengers of "God's will" to guide their followers with a root message of love and belonging. Unfortunately, these institutions can and often have become something else entirely, depending on the desires of those in charge. Religious texts and teachings are said to come directly from the Gods and, as such, true believers are expected to follow without question. When followers are offered eternal salvation in exchange for temporary compliance, many will do as they are told! We must remember that all such messages were delivered through human minds, hands and mouths. Many were translated and edited from the original messages over many years before they became what we read today.

The fear of God's wrath and an eternity in hell has resulted in some horrendous acts in the past. Blind faith and abuse of power has led to even more. There are many legitimate reasons for intelligent, kind and caring people to turn away from religion. As this fear of God wanes here, Ireland has seen a dramatic decline in church attendances and new candidates entering into the Catholic holy orders. This suggests to me that many Irish people attended church services out of a sense of duty or fear of repercussions rather than a genuine love of the sacraments or traditions. I imagine that if most people found peace, love and harmony at mass, we would continue to go in considerable numbers.

NON-PRACTICING?

I must admit that I rarely attend mass services myself, unless it is for a christening, wedding or funeral. In these cases, I go for the people involved rather than the church. I find very little in the sacraments or services to connect with. The gospels indeed give a reminder of how one might behave when choosing to act out of love, but the rest rarely holds my attention. I personally find a greater connection when looking at a beautiful sky at sunrise or sunset, take a walk in the woods or sit and enjoy the views from a mountain top. Nature is my favourite church and where I feel closest to everything. Realistically, if all is made by and from God, then everywhere is as much a church as anywhere else.

If we were to ask every person that believes in a God to describe their God, they would give us exactly that, a description of their personal perception of God. Depending on their religious beliefs and teachings, their God could have any one of many names and origins. Their God would be a collage of all they had learned and experienced with all the pieces put together in a way that fits best for them. Some would have analysed their beliefs thoroughly with deep contemplation, philosophical conversations and study of religious texts to form their God. Others would have simply believed what they were told without significant questioning.

Some would call the idea of a "sky God", or any other form of God a load of nonsense. The greater proportion of the world's population has some affiliation to religions, each with very different Gods. As such, if any one person or religion is correct about what God is and what God should be called, it would seem that most of the intelligent humans on the planet are wrong! Perhaps we are all as close to being right as each other, when trying to describe something that encompasses absolutely everything that ever was, is and ever will be?

I BELIEVE

The last few paragraphs may make me sound like a non-believer. That couldn't be further from the truth. I do believe in God, just not the bearded versions of the Sistine chapel, though I admire the artwork. I believe that everything was created by something from nothing or from itself. I believe that something continues to create our universe, around us and through us. I believe in forces that organise, move, shape and guide this creation, forces that are often unseen and yet we know they are real through their effect on our reality.

As we seek to understand our universe, we find that what appears to be solid is made of almost nothing, but the tiniest fragments of energy, shaped into atoms by unseen forces. These forces are nuclear, electromagnetic, gravitational and the recently theorised but as yet unobserved Higgs force. These forces push and pull, join and separate, organise, create and destroy all that we see and much of what we can't see at all. By most estimates, we can only see about .0035% of the light spectrum with our human eyes. These forces were believed in, by scientists, because their effects could be seen or felt before they could be proven scientifically. They were only confirmed afterwards when the belief of our greatest minds inspired them to create technology to measure them. Science is founded on the belief of the unknown and unseen. Isn't it interesting that some would try to use science to condemn those who believe in that which is unseen and immeasurable?

I believe that these atoms, thanks to unseen but organised forces, form solid, liquid and gas elements and sometimes mix together to create compounds. These then fashion the structures that make the cells in my body, each cell type with its own intelligence that organises its form and function. We call this intelligence DNA. These cells work together as part of tissues, organs and systems each guided by their own internal intelligence. I wonder if my cells know that they are part of something bigger as they go about their duties. Can they comprehend that they are linked together by the overall intelligence of the nervous system?

Within my body, and on its surface, lives a multitude of bacteria, more individual cells than I have human cells, working synergistically with my body. Together they form a whole being with a body, mind and emotions. This miraculous combination of layers and levels of organised and intelligent wisps of energy, atoms, compounds, cells, tissues and bacteria are what makes me. And what makes you! It's incredible really.

214

I believe that I have a conscious intelligence that links with the levels below as I feel the sensations of my body and it tells me when I need nourishment or self-care. My conscious intelligence, that I may call my mind or persona, is part of a network of family, friends and neighbours which form my community. We interact, communicate and affect each other with our individual and collective intelligence. My community supports me and my needs, providing me with food, shelter and many other services. My own and other communities make up my nation which attempts to serve and care for its communities.

I believe each nation, with their various traditions and beliefs, has a collective consciousness, mindset or perhaps even spirit of its own. My nation, with all the others, form the international community of our species. Humanity is but one of many species of animals and plants on our planet. Together, every single organism, in all its diversity, forms what we call life. Our planet is part of a solar system, one of many in our galaxy, in a universe of galaxies that, for us, may as well be infinite. We are made of little bits of intelligent energy and we are little bits of intelligent energy that makes up bigger bits of intelligent energy.

At each level of our reality, from the smallest that we are aware of, a similar pattern is present. Unseen forces, organised and with purpose, guide life into existence, creating order out of what could be chaos. Each level of organisation appears to create a foundation for a more complex level above. I have no reason to suppose that this pattern would peak at humanities current levels of comprehension. Our planet itself could have a form of consciousness of its own, whose language we don't understand any better than one of my brain cells understands what my mind is thinking.

Science has shown us that animals and plants communicate in incredible ways, much like the cells and tissues within our bodies. With such a miraculous universe, is it such a stretch of the imagination to believe there is a "mother earth" of sorts that feels and thinks at a level above where we are at? I expect that life and consciousness exists on many other worlds too. Isn't it possible that together they, and we, form a universal intelligence?

I believe in a consciousness and energy that encompasses all, that connects all, that is all. That is my God and for me, it is the spirit that understands that connection.

PRACTICAL BENEFITS OF SPIRITUAL CONNECTION

I get many positives from the belief that we are essentially sparks of consciousness, part of a greater intelligence, experiencing life through our bodies, minds and emotions. Life is more interesting and enjoyable, and challenges are more bearable from that perspective.

Belonging

It gives me a stronger sense of belonging which is a fundamental requirement of most humans. We are tribal by nature. We take surnames that tell others of the family be belong to. We support teams and clubs, turning up on match days wearing our colours, regardless of age or class, all together as one. We fly the flags of our counties and countries. A spiritual perspective opens me to being part of the greatest group there is i.e., everything. I too support sports teams and enjoy the banter between supporters, but don't feel a division between "us and them" as some do. I'm amazed when sports fans have to be separated at the games they claim to love, to prevent violence against others that love the same game.

Trust

My belief puts me more at ease. Trusting more in the bigger picture makes it easier to trust in the trivial things. With so much of the universe taken care of, without my control or input, I feel I can relax about the smaller details of my life. I trust that the sun will rise each morning and set each night as our planet orbits the sun at about 60,000 miles per hour. I trust that rain will fall, and water will flow. I trust in nature to provide food and other resources. I trust in the many amazing biological processes taking place within my body. I trust in the abilities that the intelligence of evolution, genetics and experience have given me. I trust in the intelligence and the spirit of humanity to balance our primal instincts, which can sometimes be short-sighted and self-centred, with an attitude that focuses on the collective wellbeing of our world. I trust in the intelligent guiding forces of our universe to continue guiding intelligently. I trust that life will find a way.

Patience

Such trust gives me more patience to wait, when my mind tells me that things aren't moving quickly enough. From an acceptance of the universe's natural rhythms, which can be seen in the orbits of planets and the cycles of our seasons, I can believe in perfect timing. This lets me trust that my plans can also bear fruit at the right time. I also find that when I ask God, the universe or the divine consciousness for help, I always seem to get it. Sometimes what I receive is so precisely what I've asked for that I now find myself taking more care to be clear in my requests. Of course, these observations could be put down to pure coincidences or my positive and grateful attitude. Either way, it works for me!

Compassion

My belief makes me care more about others. If we are all part of something greater, there is no "I", there is only "We", so your wellbeing becomes as important as mine. I wish myself well therefore I wish you well. It makes me try to be more understanding when I or others act in a less than conscientious manner, looking instead for the reason why the egos' fear-based instincts are running the show rather than the higher self. This provides opportunities to focus on alleviating the fear or to at least attempt to separate the sin from the sinner It is far easier to forgive the behaviour of somebody who we can see is afraid or simply doesn't know any better than it is to forgive those we believe to be hateful or evil.

216

Perspective

It gives me a broader perspective toward my life and the effect it has on the world. I understand that the condition of the cells, tissues and organs in my body directly affect my body as a whole. Likewise, my condition and yours, our family and friends, our communities, our nations and our species directly affect our world as a whole. The knock-on effect of my wellness and actions play a part in the decisions I make. I'm not saying that everything I do benefits the world perfectly, but it makes me want to try.

Observation

It allows me to observe myself and my own issues as a form of self-assessment and self-counselling. When we say, "I took a good look at myself", it's the observer in us that does this. When we say, "I sat myself down and had a good talk with myself", I believe that's the conscience, the higher self, stepping in to guide the rest. Regularly tuning into that clearer state helps us to stay aligned with who we really want to be and what we truly want to do.

Gratitude

It makes me more grateful for what I am and all I have. When I take time to acknowledge the scale of evolution and universal creation that took place just for me and all around me to exist, I become profoundly thankful. This stunning planet with its skies, mountains, valleys, oceans and rivers and the abundance of plants and creatures is a gift to enjoy! Even on a smaller scale, I can see that just for me to sit at my desk and write this book has involved countless people and their efforts. All those involved in the evolution and creation of the technology involved in my laptop have played a part in this opportunity. Those who invented electricity and found ways to bring it to the masses. Those who developed language and the written word. Those who developed the internet to allow us to share our knowledge and experience. I could go on, and on. We have so much to be grateful for.

Encouragement

It gives me encouragement to reach beyond my comfort zone to seek out new experiences. If everything is ok, then it's ok for me to stretch myself outside of my normal range. I can try new things without worrying about "getting it wrong" as it will be ok whatever the result. If the spirit does live through this body to experience its sensations, then I am, in a sense, satisfying my spiritual needs by trying new things. By choosing experiences that include physical, mental and emotional wellbeing, I also serve my spirit by caring for the body and mind it inhabits. If these experiences can include compassion for others, it's a triple-whammy i.e. good for me, for you and for the soul!

Acceptance

It helps me to accept and even embrace life's more challenging experiences. Rather than wallowing in self-pity when life isn't smooth sailing, taking a more spiritual perspective lets me look at it a little differently. I can say "Ok, this is a powerful, albeit difficult or unpleasant, situation that adds to my overall life-experience". "It is valuable to me and I will take something positive from it". "It will make me stronger, wiser, more patient or more understanding" It allows me to believe that life happens for us and not to us, trusting that the challenge is for my benefit, so that I can work with it.

Presence

It allows me to live in the real world. As the interested observer rather than the critic, my attention turns toward what is, rather than how I think it should be. This improves my ability to be more present. I can then seek to understand what is really going on and what may have led to this reality. Presence brings more focus to direct my energy where it best serves me. In a more present state, I also become a better listener so I can actually hear what others are saying. This makes it easier to read situations and people more clearly by picking up on the subtle signs and cues they give off. This helps me to connect with others and notice when they need an ear to listen, a word of encouragement or a little space.

Equality

It is the supreme leveller. While we can see the superficial differences between our bodies, minds and emotions, there can be no discrimination of what lies inside if we believe in an innocent, perfect spirit. Without colour, creed, shape, size or possessions, the spirit cannot be quantified. Without any means of comparison, we cannot say "my spirit is better than yours" therefore all are equal from that perspective. The word "Namaste" is a customary Hindu greeting, usually accompanied by a bow with hands in a prayer position in front of the heart. It is literally translated to "I bow to you", but I prefer a variation of this which is said to be the intended meaning. It goes, "The divine in me bows to the divine in you". Every spark of consciousness is as valuable, worthy and important and equally connected to the source. Cynics might say that if everybody is special then nobody is special. When viewing life from a more spiritual perspective, it is obvious that everyone is special. This gives me a sense of importance and humility all at once. I am great and so are you.

Freedom

It frees me from ties to religious groups, rules and regulations. I do not require the approval of an institution, book or an ordained human to earn a connection to my spirit, God or to reach a heavenly afterlife. To me, that's like a drop of water seeking permission from another drop of water to belong to the ocean they are both in. We cannot return to that which we never left. Believing in a spirit means I am already part of it, and it is part of me, always has been, always will be. However, I can see the benefits of religious teachings that encourage togetherness. "The Lords' prayer" attributed to Jesus Christ, begins with, "Our father who art in heaven...". I find it interesting that it's 'our' father and not 'my' father since we're told by the Christian church that Jesus was the one and only son of God. Throughout this prayer "we", "our" and "us" are used. Perhaps this little nugget was left by Jesus so he wouldn't be remembered as a demi-god but to say that we are all in this together. I do believe that Jesus existed, and I like the messages he left behind for us. Despite all the translations and rewritten editions, his messages of love, forgiveness and equality carried through for 2,000 years. That shows me the power and importance of these words.

The freedom of a personal spiritual connection means I can set aside the religious dogma that were perhaps suited to another time or that served the needs of those in charge of religious organisations. For example, there is the Christian idea of original sin i.e., that we are born sinners and must be baptized to be cleansed of these sins. This seems to be a very obvious recruitment drive to join the Christian church before members can choose for themselves. I can't imagine anything more innocent than a new-born baby. This "original sin" pushes current members to sign up their children within months of their birth for fear that, should they die young, they will miss out on eternal salvation. The freedom gained from believing that every spirit is always connected and innately perfect lets me trade original sin for innocence. Such freedom also gives me the space to respect the faiths and beliefs of others as I'm not tied to "my way" versus "your way". I don't need another faith to directly align with mine or use the same words to believe we are fundamentally the same and part of something greater.

THE EGO, FRIEND OR FOE?

The word "Ego" often has a different meaning in western society than it does in eastern philosophy. When we in the west say somebody has a big ego or is egotistical, we usually mean that they are very cocky and prone to bragging or other displays of their own importance. Such people draw much attention to themselves and appear to believe that their opinions and beliefs "Trump" everyone else's. The western version of the ego is indeed symptomatic of a person living predominantly through the ego but there is much more to the ego than that.

According to Eastern philosophy, the ego is the part of us that believes we are separate from everything else. It suffers loneliness as a result. The ego is dualistic in nature, judging everything right or wrong. It struggles to accept reality as a result. The ego criticises its own body, mind, abilities and value and those of others. It is often blinded to the gifts and talents it and others possess as a result. The ego seeks validation of its worthiness by attempting to outshine others with its material worth, intellect or abilities. It misses the chance to bask in the glow of others, by letting them shine, as a result. The ego finds reasons not to love and be loved. It misses opportunities to love and be loved as a result.

The ego carries guilt about the past. It struggles to live in the present moment as a result. The ego fears change and suffers when unwanted change comes its way. It misses out on the excitement and mystery of the unknown as a result. The ego attaches its self-worth and happiness to its possessions or people and suffers when they are lost, sometimes convincing itself that happiness can never return. It misses out on the chance to be happy with what it is and what it has as a result. Ego fears what it doesn't understand and creates conflict as a result. The ego is afraid of expressing its truth, so it pretends to be something it's not. It misses the chance to be real as a result. The ego is sometimes afraid to stand out from the crowd. It avoids opportunities to shine in its own unique way as a result.

Friend

This all might make the ego sound like it is our foe as it plays the greater part in so much of our mental and emotional suffering, but the ego has its benefits too. The ego is important for our bodies' survival as it helps to keep us safe from real physical danger. It warns us of risk, in the present or possibly in the near future, so that we can take precautions. Survival gives us more opportunities to have new experiences. Attaching some happiness to a future can inspire us to achieve marvellous things as we trade some instant gratification for longer-term satisfaction. Loneliness can encourage us to seek out meaningful connections and relationships with others, giving us a whole new set of life experiences. A little criticism can raise our standards for ourselves and others. Guilt from past actions can inspire us to choose more positive actions in future. Thinking of the future can help us to avoid pitfalls and make plans for our dream life. The suffering from losing a loved one can make us appreciate and respect our future relationships and those that are still with us. Some conflict can bring resolution if, even though it's through anger, truths are spoken and listened to.

There are pros and cons to our egos depending on how, where and when it controls our thoughts and actions. Believing that we are our egos and nothing more causes unnecessary suffering. Balancing the ego with a belief that we are valuable and loved beyond our wildest imagination and that we are truly connected to everything, now that can change everything.

lEtGO

During a moment of what I could describe as "deep knowing" during a meditation, where I had a complete sense of peace, faith and an overwhelming feeling of love, I believe I got to see what it means to step beyond the ego. Without the ego's illusions, I could feel and know what lies beyond it. I guess you could say I was experiencing the spirit or soul's point of view. I felt that spirit isn't restricted by the beliefs of the ego and has no fear or doubts. Spirit understands that all is ok and that everything that happens is part of a bigger plan. Spirit sees that everything is connected and necessary. Spirit recognises that all is made of energy and that energy moves, flows, changes and expresses itself in various forms but never ends. Spirit knows that we are loved beyond anything our ego minds can imagine, always were and always will be.

Having experienced such clarity, I struggled with it for several years as my ego mind tried to make sense of what it was, what it meant and what I was supposed to do with it. I wanted to return to that state of bliss and peace, leaving the fears, doubts and worries behind for good. But I didn't leave them behind completely. For a time, I saw the experience as a curse. I asked, "Why would I get to see the truth, feel such love and peace only to return to a state that included such uncertainty, worry and pain?". It took a long time before I could practice meditation without chasing that heavenly sensation. The chase left me very frustrated each time I tried and failed!

In time, I decided that even if I wasn't immersed in the state of knowing and trusting completely, that I would carry on reminding myself of what I felt during that experience. I would keep telling myself, "I know the truth, even if I don't know the reason why I had that experience or what to do with the knowledge. I still know the truth!". Eventually I came to see that the ego issues I had let go of temporarily would need to be dealt with more permanently. I now had an opportunity to learn how to work on each fear so that I could then show others. It was as if I had stumbled onto a perfect, serene spot in the middle of a forest by accident and left again. Now, I had to find my way back so I could create a map to use again, maybe one that others could follow if they wanted to. The "curse" was of course a blessing because at least I knew the destination was real and reachable!

THE JOY OF THE FINITE

So, back to the purpose of the ego. Is it a friend or foe? Is it an evil that must be conquered for us to find inner peace? I don't believe so, not for one second! I learned from my amazing meditative experience that everything is ok. Since the ego is part of everything, this suggests that the ego is ok too. Therefore, it must have a purpose. So, why would a soul, an infinite consciousness that feels only love and peace, enter into a state of separation, of limitations, living in a finite existence with fears and doubts?

I believe the benefit is in the opportunity to experience these limiting and unpleasant states and everything else that the human condition gives us. A spirit that exists in eternal bliss might choose something different. It may want first-times. There is no experience quite like the first. Humans certainly seem to chase new experiences, at least until the novelty wears off and we are drawn to the next one. We delight in the reactions of babies as they watch their new world, taste food and touch new materials. We capture their first crawls, steps, sounds and words on tape to re-watch later so we can revisit those magical moments. We remember the first days at the various stages of school. We cherish memories of our own first kisses, first loves, first jobs and pay cheques. Our first cars and homes hold a special place in our hearts.

We crave new experiences, new flavours, sights and sounds and seek them out constantly throughout our lives. We get bored when life stays the same but, luckily for us, life keeps dishing out new experiences. Our favourite songs will get played-out very quickly unless we listen to different songs, and a joke loses its hilarity the more we hear it. We look for new books, movies and holiday destinations to soak in all the "newness". Total acceptance of what we have brings a beautiful sense of contentment, but a little non-acceptance drives us to seek out more. For me, that is the difference between eating my favourite meal every day and being quite happy with it or trying out everything on the menu. Whether I enjoy each meal or not, I want to taste it all before my time is up.

We humans create stories through books, movies and video games to experience being something or somebody we aren't, just for a short time. When reading, we become the characters, feeling how they feel and experiencing what they go through in the story. When we finish reading and, having enjoyed our escape to another world, another life, we come back to our normal selves. Perhaps an infinite consciousness would do the same, living many lifetimes, playing many roles. For the greatest effect, a spirit might choose to play these roles totally immersed in the scenario. By suppressing the knowledge that this is only a temporary experience, it would become infinitely more exciting and the spirit could really get into the part it chose to play.

Embracing the ego allows us to enjoy anticipation of what may come in the future. Yes, living in the present moment is worthwhile but a little energy directed towards the future is ok too. Many of the experiences that humanity has created for itself come from that ability to plan ahead and dream of the future. The ego gives us the variety of emotions that allow us to feel wonderful one moment and miserable the next but can inspire us to create beautiful music, art and stories from such feelings. Ego's belief that we are finite and have a limited amount of time pushes us to get things done while we can, within a single lifetime. If we always approached life from the spirit's perspective, we might be too content and peaceful to do anything at all. We could become the ultimate procrastinators. What a waste of a life that would be!

To me, the ideal balance between the ego and the spirit is to know that behind the ego's illusions, everything is ok. We can use the ego's impermanence to live like every moment is precious so that we spend them wisely, while using our individual talents and skills to create the next part of the remarkable story of life. We can use our past lessons to build a brighter future. We can use fear to safeguard our vulnerable human aspects and love to open ourselves to trust and life. We can be both human and divine all at once.

As such, learning ways to allow the spirit to shine by balancing and taking care of our ego selves is the aim of the next chapter. We will work on this using the structured approach of the Chakra system.

connecting to spirit

Spirit Matters

Chapter 20

Chakras

"The body is the vehicle, consciousness the driver, yoga is the path and the chakras are the map", Anodea Judith

The chakra system appeals to me mostly because of its structured approach toward addressing imbalances in many aspects of ourselves and our lives. While some people prefer to work with colour, sound, stones and crystals or energy therapies to balance their chakras, I am drawn to working on acceptance of the associated chakra rights and taking action to express those rights in my day-to-day life. That is where I find I can use this system to make improvements in my wellbeing and my life in general. In this chapter I will give a simplified overview of the main chakras and what it is to have a chakra imbalance. We will then discuss the associated rights of each of the seven chakras and means by which we can embrace those rights. Lastly, we'll look at how to identify underactivity or overactivity of each one and how we can act to strengthen the chakras when required.

WHAT IS A CHAKRA?

Let us briefly look at what we mean by Chakras. Chakra is a Sanskrit word meaning "wheel" and refers to the points where our subtle energies i.e. non-physical energies, connect to the physical body. Basically, this suggests that our emotional and mental energies connect to our physical body through these chakras. It also suggests that these connections go beyond the boundaries of our bodies to the physical world and other unseen energies. Chakras are an integral part of many complex belief systems around the world and are believed to have originated between 1500 and 500 B.C. in India. Many of these belief systems vary slightly in the number of chakras they identify. Most of the systems I've encountered agree on seven fundamental chakras which run from the base of the spine to the crown of the head. These main seven chakras are the ones we will focus on.

We have discussed ways to improve mental, physical and emotional wellbeing in previous chapters. In this section we'll look at using the chakra system as a guideline for working on these in practical life-improving ways.

This creates more opportunities for our higher selves to shine through. You will see, as we progress through the chakras, how we can systematically work on many aspects of life. These include our physical bodies and world, emotional selves, self-expression and action, love, communication of truth, clarity of thought and connection to spirit. Much of the information in previous chapters ties in with this section.

BECOMING AWARE OF CHAKRAS

I first started learning about the chakra system at around thirty years of age. After seventeen years interest in health and fitness and eleven years working in the industry, I was already conscious of the connections between various parts the body. Not only were all the organs and systems working together, but I also could see how the mind and emotions played a very real part in how the physical body functioned. Through karate and a little time spent practicing tai-chi stretches, I was also aware of the principles of chi, prana or a life-force energy that runs through the body. The chakra system offered a way to link these various "layers", connecting them in ways that made some sense to me.

While I have studied Reiki energy healing to a small degree and do believe that energy flows through us, I am more drawn to the physical, mental and emotional aspects of the chakras. These are the means through which I feel I can work more directly on the chakras and see the results in practical ways. I often use this system to help me identify imbalances in my life. I have also noticed specific connections in my clinic clients, between their physical ailments and blockages in other areas of their lives that are both linked to the same chakra. Working to balance the chakras, for me, means working to bring balance to ourselves and our lives. This can help hugely in using our stardust in the ways we would like to.

WHAT IS CHAKRA BALANCE?

Each chakra is said to affect and be affected by our physical, our mental and our emotional states. Beyond that, they are each connected to specific aspects of our lives. A chakra can be overactive, in which case too much of our energy flows to and through it. We will know this is the case if its associations are excessive in our lives. Chakras can also be underactive when too little energy flows through them. We will see this if its associations are diminished in our lives. As energy flows where attention goes, paying too much attention to one chakra and its associations will give it more energy, but others will lack attention as a result. This is often why others become underactive.

Paying little or no attention to a chakra and its associations will reduce the energy available to it. Balancing our chakras by paying attention to each, more evenly, should give us a stronger flow of energy and a greater overall experience of life. Maintaining perfect balance all times is not necessary as some will be required more than others at distinct stages of life and under specific circumstances. Keeping them "fit", balanced, open and ready for when we need them prepares us for lifes challenges.

CHAKRA RIGHTS

Each chakra has a specific right associated with it. I suppose we could call these human rights but perhaps they are the right of all sentient beings. I view these rights as being similar to the right to vote, in that each one is meaningless unless we exercise that right and use it. We must consciously choose how to use our vote and then make the effort to cast it, if it is to have any effect in our world. When these rights are accepted and used in real terms, our life experiences can become far more enjoyable and interesting than they would be otherwise.

The full scope of the chakra system is vast, but I will briefly explain the basics, as I understand them. Some people like to wear or surround themselves with the accompanying colours or mineral rocks of a chakra they wish to energise. Some chant specific sounds, words or phrases and use certain hand positions, known as mudras, to balance their chakras. You will find lots of information online to explore these further if you choose. As "What to do with Stardust?" is a book about doing, I will focus on how our actions and habits can benefit our chakra balance. I will explain some means by which we can add energy to a chakra that is underactive by exercising its rights. If you feel that you have an overactive chakra, I would suggest diverting some of your time and energy to others that are lacking use.

Root chakra – Mulhadhara (root support)

The first energy centre, known as the Root Chakra, is located at the lowest point of the spine. Its associated colour is red, and its element is earth. Survival and support are key words associated with the Root chakra. It's main physical connection to the body is the legs, through which we connect to the earth. The root chakra relates to strength, stability and our connection to the physical world. Comparing our root chakra to the roots of a tree can help us to understand the root chakra and its influence on us. A healthy root allows a strong and deep connection to the earth, from which we would receive support, stability and strength. Strong roots allow us to weather a storm and stand our ground in the face of adversity. Deep roots can allow us to thrive, even if our environment is harsh or at times lacking, by drawing from reserves far below the surface.

A balanced root chakra brings with it a sense of safety, security and acceptance of who, what and where we are. As it is considered to be the most physical of our chakras, the grounded perspective of a balanced root chakra encourages an acceptance of our physical reality in general. We become more present when we are grounded. When we talk of our roots, it's often in relation to our ancestry, family and homeplace, where we should feel like we belong. Putting down roots means choosing to make our home in one place, where we can build a life and maybe grow a family of our own. As such, the root chakra influences and is influenced by our connection to our family and home. The Root chakra is considered the primary chakra that we must balance. Through it, we accept the first innate rights of all humans. These are our right to be and to have.

Root chakra - Our right to be and to have

We are and have exactly what we are meant to. We are individuals, bringing our own specific gifts to our world. It is the range of humanity's gifts that has allowed us to rise far beyond other species. We thrive because we are all a little different so we should embrace our individuality. What's rare is wonderful and there is nobody else on this planet exactly like us. Our set of skills, gifts, talents and attributes make us more than "one in a million". We are each one in over 7 billion! Our distinctive features mean that we can be recognised out of all the others. We must accept who we are to have genuine confidence and to believe that we do belong. There are people whose world is made all the better for having us in it. The things we do and say have a ripple effect throughout the world. We belong here and we belong now. When we go elsewhere, we will belong there too. This is our planet and our home. All humans are our people.

What we have in our possession is what we are meant to have, for now at least. In truth, we don't really own anything that can be taken away from us and everything can and will be taken away from us at some point. Kings have castles until someone with a bigger army decides that they want it. Time is the ultimate thief. Ownership is an illusion. And yet, if we choose to accept it right now, we have an entire world to explore and enjoy. We have land, skies and seas, forests, desserts, mountains and valleys to travel and experience. We have the bounty of nature's fruits unless somebody else assumes ownership of it. The night sky and its stars are as much ours as anybody else's. A deep connection to the earth makes us incredibly rich. We are as wealthy as we choose to believe.

An overactive root chakra can be indicated when too stuck in our ways or rooted in one place, becoming immovable and perhaps immobile. Overactivity can result in taking too much rest and sleep, overeating, hoarding of possessions or wealth, uncompromising stubbornness and a difficulty in moving on from romantic, platonic or family relationships when necessary. An underactive root chakra may be seen where there are anxiety and trust issues, disconnected family relationships, poverty, a poor appetite, insomnia, restlessness and a difficulty in becoming grounded and present.

To balance overactivity, we must direct more of our energy and attention to the other chakras, in particular the solar plexus chakra by increasing our movement and action and the third eye chakra by opening our minds more to other possibilities. To balance underactivity, there are many opportunities to strengthen the root chakra. We can take some time to "simply be" by sitting or lying still. This will bring our awareness to the sensations within the body, particularly to the legs. After all, we are called human "beings", not human doings or human thinkings. This allows us to become more grounded, centred and steady. As the chakra associated with our connection to the Earth, spending time in nature, barefoot helps to ground and balance us. This also reminds us of natures' beauty and value. Walking barefoot at the beach is common but we can also get out of our shoes in the woods or hills. Even going barefoot in the garden or local park can help. I do this often and find that it changes how I walk to a more natural, softer and slower step. My feet and leg muscles get a good workout and my soles feel like they've had the best deep-tissue massage for days afterwards. We can work on our physical, mental and emotional strength to bring more energy to the root chakra. Standing up for our rights and standing our ground on our opinions and values help to strengthen the root chakra also.

We can build a safe, secure home and a network of friends and family for support and stability. Connecting to our family and history can give us a better sense of who we are and where we came from, adding to our sense of belonging. We can accept the skin we're in, not despite our "flaws and blemishes" but by choosing to like our individual quirks. Such an attitude brings genuine confidence. We can accept compliments graciously with a "Thank you" by simply believing them. We can support the body with fresh and unprocessed foods, directly from the earth, just as roots would draw nourishment from the soil. We can work on accepting our right to have plenty to satisfy our needs, to have abundance even. Looking for ways to let go of fears and seeing the proof of our safety and security, that is already present in our lives, can help strengthen our root chakra. Try an "Everything is ok, even if I can't see why" attitude.

We can repeat affirmations such as, "I am safe, I am strong", "I am good enough" and, "I belong", to help accept our right to be. We can use "I deserve", "I have", and "I attract" to help accept our right to have.

A healthy Root chakra can help us live with more safety, presence and abundance.

Sacral Chakra – Svadhisthana (sweetness)

The second energy centre, known as the Sacral chakra, is located at the Sacral bone, at the centre of the pelvis. Its associated colour is orange, its element is water. Feeling and pleasure are key words as this chakra brings sweetness to life. It relates to how we feel about, and how much pleasure we get from our experiences. Its main physical connection is to our hips and pelvis, our urinary system and our reproductive system. Comparing our sacral chakra to water can help us to understand its influence. Emotions must flow and change according to the circumstances we find ourselves in, much as the sea will rage during a storm and become calm when unaffected by external factors. While calmness is desirable, to remain in the same emotional state regardless of all that is happening around us is to be disconnected from the full experience of life. Under moderate circumstances, the sea still fluctuates as it rises and falls and waves ebb and flow with the tide. Equally, it is natural for our emotions to vary from day-to-day and even from moment to moment as we encounter different people, personalities and environments. When healthy, we can easily return to balance between the highs and lows.

This chakra is strongly associated with the sweetness of life. The word "enjoy" comes from the old French word "enjoier" meaning, 'give joy to'. I like this perspective of giving of joy to an experience as it suggests that we have some say in how joyous our lives are. Our favourite meals, shows, books and relationships have many ingredients and elements that make them, but they don't contain joy for us to take. The joy comes from us and through us, should we choose to give it to the experience. Joy is created within. We bring the joy within us to the table and with a balanced sacral chakra we should find it easier to bring more joy into our lives.

While there is obvious sweetness in pleasure, there can also be a sweetness in the experience of pain. Suffering often inspires the most beautiful music, stories and works of art for those brave enough to dive into its exquisite sensations. Trying to block or indeed hold onto any emotion is akin to freezing the ocean's surface to a solid sheet of ice. When frozen, there are no lows but equally, no highs, just a cold, stark unchanging landscape with very little colour or life. This for me, is a form of depression. A balanced sacral chakra is more like a beach with waves, currents, sand, rock pools, shells, and an abundance of creatures. Sometimes it is wild, others calm. It may be hot, warm, lukewarm, cool, cold, or perhaps even frozen, but not for long. Embracing all the variety allows us to feel the whole spectrum of emotions that are essential for a fuller experience of life.

We can remember too that as water flows and changes according to its environment, its adaptability doesn't make water weak. Water shapes the land as it cuts through rock and moves huge volumes of earth with its power, yet water never becomes harmed in this process. We too can take on emotional challenges without being harmed by the experience. Water can carry extra loads, it may get dirty, but only until it calms and deposits its load again. We can do this emotionally, taking time to allow our emotions to settle and let go of what we don't need to hold. Water does not need to follow a direct path. It finds the easiest route, always finding a way to keep moving by flowing, seeping or evaporating skyward. We can find the way that works best for us. Water nourishes the growth of life. It takes a variety of emotions to nourish our personal growth.

It is through the sacral chakra that our sexuality is expressed, and new life is created. We can bond physically with our romantic partners, enjoying the pleasure that accompanies such unions. We may also create the opportunity to create our own family and enjoy the sweetness of such relationships.

When this chakra is balanced, we experience emotions in a way that is proportionate to what is going on around us, not over-reacting, nor under-reacting.

With a balanced sacral chakra, we can embrace our unpleasant emotional states more fully, until they have served their purpose by giving us an experience to enjoy or encouraged us to make life-changes.

Sacral Chakra - Our right to feel

Emotions are an essential part of experience and there are many that bring more colour into our lives. Sometimes we will feel elated and blissful, other times awful and miserable, mostly we will feel somewhere in the range between. We have a right to feel them all.

An overactive sacral chakra may result in excessive cravings for sweetness and pleasure in food or other areas. This could present itself as a sexual addiction or relationships based on sexual pleasure. It could show as intense pleasure-seeking through food, drink and substance use. This may sound wonderful but if the actions from our desire for pleasure result in more suffering, it is not truly sweet. Sugar is sweet but it is not worth a toothache. Extreme mood swings or emotional overreactions to minor challenges can also represent overactivity. An underactive sacral chakra may present itself as a lack of joy, emotional repression, shame, sexual dysfunction or loss of libido.

To add energy to the sacral chakra, we can seek out emotional stimulation through music, books and movies, as mentioned in the Emotion Matters section of this book. As this is the chakra of sweetness, we can seek, in particular, those experiences that bring pleasure and feel-good-factor. A good laugh can release tension from the body and give us a hit of feel-good endorphins. If repression of unpleasant emotions has caused us to "freeze" our emotions, we can look for the sweetness in them to encourage us to dip our toes back in. A good cry can release pent-up sorrow or fear. A 'good' argument can 'clear the air' between two people and bring up simmering issues that need to be discussed. We can embrace all our emotions and what they bring to our lives. They all have purpose.

As sexuality is connected to the sacral chakra, balancing it may involve looking at our sexual desires. The negative attitude towards sexuality by some religions and societies that are not accepting of sexuality can lead to repression and underactivity of this chakra. Likewise, unpleasant sexual experiences can do the same. Some counselling to address any issues and exploration of sexuality in a safe environment may help. As the chakra suggests, intimacy should be pleasurable, as should life, for the most part.

We can repeat affirmations such as, "I feel what I feel", and "I bring joy to my life", to help accept our right to feel. A balanced Sacral Chakra can bring much sweetness to our lives.

Solar Plexus Chakra   - Manipura (lustrous gem)

The third energy centre, known as the Solar plexus chakra, is located at the solar plexus, where the abdomen meets the ribcage, over the navel. Its associated colour is yellow, and its element is fire. Action and transformation are key words. Its main physical connection is to the digestive system as it transforms food into energy and raw materials to fuel us and to create all that our body needs to be healthy. With the root chakra governing who we are, and the sacral chakra how we feel, the solar plexus chakra relates to how we act and what we do. As such it is the centre of our personality and the expression of our individual selves. It is also considered to be the seat of our personal power.

As our centre of energetic action and transformation, it is through this centre that we interact with our world. With movement, we can explore our surroundings for new experiences. Having accepted our right to belong wherever we are, we can now go wherever we want. Having accepted our right to feel, we can now act on our feelings and our desires. We can explore our bodies and their capabilities by trying them out with various activities. We can climb, run, jump, swim, crawl and walk to see how it feels. We can go places we've never been to gain new perspectives. We can even transform our bodies, through regular action, freeing us to go further or climb higher.

We can seek and find resources to construct the lives we want. We can work towards our goals, putting energy into them until they are made real. We can build, through action, the home, career or business that will serve our needs. Much as humanity's control of fire has allowed us to work with metals, machinery and technology, transforming life as we know it, it is the fire of our action that changes our world. We can gain control over our fire, to use it according to our will by accepting our innate right to act.

Solar plexus Chakra - Our right to act

We have the right to express ourselves, living life in a way that is meaningful to us. As the chakra of action, it is here that we work to build what we truly want. Having already accepted who we are and how we feel, balance here allows us to show ourselves to the world with confidence. Imagine displaying ourselves with the same confidence as we would show off a beautiful jewelled city we had designed and built! A balanced solar plexus chakra gives us the energy to follow our dreams and goals, gifting the world with our offerings. As action involves movement, a balanced solar plexus chakra will ensure we do neither too much nor too little. Our innate right to act on our will is expressed through the solar plexus chakra.

An overactive solar plexus chakra can result in "burning out" from using up too much energy, by doing too much. Over competitive, driven and focused only on our own needs, we could burn those around us and the bridges we've crossed as we surge on towards our goals. An underactive solar plexus chakra may result in expressing what we think we should be rather than who we are i.e. living a lie. It can cause a lack of direction, discipline or purpose. We may struggle to act on our will or do what we truly want to. Movement and exercise are more difficult when underactive as energy levels are low. A sluggish digestive system is possible also when this chakra is underactive.

To add energy to this chakra, we can start to express our own individual style through our clothes and hair, how we decorate our home and workspaces and where we go to spend our free time. Doing is a major aspect of this chakra so we can get involved in activities that we enjoy. Finding others with similar interests makes it easier to express our tastes. We can take up acting or drama. Trying on various roles for size might show us a role that is a better fit for our real life. We can exercise our bodies to make them more energetic to give us a greater capacity for doing what we want to. We can become more disciplined and focused by planning our day to spend some energy on what we truly want to achieve.

We have the right to act on our dreams as they are the ultimate expression of our spirit. They tell us who we would like to be in our ideal world. There are other people living out their dream lives already, lives that were just dreams before they made them part of their reality. They acted on theirs, chasing them, believing in them and ultimately living them. It is within our power to do the very same.

We can repeat affirmations such as, "I act according to my will", and, "I express who I am", to help accept our right to act.
With a balanced solar plexus chakra, our actions can bring great benefit to us and to our world.

Heart Chakra – Anahata (unstruck)

The fourth energy centre, known as the Heart chakra, is located at the heart. Its associated colour is green, its element is air, and love is a key word. Its main physical connection is to the heart and cardiovascular system. The heart chakra relates to loving and being loved. A balanced heart chakra is "unstruck" or unhurt. Without hurt, it sees no reasons to withhold love from anyone or anything, therefore it can love unconditionally. There are few feel-good factors that compare to loving others, be that the love for a partner, family member, friend, pet, an activity or for life itself. Imagine feeling love for everything around us, it would be a blissful way to exist.

As love is a two-way street, giving love accounts for only half of this chakras purpose. A balanced heart chakra also allows us to accept love and its benefits. While we may not always be aware of how loved we are, there is still great benefit to us from the support, kindness, physical contact and caring we receive from those that love us. Accepting that we are loved by others can also help us to love ourselves, which leads to a higher level of self-care. Balancing the heart chakra can allow us to love and be loved unconditionally, bringing acceptance, kindness, patience and joy to our relationships with others and ourselves. Our innate right to love and be loved is expressed through our Heart chakra.

Heart Chakra - Our right to love and be loved

We all have the right to love and be loved. It is illusion of the mind and criticism of the ego that suggests otherwise. When I chose to fully let go of fear and judgement, I felt that love completely. It was overwhelmingly beautiful. The best part was realising I had only forgotten how much love was possible and how loved we already are. I didn't earn that love by letting go of fear, the love was always there.

An overactive heart chakra sounds like it should make for a wonderful existence. "How can we love too much?" you may ask. It's not that loving too much is a problem but by directing most of our energy to this chakra the others will lack attention and become underactive. We would then become less grounded, less able to feel other emotions, less likely to express ourselves, unable to speak and hear truth and find difficulty in seeing reality. We would become blinded by love and lose our sense of self within a relationship. This could leave us very open to being taken advantage of. Excessive love for one person can become obsession and we may sacrifice our right to be who we are, to feel, to express our desires and to enjoy love through our other rela-

233

tionships. Overactivity may confuse platonic love with romantic love, seeing potential partners where such a union is unlikely or inappropriate.

An underactive heart chakra has difficulty with self-love and loving others. This can make us very critical, judgemental, cold to ourselves and others, and fearful of intimacy.

To add energy to the heart chakra we must take advantage of opportunities to feel love. Love is felt and expressed in many ways. It exists in family relationships, friendships, towards our pets, towards colleagues, romantically, and in activities we enjoy such as music, art, nature and sport. Love can be the compassion towards a stranger or the self-care we give to ourselves.

Love, in its purest form, is given unconditionally. We know if we are loving when we feel it. Our actions when we feel love are acts of love. A person acting from a place of love is gentle, accepting, supportive, encouraging, forgiving, kind, trusting and wishes only to see the other shine brightly. This does not mean that we should accept behaviour that infringes on our rights from those we love. That would show a lack of self-love. Such behaviour must be addressed or perhaps avoided but this too can be done with love. Human love is a little more flawed, as we are, because we are susceptible to fear which interferes with our ability to love unconditionally. Looking for connections, common interests and seeing the beauty and value in others makes it easier for us to love them. Understanding our value and importance makes it easier to believe we are worthy of love. Bringing more love into our lives requires us to bring more love into our hearts.

Although we absolutely have the right to be loved, love cannot be taken. The wonderful feeling that comes with love is in the giving of love by allowing its energy to flow through us. Being loved by somebody isn't obvious to us unless we know and accept their love. We don't feel more loved when a secret admirer loves us as. Without knowing we are loved, this love has no effect on how loved we feel. We all have people that love us dearly, but do we feel the warm fuzzy glow, every day as a result? If we did, famous pop stars with all their admirers would be ecstatic all the time! If we want to be loved more, we must open ourselves to the possibility that we are lovable, as we are. In a sense, we have to give ourselves love to even believe in the possibility of receiving it from others. We must also create opportunities for others to love us be letting them see who we really are. How can anyone be expected to truly love us if they don't know us? It also helps to show others that it is safe for them to love us and that we will respect and appreciate their gift.

We can love and care about anybody platonically. Romantically, there are some boundaries of course, with age being the top one to protect those that haven't reached adulthood and emotional maturity yet. Thankfully, the world has taken huge steps in accepting the rights of consenting adults to love with the Equality movement promoting equal rights for couples of all orientations. This fills me with the hope that we, as a species, are becoming more loving as we evolve.

Love is sometimes confused with infatuation and attachment, as demonstrated in so many love songs and movies. Feeling like we cannot live without somebody, that we would die for them or that they are our other half or world is not love. Love is gentle and patient, kind and considerate. Love gives freedom to the other to stay or go, knowing that if they too love us, and their needs are met, they will want to be in our lives. If they were to leave, it is not love that hurts us. What hurts is the grief for the loss of what we thought we had or for what we wished to have with them for the future. Coming from a place of real love, we could let them go, wishing them well. There is one guaranteed way to enjoy a love affair that will last a lifetime and that's to love everyone including ourselves.

On a trip to India several years ago, I had some interesting conversations with my driver, a local farmer that alternated, every three weeks, between working his farm and driving in the city to fund his children's education. He was in an arranged and happy marriage. His wife had lived in the next village to his own and was "found" by his father and brother having gone there to look for a bride. Once his and her family deemed them a suitable match, arrangements were made, and they were married. He believed that western "love" was doomed to failure because it was, in fact, confused with passion, which would run out eventually. He felt that the love he had for his wife, based on respect and commitment, grew over time and became stronger. I wondered how many of these arranged marriages would survive if societal and religious pressure to remain together was gone? A little passion helps too, but I do agree with the respect side of his argument and see its value in any long-term relationship. We can repeat affirmations such as, "I love and I am loved", and, "we are all worthy of love", to help accept this right.

Hate

While we're on the topic of love, I would like to briefly address the topic of hate. Anahata, the Sanskrit name for the heart chakra means unstruck or unhurt. Hurt is the precursor to hate. We don't hate people that mean nothing at all to us or have no effect on our lives. We hate those that we believe have already or may hurt us in the future. We may hate an ex-lover if they withdrew their love or treated us in a way that suggested to us that we were unworthy of love. Maybe we foolishly attached our happiness to them, so it left us when they did. We may hate those that have harmed somebody we love. Perhaps their religious beliefs, sexual preferences or lifestyle choices don't fit with ours and we feel threatened by them and so we hate instead of love. We might convince others to hate with us, believing that we are sparing them from the possibility of getting hurt if they are forewarned. Hatred can spread through races and generations for this reason.

Countries take one another's lives in the name of war, sometimes under the guise of bringing about peace, causing much hurt. They fear the hurt the other side may inflict in the future, so they hate one another. They stop seeing each other as valuable humans, deeming them unworthy of love. It is almost impossible to take the lives of those we love, but if we don't care for them, it is possible. Ridding the world of those we believe to be dangerous becomes easier, perhaps necessary, in their minds. The killing, the hurt and the hate continues in an endless cycle. Past atrocities tell us we have reason to fear, but the future is unwritten and can be different if we all choose it to be. Love can break these cycles, bringing forgiveness and peace. Over time, when each side sees the other means no harm, trust may grow, and relationships may be built. As individuals, communities, races and nations, we must get beyond our past hurts if we are to move forward and love freely.

Throat Chakra – Visuddha (purification)

The fifth energy centre, commonly known as the Throat chakra, is located, as its name suggests, at the throat. Its associated colour is blue, and its element is called akasha in Sanskrit which can be translated into ether or space. Communication and truth are key words. Its main physical connections are to the throat, ears, nose, neck, shoulders, arms and hands. The throat chakra relates to pure communication i.e., communication of truth. While truth may be subjective and will vary according to perspective, our own personal truth of what we believe is real to us. A balanced throat chakra allows us to communicate our truth through the words we speak and the songs we sing. Our hands and shoulders are also very effective communicators through our gestures and the postures we assume. It is through our hands that we write, use sign-language, paint and draw. It's believed that in a typical, face to face conversation, only 25% of our communication is through the words we speak. The remainder is expressed by tone of voice, body-language, facial expression, posture and hand gestures. These often communicate the truth when our conscious words may not.

A balanced throat chakra also helps us to receive truth more easily. It allows us to listen fully to what others have to say, not just what we want to hear. We can then pick up on the subtle tones of their voice and perhaps hear what is being unsaid. As we openly communicate our true ideas, feelings and opinions we may find that others do the same and truth comes our way more often. I have found that people often open up to me during clinic sessions and outside of them about personal issues, often surprising themselves at their level of honesty. I feel this is simply because I try to speak openly and to listen. This creates a safe space for truths to be told. Through the throat chakra, we express our right to communicate truth.

Throat Chakra - Our right to communicate truth

We have the right to speak and to be heard. Communication is one of the greatest of human gifts. It allows us to share lifetimes of learning with the next generation, knowledge that each generation can build upon. We have seen an unprecedented rate of technological advancement due to the sharing of information through electronic means. By sharing our knowledge, many minds can work towards scientific progress, each adding pieces to the puzzles that present themselves. We're getting better at communicating through the technology of text message and email but, with so many eyes glued to small screens, I wonder if we are losing the art of real-time conversation. This, with other factors can lead to imbalances.

An overactive throat chakra may result in talking lots but saying little of importance. While speaking our truth is a good thing, overactivity here could lead to the revealing of information at inappropriate times. Some discussions do not need to be heard by the innocent ears of children, some truths can be tempered with diplomacy to spare hurt, and some information does not need to be shared on Facebook! Overactivity can also result in a tendency towards gossiping, listening for information that does not concern us and sharing it without compassion for those it concerns.

An underactive throat chakra may have difficulty with communication with others, singing or speaking up for oneself i.e., trouble finding our voice. Attitudes where children should be seen and not heard and kids being told to stop asking stupid questions or speaking their mind has led to many people losing their voice, metaphorically. They learned at an impressionable age that what they had to say was not worth saying or hearing, so they gave up this innate right to speak and be heard. It takes practice to accept it and use it once more.

We can develop our throat chakra by using our communication skills to express ourselves and our truths. We can write stories, poems and songs. We can write about our observations of the world around us or how we feel inside. We can recite poetry, tell our stories and we can sing our songs. We can share advice and give kind words or compliments to others. We can speak out when we feel something needs to be said.

Using our voices can bring happiness and comfort to others by way of advice, a compliment or a kind word. These are free and so easy to give but may be invaluable to the receiver. We all have life experiences and wisdom that could be beneficial to those going through the challenges we've already overcome. A chat can point them in the right direction and take much stress and worry off their shoulders. As regards compliments, there's always something positive to be found in everyone. Look for these and point them out. Most of us are too hard on ourselves, with internal chatter telling us we're not good-enough. That one compliment could turn somebodies day around for the better!

Singing can add greatly to our sense of well-being, especially when it's a cheery, upbeat song! I sing with a choir and always feel the benefit from our practice sessions and performances. The positive feedback from the crowd afterwards shows the feel-good benefits for them too. Music can also help us tap into our suppressed emotions. When feeling down we sometimes struggle to express it, internalising our pain instead. Singing a song that taps into the emotional well can let us stir it up and let it out. I took up guitar in my late twenties, even though I had one for 10 years sitting in a case, following the break-up of my family. I didn't notice it at the time, but I found myself drawn to playing and singing deeper, more emotional songs. I wasn't open to talking about my feelings then and few would have known how difficult I found it being separated from my children, when I denied it even to myself! I definitely vented some of my sadness in those music sessions, at home alone on my guitar when I would get lost in a song and allow myself to feel it. In the years since, I have also taken up a little amateur song writing to express some of my thoughts and feelings.

Speaking out is also a way to express our needs and desires, after all, "it's the squeaky wheel that gets the grease!". If we are speaking but not being listened to, we may need to change tactics. Some will block their ears to a shout but listen closely to hear a whisper. Finding a quieter and softer way to communicate may make it easier for somebody else to listen to us. The opposite may apply if we have tried the softer approach, and we may need to raise our voices to a roar! Timing can be important too. So, if you want to be heard, choose a time or situation when the other is more receptive to what you have to say.

Listening is a skill that is waylaid by distracted, busy minds or a strong need to tell people what we think. Often, when in conversation we're already rehearsing what we will say next, our opinion, the advice we'll give, and what they should do. There can be so much going on that we barely hear what they're saying over the noise of our own inner voice. On a course I attended several years ago, our group was paired off. My course partner and I were sat, face-to-face, about two feet apart and given a topic to speak about. The topic was - 'the masks we wear', only it wasn't a typical two-way discussion. The rule was that one spoke as the other listened for 10 minutes. My course partner spoke first. I thought listening would be far easier than talking for 10 whole minutes. It wasn't easy at all. I struggled. My mind started to wander within the first minute. As the words she spoke connected with my own experiences I found myself getting pulled into my own memories. I wanted to interact, sometimes to make suggestions, at times wanting to sympathise.

When distracted, I had to consciously pull myself back to her voice. This took some effort which showed me that listening wasn't a strong point of mine and a skill I needed to improve. I did manage to avoid interrupting though so I was halfway there. As she spoke and I listened, she came out with insights and answers she didn't know were in her. She figured her problems out as she spoke, uninterrupted. When it came to my turn, I too found it easy to talk for ten minutes, also finding myself saying things I hadn't expected to hear. As my words flowed, so did my realisations. I'm sure she got distracted and tuned out at times, as I did, but still those 10 minutes were worthwhile. This proved to me that sometimes taking off the fix-it hat to just listen, giving a little of our time, is the best help we can offer.

Though sometimes it seems easier to use white lies, we can trust that by speaking the truth, all will work out for the best, for us and others. People often need to hear the truth, even if it hurts a little, to learn what they need to. Lies are difficult to remember and become more and more complicated to sustain as time passes. I find that the truth tends to find me when someone has withheld it for any reason. Being brave enough to speak our truth and courageous enough to demand truth from others will strengthen and open this chakra. We can repeat affirmations such as, "Truth is mine to speak and hear", to accept our right to truth. A well-balanced throat chakra makes us more effective in our dealings with others. The greatest speakers often become the greatest leaders by connecting with people and bringing them together to work towards a common goal.

Third eye Chakra – Ajna (to perceive and to command)

The sixth energy centre, commonly known as the Third eye chakra, is located behind the point between the eyebrows. Its associated colour is indigo, its element is light (or the combination of all other elements). Its main physical connection is to the eyes and brow and this chakra is associated with thought. Understanding is a key word. The third eye chakra is about perceiving reality with clarity, unaffected by the distorting effects of judgements and beliefs that we usually apply to what we observe. A balanced third eye chakra allows us to look beyond our own mental filters so that we may see what is truly going on in front of us. It can also allow us to revisit past situations that we may have misunderstood, through our lack of knowledge or understanding, to resolve them.

A balanced third eye chakra creates an open mind that can learn new ways of thinking, and living, freeing itself from old and ineffective patterns. An open mind is interested in many topics and will have ample room for new knowledge. An open mind can "think outside the box", as it doesn't limit itself to what it already knows, finding solutions to challenges that a narrow mind never will. Those with balanced third eye chakras can see the connections between all people and the purpose behind events. Their ability to look with clarity affords them a far reaching, "big picture" mentality to develop successful plans and foresee obstacles and challenges that may be avoided or overcome.

Without the distractions of a cluttered mind, we can enjoy a sharper mental focus. Such higher concentration improves the mind-body connection, hence the use of sports psychology to improve the performances of top-level athletes. Our physical abilities are of a higher quality when we are totally focused on the task at hand. Likewise, if giving commands or directions to others, a clear mind can offer simple, logical orders that all can understand and follow, increasing the likelihood of our plan being followed correctly. Educators with a clear mind can simplify their subject without the use of technical jargon or rehearsed phrases, making it far easier to comprehend.

By seeing our reality clearly, we can work directly with what truly is rather than our own version of the truth. Through the third eye chakra we express our innate right to see with clarity.

Third Eye Chakra - Our right to see clearly

A clear mind allows us to see the truth, how things really are rather than how we believe or want them to be. We can be influenced by the opinions of others regarding a person, situation and even ourselves. We are programmed by whatever we see and hear repeatedly. This programming is reinforced each time we encounter the same information until we take it as truth. With a balanced third eye chakra we can question such beliefs with logic and an open mind.

An overactive third eye chakra may result in an attitude of detachment and indifference to life. We may become great observers but could sacrifice the interactions of doing and feeling. We would then miss out on two-thirds of the experience of living. We could obtain a great understanding of how the world works and why things happen but with less energy going to the root chakra, we would become less invested in this world. Without sufficient energy flowing through the heart chakra we would care less about what happens. As this chakra is associated with thought, overactivity here can lead to over-thinking even to the point of losing touch with reality through hallucinations and delusions as the lines between our thoughts and reality become blurred. Overactivity may cause excessive focus leading to obsession. With our sights firmly fixed in one direction, we could become blinkered to all else.

To bring calm to an overactive mind and reduce overthinking, I recommend grounding oneself. By bringing energy down to the root chakra, through the others, we can draw some energy away from the third eye. Grounding involves bringing awareness to the body, in particular the legs. Getting out into nature, slowing down, feeling and doing with less thinking can all help. Enjoy physical activity, especially physically pleasurable activities to open the flow to the lower chakras. Aim for more 'be-ing' and less thinking when over-thinking is an issue.

An underactive third eye would have difficulty in 'seeing clearly' or with focusing. This may present as problems with physical eyesight and forward thinking, and those with underactive third eyes may experience lack of clarity, poor memory and a limited concentration span. An inability to see truth will bring an inclination towards denial of oneself and what's going on around us and a tendency to be fooled.

To add energy to this chakra, which is essentially to open the third eye, I highly recommend taking time every day to quieten the mind and let go of preconceived notions and beliefs. This lets us take a neutral perspective and open the mind to other possibilities. It also helps to be mindful of the thoughts that arise, listening to what our inner voice is saying to see if that pattern of thinking serves us. We can aim to observe more and judge less. We can study ourselves and our own nature to learn why people do what we do. We can seek knowledge that gives us a better understanding of ourselves and our world so that we can interact with it in more meaningful ways.

The French word clairvoyance literally means "clear vision". It's often used to describe an extra sensory perception, distinct from our five senses of touch, taste, smell, hearing and sight. I believe, that by clearing the obstructions of our mind, by letting go of our own ideas and opinions, we take in a lot more information that allows us to read a person or situation better. Over time, through the practice of observation, we will also recognise patterns, subtle cues and commonalities that can allow us an almost supernatural understanding of what's likely to be going on now and what may happen in future. We may all possess the ability to foresee events to various degrees and call it intuition or a hunch. Perhaps some have developed this ability to such a high level that they appear to know the future. We can use affirmations such as "I open my mind to clarity" and, "I accept reality as it is", to help us accept our right to see. With a balanced third eye chakra we no longer need to subscribe to illusions about our reality and can see and accept life for what it is.

Crown Chakra – Sahasrara (thousand petal)

The seventh energy centre, commonly known as the Crown chakra, is located at the crown or highest point of the head. Its associated colour is violet or white. It has no element as, though it connects to the physical body, this chakra is not of the physical realm. Its physical connection is to the central nervous system, namely the brain and spinal chord. The crown chakra is all about our connection to divine knowing and bliss. It's our link to the universal consciousness whose strands connect everything in our universe, forming this web of life that is no more visible to us than the wireless internet connections of our computers and phones.

An overactive crown chakra can lead to a sense of detachment, of not being part of this world. We could find ourselves existing in a timeless state of non-thought, a beautiful state to visit but impractical if we want a human experience. In a pure spirit state of bliss and non-thinking we would miss out on the physical sensations of touch, taste and smell, the sea of emotions, the doing and creating, the complexity of human love, the communication through word, body and song and the opportunity to observe our fascinating universe. Maybe a perpetual state of bliss gets boring after an eternity and this human experience is the gift that spirit gave itself for something a little different.

An underactive crown chakra limits our ability to tap into our divine inspiration and knowing. It can prevent us from understanding that we are divine sparks experiencing a temporary human existence. Knowing our true nature gives us power and freedom to dive into life, fully embracing what comes our way, relying on the ego only when we need it to keep us safe from real harm. When the crown chakra is underactive. We may become detached from the knowledge that we are spirit, existing in a human state. We then identify only as the ego and become tied by its fears, doubts and inhibitions

A balanced crown chakra, with a strong connection, allows us access to the source of all bliss and knowing. Through this connection we receive inspiration to bring ideas into existence through our actions, so that we may become part of the continuing process of creation. A fully opened crown chakra is said to be devoid of thought, as no thought is necessary. The information passing through it, from the divine source, is pure knowing. Through the crown chakra we express our innate right to know.

Crown Chakra - Our right to know

We have the right to know how connected we are, that all is love and that in the grand scheme of things, we have nothing to fear. Quantum physicists believe that every particle of matter that comes into contact with another, becomes connected to it forever more, regardless of the distance between them. This process is called quantum entanglement. According to the scientific 'big-bang' theory of universal creation, the whole universe started out as a

241

small ball of energy containing all the particles that would become everything we know now. This entanglement may very well prove what spiritual philosophies have been teaching for thousands of years i.e. everything in the entire universe is still connected.

Science also tells us that all the energy that exists in the universe now was present within that original ball of energy, no more and no less. All matter is energy. This matter and energy has been formed and reformed countless times but none has been created or destroyed since time as we know it began. Nothing in the universe every truly dies or ends, it just changes into something else. This is our universe. This is life. Life will always continue in some form or another. This suggests that we will continue too, just in another form.

We have a right to divine inspiration. If we are indeed spirit or consciousness that took on human form for the experience of life, perhaps we did so with a purpose or intent for what we wished to achieve while here. Some might call this a soul-purpose or a raison d'etre i.e. reason to be. An open connection to this state of knowing could help us to remember what that intent or reason was. Once recalled, we can act on it and fulfil our purpose.

All that humanity has invented or created, throughout our history, didn't exist at one point in time. They were impossible until made possible, they were dreams until they were made real. Perhaps they came from somewhere, some other plane of consciousness where dreams wait for those who dare to dream them. Maybe there are ideas waiting to be brought into existence should we open ourselves to receiving them. I would suggest daydreaming, doodling, writing or inventing with the limitless imagination of a small child or a nutty professor to open the mind to receiving such ideas. We might come up with the next great song, story or world-changing invention! We could just get to enjoy the fruits of our imagination. All are worthwhile.

If we can allow such inspiration to work through a body that is strong and healthy, emotionally balanced, willing to act, with love, using honest communication and the abilities of a sharp mind, the possibilities are far reaching. Such a person would have incredible energy, a powerful intention to make the world a better place for all and the ability to bring others together to achieve inspired goals.

Practical Chakras

So how does this chakra balancing help us live more spiritually? Well, as I've said already, I believe that we serve our spirit by providing it with experiences and by living more in a state of connectedness and love. Using the chakra system to bring more balance to our lives can free us to enjoy a greater range of life experiences while caring for others too.

Through balancing of the root, we can become more stable, secure and self-confident. We accept ourselves and others' right to be who we are and to have what we have. We can develop a stronger connection to our planet which will make us want to care for it. We would appreciate our family roots and enjoy the support they provide. We would develop a solid foundation on which to build our lives.

Through the sacral chakra we can experience the sweetness of the complete range of emotions and bring more pleasure or feel-good-factor into our lives. We can enjoy and express our sexuality without shame. We can bring new life into this world.

Through the solar plexus chakra, we would accept and realise our personal power. We can become more active in pursuing what we want to experience. We would confidently choose how we want to express ourselves and how we would like to make a difference in this world.

Through the heart chakra we feel more love for others and allow them to love us in return so that our actions become more about "we" than "I". We would naturally feel compassion towards our fellow human beings.

Through the throat chakra we can communicate and express our truths, sharing our knowledge to combine our efforts with other like-minded people. This results in even greater opportunities for experiences that would be impossible alone. We can create opportunities to connect and build relationships.

Through the third eye chakra, we gain a clarity that allows us to use the mind and its abilities to their fullest potential. It can help us to analyse our situation and to understand others better. We can visualise what we want to achieve and figure out ways to plan the best way to reach our goals.

Through the crown chakra we can know how loved and connected we really are and tap into divine knowledge and inspiration. We can live and act from the best part of us i.e. the human spirit.

With all of our chakras and beliefs working well together, we can expect to live interesting, enjoyable and fulfilling lives. Rather than following religious rules or somebody else's philosophies, we would naturally live from spirit.

The best in us would automatically shine through!

For more on the chakra system visit www.highestpotential.ie

PART 7

Future Matters

Chapter 21

Building the Lives We Want

"Ask yourself what is really important, and then have the courage to build your life around the answer"

At the beginning of "What to do with Stardust?" I explained how this book's main aim is to help you to realise your potential in two distinct ways. The first way is to realise just how much potential you possess. I hope at this point that you are beginning to embrace this and are feeling the power such potential offers, power that you held ever before you started to read this book. The second way is to help you to make something real of your potential to have, to be and to feel what you would choose. The last realisation we must embrace is that turning potential into reality requires action.

While there may be similarities between them, your dreams are yours and my dreams are mine. I cannot know exactly what your dream life entails nor could I lay out for you, step by step, the exact route you should take to reach it. This is good news because half the fun is in the planning. My goal in these remaining chapters is to guide you through the process of designing, planning and building towards your goals. We will look at ways to identify our true desires, discover the resources at our disposal and incorporate efficient ways to make these dreams a reality. We will also address means to remove some common obstacles to our success. Let's find the easiest ways to get where we want to go.

MAGIC MOMENTS
I like the analogy of building a life in the same way that we would build a home. I imagine that every thought and action is like a brick that we can put to some use. In each new moment we get another brick, as if magically appearing in our hands. We then choose how to use each one.

If this sounds like a lot of effort, I would remind you that we are already laying bricks, every moment of every day, regardless of the outcome. It is impossible to do absolutely nothing at all. Even lying down is an action. Though it spends only a little energy, lying for an hour costs us as many moments as an hour engaged in any other activity. By going nowhere, it's as if we

247

lay our bricks around us. Do this for long enough and we will find ourselves blocked in by our own idleness until we finally decide to climb out. Some use these bricks to create defensive walls, which give the illusion of being protective, but will ultimately make us prisoners of our own fears. Some we may waste by blocking or throwing them to harm others. I see the bearing of grudges towards others as comparable to throwing our bricks at those we dislike. We lose the opportunity to do something constructive, our targets are harmed, and nobody benefits. Or we might discard them mindlessly around us, achieving nothing of any use, but making quite the mess of our lives.

However, when we have a purposeful design in mind and apply some effort, we can lay our bricks constructively. These bricks i.e. our thoughts and actions, can be used to lay a path in the direction we wish to go. Perhaps it will become a path for others to follow in our footsteps. Creating such a path towards that which is meaningful to us, gives us an opportunity to connect with others on similar paths. We may enjoy their company, build close relationships and maybe combine our efforts as we lay such paths together. We can use our bricks to build a home both literally and metaphorically, creating an environment that is safe, supportive and pleasant for all who enter. We can build bridges to overcome obstacles by focusing on what we can do rather than what we cannot, solutions rather than problems. We can build steps that will allow us to reach greater heights and perspectives. The height and strength of a pyramid is largely determined by its foundation and base layers. The more blocks laid with care and precision, the more magnificent the overall structure. Our bricks, our moments and our efforts can be used to build a life and a world we want. The collective moments of one life are significant. Combined, the possibility of what many lives can build is astounding. As with the man-made wonders of the world, our legacies can last long after we are gone to be enjoyed by our descendants. If we consistently choose to use our bricks, moments, thoughts and actions consciously, they can become extremely constructive. They are valuable. Use them wisely!

IMAGINATION

To dip into our desires, we must imagine being, having or doing something that is not currently part of our reality. Recall the times when you said, "I wish I was ___, I wish I could have ___, I wish I could be ___", or, "I would love to ___". Fill in the blanks and write them down. Make a list. The imagination lets us explore our desires unreservedly. Set it free to determine your deepest desires.

Alan Watts a British philosopher, writer and speaker on Eastern Philosophy would ask people "What would you do, with your life, if money were no object?". I really like this aproach as earning a living is often the overwhelming deciding factor in how we spend much of our lives. I can honestly admit that if I had the funds over the last few years, I would have reduced my clinic hours to focus on writing and developing wellness programs. This simple question can help us get right to the root of how we can best serve the world and ourselves. If you would always have enough money to meet your basic needs, what type of work would you do? What job or activity would make you want to get out of bed in the morning, excited for the what the day will bring? What work would make you lose track of time because you're so engrossed in it? What would you be happy putting in extra hours for? Would you play music, travel, write, play sports, cook, eat, drink, sketch, act, write, research, explore or care for others? What do you do on your weekends and with your free time when the chores are done?

Living like that may sound like a pipedream as bills must be paid and the mundane jobs must be done. Surely, we can't all work at what we love? Or can we? Mr. Watts made the point that, if you do enough of what you love, you may eventually become an expert in that area and people will want your expertise. Luckily, people are generally willing to pay for an expert's knowledge or skill. There are people all over the world paid to play music, travel, write, play sport, cook, eat, drink, sketch, act and explore. There are people that love to clean-up, mess up and dress-up, make stuff, break stuff and shake stuff, and they get paid to do it! There are actors getting paid big bucks to dress up like superheroes, models to try on clothes and footballers to kick a ball into a net. Demolition experts bring down buildings safely, but they still get paid to blow stuff up. Comedians get paid to fool around and make others laugh. People even get paid to taste chocolate, wine and beer! There is proof everywhere that we can work at what we love and make a living from it. Even if we can't immediately make a good living from our hobbies and interests, balancing the mundane chores with exciting pastimes makes life far more enjoyable. This I know from experience!

CLARIFYING OUR DESIRES

"Be careful what you wish for, you just might get it!". Rather than a warning, I see this old saying as encouragement towards clarity when designing our ideal life. The imagination's ability to dream is vast but our time, energy and resources available to achieve such dreams have some limits. Refining our goals can help us to use our resources more efficiently so we can reach our potential with more ease.

Abraham Maslow, one of the most influential psychologists of the 20th century, developed a theory about the importance of fulfilling fundamental human needs before we can reach our full potential. Maslow's hierarchy of needs begins with our physiological needs i.e., food, water, warmth and rest. Secondly, he suggests that we require security and safety. Both our physiological and safety needs are defined as our basic needs. Following these are a sense of belonging and love we receive from close relationships, then our self-esteem needs from feelings of accomplishment. These are defined by Maslow as our psychological needs and, along with our basic needs, are deemed essential before we can realise our fullest potential. This is why the early chapters of this book focus on understanding our innate value and then on developing habits of self-care in our day-to-day lives. These build a foundation that can give us the belief and energy to go beyond our basic functions to dream and live more meaningfully, becoming co-creators of our reality.

I feel at this stage, it's beneficial to separate our basic needs from our wants as there is a limit to the financial, time and energetic resources we can commit to each. With our basic needs met, we are free to explore our potential and desires. Spending too much time eating, drinking, resting or in our loved one's company may give little or no time for anything else. An excessive amount of our disposable income directed towards basic needs e.g. eating out or socialising will leave little for other activities. Working excessive hours to fund a house, car, holidays, fashionable image or lifestyles far beyond our basic needs could deny us more satisfying opportunities. We sometimes find that we only truly feel like we're living when we go on holidays and escape our normal lives. Does two weeks out of fifty-two measure up to a great life? Is living for the weekends indicative of somebody that is living well?

WHAT DO WE REALLY WANT?

When choosing life-changing goals, or even small personal goals, I would suggest taking time to specify what your actual desire is to save time and energy on its pursuit. Examples of common goals are a fit body, bigger house, more money, fame, a high-powered job, sporting success and a new partner. It's worth looking at what each one may represent to you.

Striving for a fit body may represent a wish for increased health and confidence. Some aim to develop the 'perfect body', which in my experience drains a vast amount of time and energy, and still seems to be out of reach to even the most fitness dedicated. I never got the perfect body in my gym days, but I gave a lot of myself to the attempt. Perhaps too much. Instead, we could focus on health, well-being and becoming comfortable in your own skin, whatever body-shape our healthy self takes. This can be achieved with 4-5 hours of exercise per week and some self-love. We can enjoy a healthy body without the risk of using unhealthy measures such as extreme diets, extreme workouts and steroid abuse. We'll also have time and energy to spend elsewhere.

A big house may represent a wish for a home with space to do all we want. I often dreamt of a spacious house in the countryside with a library, music room, gym, yoga studio and an orchard garden and vegetable patch. These came with the usual living room, kitchen, bedrooms etc. Luckily, I rented a 7-bedroom house for a time, in the countryside with a fine big garden, which I found was too big. I used to jog down the hall because it seemed to take ages to walk it and I rarely went upstairs as I didn't need to! My current home has a living room with musical instruments in one corner and a bookshelf in another, my home therapy workroom is also my gym and yoga room. My kitchen has a small DIY recording booth and my "creation station" with laptop, screen and graphics pad. I love this home. It is perfect for me! I don't have an orchard or vegetable garden, but since I can barely keep houseplants alive and don't make time for gardening, that's a blessing in disguise. I have easy access to the town centre and woodlands plus my house is easily accessible to my clients. Working from home means that I only commute twice per week. The daily drive time spared is mine to use as I choose as is the money saved by living in a smaller space. If your goal includes a new home, remember the size of your house may be less relevant than its location and cost. It might be more beneficial to aim for a home you love with a sense of security and comfort that serves your needs perfectly. With reduced cost and maintenance, you can apply your time, money and energy to other areas.

A wish for more money generally reflects a wish for that which costs money, rather than a desire to look at a larger figure on our bank statement. If that's the case with you, write a list of the first things you would spend extra money on. Remember that once our basic material needs are met, everything else is novelty or luxury and perhaps not as important as we deem them to be. Expensive clothes, cars or holidays may represent a need to show others our success, to get their validation.

I'm not suggesting there's anything wrong with high-end clothes or cars, in fact I love to see those with financial abundance spending and enjoying it. It's only an issue if it drains finances to a point where it causes stress or limits other opportunities. If validation is the root goal of presenting a successful image, a more practical goal may be to work on seeing clearly how valuable you, as a person, already are. This will bring confidence and the freedom to spend your money in a way that enriches your life experience. If your money-raising goal is to pay for travel, you could start a simple manageable savings plan. I often remind myself that for every extra twenty euros per week I save, I will have a thousand euros at the end of the year. I then work out how many of these weekly twenties I need to take a trip or pay for a course. This breaks it into very achievable, bite-size chunks, making the course or trip an option for me.

Climbing the professional ladder or striving for sporting success may also represent a desire to receive acknowledgement of our talents and gifts by proving ourselves to others. If so, we could instead focus on finding a job where we are valued by co-workers. We could also benefit from working on our own self-belief so that validation from others becomes less important. As a result, job satisfaction may come ahead of promotion goals and working hours can be more easily balanced with personal time. If we are simply passionate about our sport or profession, then we are probably right where we belong. We can use that energy to rise to the pinnacle of our field. Engaging in a sport or profession suited to our natural talents and abilities will bring the best results.

A longing for a new partner may represent a wish to love and be loved. This is a common wish, and as Maslow suggests, a fundamental need for most humans. With that as our focus, we could aim to bring love, in all its forms, into our lives through cultivating relationships with friends and family. If required, we can work on self-love to strengthen our belief that we are worthy of love, so we are open when opportunities come along. The subtle confidence of somebody that is happy in their own skin is very attractive. To increase our odds of attracting new friends and maybe a life-partner, we can engage in activities we enjoy with like-minded people. Also, to remove a potential barrier, we can look at how specific and perhaps unrealistic our prospective partner checklist is. If it comes straight out of a Disney cartoon or a magazine, we won't find them in the real world! We may need to give a real person with real flaws, but also a real heart, a chance to love us back!

Taking the time to evaluate our current situation and what we truly want to bring into our lives, will make us focus on our real goals. We may also find we become a little more flexible and open-minded about how we achieve them. With our true desires in mind, we can go about planning how to build that dream life.

MOTIVATION

There is a growing trend in our teenagers to see financial wealth as a primary life goal, followed closely by fame. With money and fame as their goals, all the mastery our young people attain and all the good they do for the world will be overshadowed and made meaningless to them unless they become rich and famous. Wealth and fame are relative to the wealth and fame of others. Only a small percentage of the population of any society can attain financial or fame levels far beyond the average. As such, these goals are unrealistic for most and we should encourage a focus on other rewards to motivate the next generation. They will become the caretakers of their lives and our world. They must realise that neither thrives solely on bank balances and Instagram followers.

An interesting lecture worth mentioning, relating to motivation, was given by Daniel H. Pink, at the RSA (Royal Society for the encouragement of Arts, Manufactures and Commerce) on the surprising truth of what motivates us. In this talk, Mr. Pink explains why money, as a motivator is limited in its ability to get the best from us. When undertaking very simple financially rewarding tasks, for example building a wall and getting paid for each brick that's laid, money is indeed a good motivator for getting results. We would work harder to lay more bricks and earn more money. Bonuses for laying a certain number of bricks per day would push us even harder to achieve goals. But when this approach was applied to jobs that required more cognitive function i.e. imagination, creativity and thinking outside the box, it didn't work. Mr. Pink explained that big bonuses to encourage extensive ideas, tend to lower our productivity. Money seems to complicate the issue, as if the pressure of earning the extra money diminished the creative side of the brain's ability to work well!

The essential factors that were found to encourage the greatest ideas were self-direction i.e. being allowed to work on our own initiative, fulfilment of needs i.e. having enough money meet our needs, so we're not distracted by money worries and mastery i.e. our desire to get better at what we do. In his talk, Pink referred to a company that would allow their employees to spend one day per quarter working on a project of their own, working on whatever and with whomever they liked. The employees must then share the details of their projects and findings with the company at a fun meeting. The company found that what their employees came up with, from those free days, was of high quality and benefit. These provided the company with solutions to software problems they had and new product ideas to develop. He also explains how we have an innate drive to contribute to the world, making it a better place. No surprise there!

These findings can explain why most of us don't simply work seven days a week to make more money. Instead we take up unpaid but enjoyable hobbies that interest us. We take courses to gain mastery of a subject or skill. We volunteer our free time to coach sports and help with charity fundraising. I can completely relate to these discoveries, especially over the last few years, as I have found myself drawn more to that which interests me rather than that which is most financially rewarding. I am at my happiest when I do enough clinic work to keep the bills paid, leaving free time for other projects.

This theory fits in, for me, with Maslow's hierarchy of needs. When our primary needs are met, we are free to develop our true potential. When we are safe, secure and nourished, our "survival" brain doesn't need extra activation, so it takes a backseat of sorts. When we have close intimate relationships and feel valued by our abilities, our "feeling" brain is satisfied so it too can run in the background. The remaining higher functions of the neo-cortex or "thinking brain" are free to take centre-stage. As the neo-cortex is the part of the brain involved in sensory perception, motor commands, spatial reasoning and conscious thought, these may peak when our attention is not diverted towards survival. This suggests that having our basic needs met should help us to become more aware and observant, move with greater control and think more clearly. Many regular meditators, would tell you that this is indeed the case.

In summary, it seems we are at our most creative, enthusiastic and motivated when we choose what we want to do, don't worry about money (or anything else for that matter) and strive to master our skills with an intent to make the world a better place. That is how we get to shine brightest!

SACRIFICE

With a limit to our time, energy and other resources, making positive changes usually requires some sacrifice. To put time and energy into a new habit, we must take some from an old one. We can begin by sacrificing those habits that are ultimately of no great benefit to us. We can take a proverbial, sacrificial knife to the junk food that stresses our bodies and lowers our energy levels. We can replace it with nutritious food that energises us and nurtures our wellbeing. We can cut out the late nights, watching meaningless tv or social media that drain our batteries to wake feeling refreshed and enthusiastic for the day ahead. We can remove the junk television soaps and dramas, to use that time to improve our own stories and develop our own characters.

If abusing substances to escape an unhappy life or to get some buzz from it, we could trade them for a more interesting, exciting life that we want to be present in. We can sacrifice impulse purchases that give short-term feel-good-factor until the novelty wears off, for experiences that create life-long memories. We can cut out judgement and criticism so that we can see our own magnificence and the brilliance of others. We can remove ourselves

253

from relationships and situations that no longer serve us to make time for ones that bring joy and fulfilment. We can cut the chains of limiting mindsets and beliefs, freeing ourselves to possibilities, challenges and growth.

Sacrificing the "dead-weight" of our lives gives us time, energy and resources to make significant changes. In situations where we must sacrifice that which we do enjoy it helps to view it from a positive perspective. In such a situation, rather than focusing on the loss, we can look at how we have two great options to choose from and we get to pick the best one. Some sacrifices may be challenging but it's quite likely that we can keep all that we value most, in the pursuit of our dream life.

COMMITMENT

I have always found willpower to be over-rated as a means to achieving goals. In using willpower, we make a choice each time based on the options available as we ask, "Will I, or won't I?". "Will I eat junk foods, or will I eat healthy foods? Will I play video games, or will I work on my book? Will I stay in bed or will I get up early to exercise? Will I watch more television, or will I practice that instrument I want to learn? Will I go to bed late or will I go to bed early, meditate before I sleep and wake up refreshed and revitalised? Will I get to work on my dream life, or will I scroll through social media and look at the fantastic photos of others living theirs? If we give ourselves options each time, every day, there's a chance we'll make a productive decision and a chance we won't.

We can take chance out of the equation with commitment. We make it easier by reducing the daily decision-making to just one at the beginning. Choose, when in a positive, balanced and motivated frame of mind, what life improving habits we are going to take on, then follow through with them whether we feel like it or not. This is easier than you might think! We do it every day. We do it when we go to work or school each day, wash our bodies, brush our teeth and pay our bills. We do it when we put on school or work uniforms. We do it when we clean our houses, cut the grass and take out the rubbish. These are normal everyday activities that we perform without question. They become part of our routine. Rather than making these optional, we, as the Nike slogan says, "Just do it". It's easier that way. We get on with it and enjoy the benefit of an income, education, hygiene or services we've paid for.

MAYBE, THE MOST POWERFUL WORD

Maybe I'm good enough, smart enough, strong,
to write my own story, sing my own song.
Maybe I'm worthy and soon I will see
that anything's possible, if I add maybe...

Belief in our ability to succeed is of primary importance when committing to the actual work necessary to get the results we desire. It gives us the courage to start and then stay going until the end. Often our self-belief is based on our past successes. If we have already accomplished something, it is easier to believe that we may be successful again. If we successfully perform a task consistently our belief becomes expectation. Remember that everything we have achieved heretofore, we did so for the first time. There have been so many first times from crawls, steps and schooldays to jobs, cars and qualifications. We should use these as proof that we will continue to have successful first times. There will be first days at the job we want, first times travelling to new and exciting destinations and first meetings with those we will come to love dearly. We get to choose how many more firsts we get to enjoy.

I would also remind you that none of us are exactly who we were last week, last month or last year. In fact, you are not exactly who you were before you read this line. You have added it to your memory therefore you have changed a little. We exist in a constant state of change so being "stuck" is an illusion. You are not stuck. This is a natural law of the universe and we have some say in the direction our changes take. We can embrace this inevitable change to add strength to our belief in what we can achieve when we steer our course.

We admire others for grabbing life by the horns and chasing their dreams. They inspire us and we applaud them for their achievements. Remember that they, and you, are made of the same miraculous stuff. The differences between us are minute in comparison with the similarities. There is one subtle difference between those who strive for success and those who settle for less. Those who strive believe in their right to have what they desire, so they make the effort and go get it. We can use their successes as proof of what is possible, to add to our belief in ourselves.

MAYBE I…

To create vast space for our belief in possibility, the most powerful word I know of is "Maybe". Adding the word "maybe" to a statement of intent makes it instantly plausible i.e., "Maybe I can ____" or "Maybe I will ____". Humanity dreamt of flying, diving, sailing and touching the moon before somebody went beyond "If only I could" to "Maybe I can?" and started to work on making that dream real. Maybe is a key to locked potential. Maybe opens the door to possibility and lets us take a peek through without asking us for a huge leap of faith. Maybe lets us then a step through this door into a world of possibility. It lets us look at the mountain and say in truth, "Maybe I could reach the top". Maybe lets us see paths as real options. Maybe encourages us to create paths where none exist. Maybe helps us to reprogram, "I can't, I couldn't, and I shouldn't". It helps to dissolve any pre-existing limiting beliefs replacing them with the freedom to explore, to try. Maybe is and will always be one of my favourite words.

We're made of Stardust, formed by 14 billion years of cosmic evolution. This sounds quite impossible and yet here we are. We are already more miraculous and more unbelievable than anything we might want to do. If we are possible, then so are our dreams. Maybe, just maybe, choosing to make the most of our Stardust will allow us to shine brighter than ever before.

Chapter 22

The Design Stage

"Every great design begins with an even better story", Lorinda Mamo

SERVING A PURPOSE

When we build any structure, we do so with an intent to enrich our lives in some way. It may provide shelter, a space to live or work, educate or entertain. It will serve a purpose and it will serve our needs. When designing a life that lets us use our stardust in a meaningful way, we can apply a similar approach. We can aim to serve a purpose and also to create a lifestyle that serves our personal needs.

If the idea of serving others sounds unpleasant, I would remind you that we are all servants already, in some form or another. Along with those working in the retail, food or financial service industries, everybody working in agriculture, construction, education, healthcare, entertainment or communication is serving someone's needs. People serve in the army, police force and in government positions. The CEO of a company serves its investors. Even the president of a country is a servant to its people. Parents serve their children with food and shelter. Many children end up serving their parents at some point in their lives. We serve when we volunteer to help, hold a door open, allow somebody ahead of us in a queue, or help someone across a street. We call it our good deed for the day. Service is part of our nature.

Serving others is, for the most part, a pleasant experience particularly if our efforts are acknowledged. It's not that we do it for thanks, but such validation reminds us that we are indeed of use to our fellow man. This adds to our sense of belonging, one of the fundamentals of Maslow's hierarchy of needs. Working together is also one of the key factors in the success of humanity over other species. I scratch your back, you scratch mine. I serve you and you serve me.

In my clinic work, I get great satisfaction when a client is feeling better after our sessions. I get even more when I meet a client, months or years later, and find that they have been well ever since. I get a similar buzz when a parent tells me their son loves our rugby training, when somebody likes a song I've written or sung or when someone enjoys our choir performances. I'm

257

sure I will enjoy hearing from you if this book has served you in any beneficial way. Serving others is not a completely altruistic act, nor does it need to be. The server and the served can both benefit from the exchange. I believe that when we find ways to use our talents and gifts, putting the best that we have to offer out there in service to others, everybody wins.

Creating a lifestyle that serves our needs or indeed, our wants, comes from balancing our service to others with the service of others to us in return. In doing so, we grant them the same sense of purpose and belonging, with opportunities to use their own talents in a meaningful way. When we take time to be entertained by sport, music, art, books etc, we get to enjoy a new experience and the sportsperson, musician, artist or writer gets to do that which they love i.e., entertain! When we share a workload with others, we all get a sense of purpose while improving our work-life balance. This affords us more time-off to rest, relax and enjoy other experiences. When we create a home that truly feels like home, all who enter may benefit. When we choose to be educated, we give teachers the opportunity to teach. When we are healthy and full of vitality, we can be of greater service while serving our own feel-good-factor. When we pursue our interests, for career or personal reasons, we often put more effort into developing our expertise. That passion and expert knowledge may become very useful to our fellow man. A self-serving attitude can be very positive, if not at the expense of others.

Designing our ideal life, I feel, should incorporate how we can best serve others and how our lifestyle and habits can serve us. In the next chapter, we'll look at identifying our talents to see what gifts we can use to be of service. For now, we'll focus on clarifying our own desires.

OUR COLLECTIVE VISION
"We do not inherit the world from our ancestors, we borrow it from our children" - quote origin unknown.

Our visions for the future must include our world and the condition we leave it in for future generations. Our climate is changing rapidly, and we must accept the large part we have played. Only then can we take responsibility for fixing our mess by making a real effort to start living in harmony with nature, in sustainable ways.

As it stands now, the earth is on the brink of ecological disaster. Our world is getting warmer, with devastating results. NASA's official stance on the current warming trend is that it is extremely likely (greater than 95% probability) to be the result of human activity since the mid-20th century. This trend is proceeding at a rate that is unprecedented over decades to millennia. Glaciers are melting, sea levels rising, extreme weather events increasing, and our oceans are becoming more acidic. Plastic seems to be wreaking havoc in our oceans and, since it takes hundreds of years to degrade, unless we clean it up it's not going away anytime soon.

Agriculture has changed the face of the planet as we clear land for farming, destroying the habitat of countless species that share our world. Forests still cover about 30% of the world's land area but that's approximately half what it was when humans started felling trees and it's still going down rapidly. Between 1990 and 2016, according to the World Bank, over half a million square miles of forest have been cut down. That's an area larger than South Africa. Trees convert carbon dioxide into the oxygen we breathe. That same carbon dioxide is deemed to be largely responsible for climate change. It's simple math. It needs to be reversed. We are the problem and we must become the solution not just for other species but for our own.

We live on one planet with one atmosphere and one water supply. When we burn, dump or flush our waste it doesn't disappear, it simply goes elsewhere within our living space. Our smoke is released into the air that we must then breathe. Our waste is released into the water that we must then drink. Our footprints stomp everything that gets in the way of our progress. We have more footprints now than we have ever had. There are now more than seven and a half billion of us on the march. The 20th century saw our numbers increase four-fold. Think about that for a moment. Fewer than 2 billion humans existed on Earth in 1900 and it took hundreds of thousands of years for us to reach that number. Estimates for the end of the 21st century range between 10 and 13 billion. That's a lot of new footprints in itself but even more worryingly, our individual footprints are getting larger.

As our societies develop, so do our wants, needs and expectations. Our houses get bigger as does our demand for furnishings. I live in a house roughly twice that of my parents but with fewer children. Our mechanical and technological requirements increase too. I say requirements but many are luxuries, not necessities. I don't need the big tv in my sitting room, I just want it for the rare occasions when I watch sports or movies. I was 15 when my father got a car, but my kids have always been driven in cars bigger than their grandfather ever owned. I was 19 years old when I first stepped onto an airplane. My 15-year-old son has visited about a dozen countries already. Again, I have no issue with abundance nor with progress, in fact I wish both for everybody. Still, all of these extras require more resources and materials which are limited, and more manufacturing and transportation which use fuel and produce emissions. Material abundance for every human means more mining, more felling, more plastic and more smoke!

Is this to be our legacy to our children and their children? More house space, screens and gadgets but less natural beauty. Less life. More doing but less being. Instant world-wide communication but fewer meaningful connections.

I can think of a few species that became extinct in recent years due to human activity such as the dodo bird, the great elk and the mammoth. These are but a few of many. How many more species will disappear on our watch? How many have already disappeared that we don't even know about? Even bees are at risk and if they go, how long before we all follow? How many forests must be cut down? Will a time come when much of the life on this planet exists only on recordings? If we survive long enough for them to ask us why we let such things happen, how will we answer our grandchildren?

259

OUR ROLE AS CARETAKERS

Our world is a paradise. If you haven't already, I suggest taking some time to watch nature documentaries such as the BBC's "Blue Planet" and "Planet Earth". Marvel at the variety of species of plants, birds, mammals, fish and insects and the habitats in which they live. These are not distant, alien places, not really. It's all one world, yours and mine and all its living beings are earthlings. Listen also to sir David Attenborough, a man that has dedicated his life to the study of nature, when he says we must care for these or they will disappear. We have stepped out of the natural food chain of our planet and none but ourselves can keep our numbers in check now. We have taken the role of caretakers and must take that position seriously, for the sake of this world and future generations.

Some suggest that should all humans become vegetarian our beautiful planet could be saved. I see that there are valid points to this but am a little sceptical about this solving all our environmental issues. Yes, our farmed animals require substantial land space and resources while adding to methane gas emissions, but without them we would still need vast acres of land to grow grains, fruit and vegetables. Such change wouldn't stem humankind's desires for the finer things in life. To the best of my knowledge, first-world vegetarians don't all limit themselves to homes and clothing made exclusively from local, naturally harvested and sustainable materials. Nor do they travel solely by leg power or shun the benefits of technology.

SELF-CONTROL FOR FUTURE GENERATIONS

The most viable solution I can see to spare our planet, while giving all human societies the opportunity to develop in the direction we seem determined to go, is a significant reduction of our population. Add a major shift from fossil fuels to clean and renewable energies plus large scale recycling of the materials we have already created or mined. Finally, if we massively reduce our use of harmful chemicals agriculturally, commercially and domestically, we might just save the world.

The least devastating means to reduce our numbers, I believe, would be for a general consensus to have only one or two children per couple, for several generations. By this, I mean world-wide decision made by couples themselves rather than an enforced law. I know this is controversial on many levels and would be difficult for the generations involved but without drastic changes, we could ruin this world for all humanity.

This approach was attempted in China for 35 years, finishing in 2016. It was seen as a failure as population numbers still increased in that time. However, it is estimated to have prevented 400 million births over that period. A major issue with the success of this attempt was that it was instigated by the government rather than chosen by all the people. As such, many did not tow the proverbial line. Particularly in rural areas, many Chinese couples traditionally wanted a son to carry on the family name and take over the farm. For this reason, when blessed with a girl, many families continued bearing children until a son arrived. At its worst, there were cases of infanticide and abandonment of new-born baby girls. Perhaps if equal value were placed on both daughters and sons, this population reduction measure might have worked. It still could work for us worldwide, but I feel it would need to be a conscious decision that we make for the benefit of all our descendants.

There would be many challenges with such a plan and, I would imagine, it would take hundreds of years to reach a sustainable population and a rebalancing of the Earth. Some plans take a long time and are fulfilled by those who will never get to enjoy the end result. They are worth it, nonetheless. I've always admired those who plant our longest living trees, knowing they would never see them reach their full glory or sit in their shade. Instead, they toiled for those who would come after. This plan would require such an attitude from humanity. We would have to educate our people so there is a clear understanding of why it is needed, and we would have to make sacrifices for the sake of our great, great, great grandchildren.

During those years, we would see our average population age increase but with fewer young people to work and to take care of our elderly. I would hope that technology would allow our children and grandchildren to handle the extra workload and still live fulfilling lives. A shift by all of us towards the practice of long-term self-care could give more independence to our elderly so we don't become so much of a burden on these young people. This should be a "no-brainer" as we would want a high quality of life and not to burden to our families. We would see generations of "only-children". So that they don't become "lonely-children", we could ensure they get lots of contact with other kids, letting the children be raised together, by the village, again.

Over time, as our populations reduce, we should see a lessening of our destructive effect on this world, giving it the opportunity to heal. We should be free to return farmed and populated land to nature. We could expect more space and materials to be available to each person with fewer of us competing for them. Inheritances such as farms, properties and savings, that are typically divided between siblings, would be passed on directly. One would hope that unemployment and housing crises could become a thing of the past. Our descendants could live in the less crowded, newer, safer and more comfortable properties. As towns and cities shrink, the older, unused and unsafe buildings and the land around them can be cleared. Constructions that took many hands to create fifty years ago can now be removed by only one or two people with the right equipment. Perhaps we would see the end of malnutrition in third world countries with fewer mouths to feed. There could be abundance for all. All of this may be an idealistic vision, but we must visualise our ideals and work towards them. Blindly careering into the future, as we have been, is no longer an option for us.

IMMEDIATE ACTION

In the immediate future, we must make a concerted effort to, as the slogan says, "reduce, reuse and recycle". This is the ideal order. Reducing our purchases of plastics and packaged items means there will be less to process later. Reusing and upcycling items means we are not purchasing anew and dumping the old. Many of our furnishings and technologies are designed to be disposable rather than building them to last. I would love to see this change back to "built to last" manufacturing. At the very least, we should design these to be more easily stripped down and recyclable.

Lastly, recycling wherever and whenever possible so that our waste does not end up in landfills, burned or poured into our oceans will go a long way towards reversing the mess we've made. Taking our reusable containers to local greengrocers, butchers and fishmongers cuts our packaging waste drastically. My butcher was delighted when I first arrived with my own container. My fishmonger put a sign up to encourage others to bring their own after several other customers commented on how they should do the same. Change is often just a matter of showing people that we have choice.

Along with helping the environment, this gives us access to fresh produce while supporting local businesses and farmers markets. Glass is easily recyclable and far less environmentally harmful than plastics. Glass jars and bottles are reusable too. There are waste-free shops popping up in cities for people who bring their own containers. Charity shops often sell high-quality goods, new or barely used. Pop in occasionally for a look. You'd be surprised what you could find. We vote for the world we want daily through the money we spend. Environmentally friendly businesses grow and become more common if we use them regularly. The big corporations will follow suit if that's where the money is to be made. Cast your money-vote wisely.

I understand that I'm simplifying a theory that is far more complex than a few lines can fix, but it seems that we are rapidly running out of time. I believe we must start thinking along these lines and acting now, each and every one of us. Our alternative, if we continue, is a ruined paradise and wars for food, clean water and space. Is that to be our legacy? We have only begun searching the stars for other worlds like our own. There are some that seem to lie in the "goldilocks-zone" of other stars i.e., not too hot, not too cold but we're not ready to go anytime soon, even if we found one suitable for us. There is no Plan(et) B. If we consume everything else on this world, will we then eat each other?

I apologise if that section seems morbid and apocalyptic. Sometimes we need a jolt to add a new goal to our mindset. The huge positive for us is that we can create a bright and beautiful future for our descendants. We can combine the best of our technologies to live very comfortably in harmony with nature. I can see towns and cities with greenery and life woven into their design and powered by clean energy that add no toxins to our land, water or air. I can see native species returning to the land we give back to animals, plants and insects. Our descendants can enjoy acres of unspoilt forests, wildflowers and grasses. I can picture active, healthy people, of all ages, full of vitality exploring nature, breathing fresh air and drinking clean water. I can see nature's return to balance encouraging us towards more work-life balance, taking time to appreciate the simple pleasures. I see us exploring our own gifts, creating new experiences rather than watching others do so on-screen. This is the potential we have collectively. We simply have to realise it.

MULTIPLE GOALS

It is possible to have several goals to work towards in tandem with one another. Sometimes having several dreams can seem overwhelming, preventing us from chasing any for fear of going the wrong way.

I found myself "stuck" a few years ago when trying to figure out my own direction. I was working as a Neuromuscular therapist and, while I enjoyed the work and the job satisfaction it gave me, I wasn't fulfilled. I had already named my practice "Health Matters Multi-Disciplinary Clinic" as my aim was to bring other therapies and therapists together under one roof. I could see the benefit of providing a wide range of mental, physical and emotional treatment modalities. In my plan, practitioners would learn from one another while providing comprehensive care for patients that needed more help than any one therapy alone could offer. I could easily visualise such a centre and put together a business plan based on a property that was for sale in the hills near my hometown. I envisaged several treatment rooms that could be occupied by various therapists, on different days to provide many forms of therapy from one centre. I foresaw indoor and outdoor meditation and exercise areas, nature walks and hikes, tai-chi, yoga, healthy eating and cooking classes, group health sessions, weekend holistic-health retreats, training courses and more. While the business plan didn't bear fruit at that time, this idea never left me and remained a path I wished to follow.

I also had the seed for this book germinating in my mind, ready to sprout into something real. I had been thinking about it for several years at this stage. I had much of the information ready to put to paper, or at least I thought I had at the time. The content naturally grew and changed over the 4 years as I worked on it. Still, even then I knew there was a story I wanted to tell with a message of self-care, self-belief and possibility. I understood that this would involve time and effort to write, publish and promote. My plan included a multi-media approach to connect videos, audio podcasts, corporate workshops and school programs to the book. It would be a major undertaking to fit this in around my work and family life, yet it was certainly another path I wished to explore.

As if that wasn't enough, I wanted to start working on producing guided meditation CD's. I had found meditation practice to be very helpful to me over the years and wanted to share this benefit with others. I also felt that many people worldwide are enamoured with the magic and mysticism associated with Ireland. I saw that as a possible vehicle to carry my work further afield. As luck would have it, a good friend has a recording studio of his own and was interested in working with me on this project. This presented me with another path to follow.

On top of those, I had spent several years coaching rugby, having been asked to help with my son's team when he joined the local club. I enjoyed coaching and felt I had something to offer as I could use my experience from working in fitness along with my belief in positive motivation. I had benefitted massively from the sport of karate as a youth and coaching rugby gave me an opportunity to give something back to the youngsters involved. I saw a possibility of going further down that line by developing my coaching skills and gaining more experience. Commitment levels increase as you go further in coaching so I knew that this path, should I take it, would mean sacrificing others. And yet, it was enticing.

Lastly, I enjoyed singing and song-writing. I had begun exploring my creativity and found that lyrics would come to me quite easily. I never considered myself musical, I'm still not sure I would use that term but there was some music in me, and I wanted to explore this further. I saw an option for writing for other artists or, ideally, performing my own songs. Writing, performing and recording to a high standard would also require much commitment. It seemed impossible to follow this path and turn my back on the others but how could I leave this path unexplored?

CAUGHT IN THE MIDDLE

My greatest obstacle was that I viewed myself as standing at the centre of a crossroads, each path pointing in a different direction and not knowing which one to choose. Health clinic developer, author and illustrator, meditation CD producer, rugby coach or singer and songwriter. Which one of these options should I direct my energy towards? I would venture down one path a little, then find myself pulled towards another. I felt like I was going back and forth but not really making any headway with any of them. At times, all the things I wanted to do seemed so impossible that I did nothing. Instead of doing something to help achieve one of my goals, I would scrap it all to play video games!

As with driving on a motorway, our sign appears just before it's time to change direction. The sign I needed to overcome my limiting belief came when I visited an energy healer and clairvoyant. This happened through a recommendation from my sister Lisa following her own astounding experience there. In fact, it was my mother, Helen, that wanted to go and, since she didn't drive, I offered to bring her. I decided to book myself in for a session while I was there. Caroline, the energy healer, was so busy when I called to make a booking, we would have to wait nine months for the next available appointment! In the car, on our way there, I suggested to my mother that I would go first. I am generally open-minded but approach such things with a healthy dose of scepticism. I knew the sceptic in me would not have trusted in Caroline's abilities if I thought my mother had inadvertently given her information about me.

My mother was happy for me to go first and I had an energy healing session to start. The main thing that Caroline spoke of during that part of the session was my abundance of energy and potential. She repeated this several times, as she did again during the card-reading that followed. She spoke about several very specific areas of my life that she could not have known through any Facebook or Google search. Believe me when I say these were not vague or general comments that any client could easily relate to their lives. These were detailed and quite personal statements that I knew to be true. Some were relevant, right at that time. She spoke to me as if she knew me and my life. I should point out that even my close friends and family wouldn't have known some of this information. Again, my sceptical side takes everything with a proverbialre open to her opinions regarding my potential.

ENCOURAGEMENT TO MOVE FORWARD

She related how I had learned so much already, telling me there was "a book in me". I already knew I wanted to write a book but hadn't told anybody. As an example, Caroline explained how a terminally ill client of hers had left small written notes for her children in a tissue box, to leave them advice to follow after she had left this world. The box was later found by her husband and published as a book. This resonated perfectly with me. My initial reason for writing my thoughts and what I have learned was also to pass some advice to my children for when I wasn't around or when they were struggling but simply wouldn't ask for help.

She went on to speak of both my analytical and creative sides of the brain working very well together. She spoke of delivering talks and lectures without needing educational qualifications of the highest level, giving an example of another client of hers who did just that by becoming a motivational speaker. My work and family commitments wouldn't allow a return to full-time education, but Caroline reminded me that sometimes the experience and knowledge is enough. Mostly she spoke of potential. She said, "It's all there for you, right in front of you!" then asked me a simple question, "Do you not want to be famous?". As I explained that I had a few options in mind, she politely interrupted with, "A few? There are thousands. You can do anything you put your mind to!"

ONE DIRECTION

I chose to take her words on board and adjust my mindset. This allowed me to look at all my paths, not as alternate directions, but as one path with several destinations along the way. I also pondered her, "Do you not want to be famous?" question. I acknowledged that I enjoy the freedom that comes from anonymity to do what I want, when I want, without anybody really taking much interest. However, I understood that if I want to share a positive message with many people, I may have to become more well known. It was time to step out of the box and put myself out there, so to speak. It also occurred to me that an album of my own songs, meditation CD's, Youtube videos and published books could cross-promote one another, each bringing my work to a greater audience. In time, maybe these could help fund the clinic I dreamed of and connect me to others that would work or invest in such a venture. Rugby coaching could still remain a hobby to give me a break from these other goals, or perhaps it would fit into the grand plan later. I understood that I didn't need to sacrifice the rest of my interests to focus solely on one. Suddenly it seemed many pieces of my life, that I had believed to be separate, were fitting nicely into place. I just needed to take my plans and turn them into something real through action.

I have found that my attention span for writing, singing and illustra-

265

tions is limited to an hour or two per day. Occasionally I will get absorbed and spend longer, but I'm quite happy when I've given that much time to each, several times per week. I see steady progress, each project remains fresh in my head, and they can all fit into my free time. The clinic plan can wait until after these others are finished and out there generating funds and connections. With a little time-management, I also leave space for family-time, exercise, socialising, relaxing, reading and watching tv or movies. As they say, "All work and no play makes Jack a dull boy"!

MAKING BIGGER PLANS

Once we've accepted that we can work towards several goals at once, we can start entertaining bigger plans. A grand plan of sorts. Sure, it's important to live in the moment but some plans take years to complete. This is not news to anybody with a mortgage, pension plan, or college degree. In such cases, we sign-up to the terms and conditions and put in sufficient money or effort over an agreed term. After a few years, we get the reward of a house, money or qualification. It's simple really. Not always easy but simple, nonetheless.

We commit to long-term goals such as these more easily as they are commonplace. As such, we are inclined to view them as achievable. Lots of others are doing it so why not us? It takes the fear out of signing the contract. If you have a big goal in mind, look to those that have already achieved something similar for reassurance that it is possible. If you haven't, consider adding a bigger, long-term goal to your plans. The years will, hopefully, pass regardless. Lay the foundation now. We will discuss in the next chapters how to divide big goals into bitesize, manageable chunks and how to maintain consistency and momentum to see them through to completion. For now, we'll focus on choosing a grander plan.

Where do you see yourself in 5 years? Or 10? Or 20? These questions are commonly asked in job interviews to assess the mindset of the candidate. I prefer "Where would you like to see yourself?" as this removes the limiting effect of self-doubt on the reply. I see self-doubt as one of the greatest obstacles we face when reaching our true potential. It holds no place in the initial design stages of dreaming ways to use our stardust. At the planning stage, we can use self-doubt to identify areas where we might need to adjust our plan or get some expert help. At the building stage, we can put supports in place to counter unnecessary self-doubt, so construction continues regardless.

Making bigger personal plans works on similar principle to a mortgage, requiring just as much commitment, but we set the terms and conditions for ourselves. We decide how much time and effort we will invest. That can be the tricky bit. Without somebody looking over our shoulder to penalise us if we slack off, it's easy to take days off and work with less diligence. These terms and conditions will decide how likely we are to achieve our goal and how soon. We must remember that whereas much of our mortgage investment goes to the bank, we are the sole beneficiaries of our personal investment. We get to keep the interest.

A grand plan need not be grand in the physical sense. Reaching our long-term potential doesn't necessarily require fame, fortune or some huge project. It can be a long-term plan for wellbeing, new experiences, knowledge or peace. It could be a travel destination that takes several years to plan and save for. It can be an ongoing commitment to self-exploration. Thinking long-term opens us up to continued development, growth and change. We could aim to be a shining light for those around us, one that brightens up the rooms we enter and the lives of the people we meet. Maybe we'll be that ray of hope, or guidance for just one person, maybe we already are. That's enough to make you a valuable member of society and invaluable to that one person. Grand plans are about quality, not quantity. We should let our plans reflect the abundant potential we have.

CREATE A VISION BOARD

To solidify our design and make it a little more real, we can create a vision board. This is a board, poster, sheet of paper or even a screen saver that displays our vision for the future. On it, we can put words and pictures of all that we want, giving our priorities centre stage. We can include the most important things we already have to remind us to appreciate them. If we don't appreciate what we already have, these may leave our lives. We should make it exciting so that it inspires us. It is a vision board, not a vision "bored" after all! Your vision board should be all about your vision, but I would ask you to consider including nature. All of our other long-term plans will be rendered meaningless if we don't care for this planet.

I would suggest the inclusion of key words such as contentment, satisfaction, appreciation, peace of mind, happiness, health, balance and love if these are what you ultimately want from life. I would suggest that you get more specific with your terms by adding definite health or fitness goals, the type of love you want, destinations or plans that you feel would be adventurous and exciting. These will give you targets to aim for and make you want to do what is required to reach them.

How you will achieve your vision board goals is irrelevant for now. What's important is that you put all you want on it and place it somewhere that you will see every day. Give it pride of place in your home. Let other people see it so they too can be inspired. Let your vision board become a promise that you will keep to yourself and all that view it. Make it bright and pleasing to the eye so that you want to look at it. This will remind you to take action to achieve your goals. Perhaps you could also include some ways to help your fellow man as this is the means by which our societies can best work towards a bright future. That could mean a commitment to being conscientious to those you encounter each day. It could mean volunteering some of your time where it is needed.

The more you see your goals on your board with your eyes, the more your mind will accept it as a real possibility.

Future Matters

Chapter 23

The Planning Stage

"Success is the residue of planning", Benjamin Franklin

Now that we've dreamed the dream, it's time to get practical if we are to turn it into something tangible. The planning stage is where we prepare ourselves for success.

To plan any structure, we take our design ideals, identify the resources available to us and figure out the most efficient way to transform our resources into what we want. Our resources include time, location, funds, materials, equipment, knowledge, experience, skills and labour. Plentiful resources give us more options and greater scope to build with. Top quality materials and skilled professionals with the right tools will get the job done more easily and efficiently. That said, people have built structures from mud, ice, sticks and leaves for many years. Sometimes we have to work with what we've got!

As the old Irish saying goes, "Tús maith, leath na hoibre" – "A good start is half the work". It helps to be well prepared before starting construction. Of course, we can still improvise, adjust where needed and bring in new tools as the job requires it. We don't need absolutely everything in front of us at the very beginning. It is comforting to know, however, that we can access them when they are required. This same logic applies to planning for success in reaching our personal goals. We must identify where we will build and which resources we will build with.

TIME WAITS FOR NO MAN

Most constructions must be built within a limited timeframe. Leaving a building site idle for months or years usually means scrapping the project or starting over completely. A site will become overgrown and the materials tend to degrade so starting over can be even more difficult. It's easier to keep working once we begin.

Time factors apply to building our dream life too. At this point we must answer some important questions. When do we want to reach our goals? How much time can we commit each day, week or month to achieving them?

When does each stage need to be completed to keep our momentum and get to the end? I have to admit that I have tended to drastically underestimate how much time my various projects will take to complete mainly because, in my head, I can visualise them already done. Perhaps I wouldn't have started some, if I knew how long they would take! I believed this book would take six months. Three years and six months later, I'm putting the finishing touches on it. I hadn't set a deadline by which time it had to be finished, and nobody else was counting on me to finish at a specific time. As such, going beyond my initial estimate was fine for the first book but I'll be more realistic in future.

Much of that extra time can be accounted for by my lack of consistency in the initial stages of writing. In those first two years, I would go weeks at a time without writing a word. I could say that I wrote on and off, but I was more off than on. In the remaining eighteen months, I committed an hour or more, most days of the week. I started to set myself mini goals. I would aim to get a set number of pages written per writing session and set dates to have chapters ready to send for editing. These time-related goals helped me to create consistent habits and get the necessary work done. This approach is absolutely essential for goals with specific deadlines such as exams, travel dates, events or competitions. We must have sufficient study, savings or fitness training accumulated to realistically expect success.

Dividing our efforts into bite-size, achievable goals makes our work more manageable. It lets us study page-by-page, save euro-by-euro and get fit step-by-step. As a resource, time is limited for all of us and should be spent wisely, with intention, on what we want to build. We will discuss the benefits of using a diary later to help utilize our time more efficiently.

LOCATION, LOCATION, LOCATION

A solid foundation and a suitable location are key elements of planning. We don't build on shifting sands or put bridges where nothing needs to be crossed. To fulfil its purpose, our construction must be located where it is likely to serve most and for as long as we require it. We too must identify the places where we can be of the greatest service, where our gifts will be appreciated, and our talents will be used. We must also begin looking for the best locations to work on our goals. In such places we will find support, encouragement and advice. The people there will want us to succeed as much as we want it for ourselves. These locations may be found in our own locality, further afield, online or perhaps a combination of these.

If wellness is a goal, where can we find sports clubs, health centres, cycle or running tracks, forest trails, dance halls, yoga studios, meditation groups, counsellors or nutritionists etc? Once located we can pick one, or several, that suit. If education is our goal, what institutions are available to teach us? Where can we study? For a business plan, where is our service needed most and where can we find advice or support? Perhaps inner peace is our goal and we must go inward or find settings with fewer distractions where we can do our inner work. We can look for places where others with similar goals reside. There are groups that meet and practice together. There are places that naturally encourage calm. Whatever your goal, find the places and the people where you will thrive.

FINANCES

In the case of physical constructions, money will be required to pay for materials, labour and a host of other expenses. They say, "A fool and his money are easily parted", so we must be conscious in how we spend it. Money is limited for most of us but can be spent wisely on quality materials and genuine skilled tradesmen. This ensures we get value for money.

Meeting our basic needs can absorb much of our available funds. It is our disposable income that we are free to spend as we please. Creating a budget for our day-to-day spend can help us to free up some money to fund other goals. Looking out for better deals on household bills could save us from unnecessary spending. A door-to-door salesperson recently advised me to call my gas and electricity provider for a better deal, even though he worked for them. I did and when they couldn't offer a better rate, I changed supplier. An hour spent on some research and an enquiring phone call brought significant savings. That extra money can fund an educational course, a trip to a new destination or a membership to a club, gym or subscription service.

SPONSORSHIP

The world benefits from our success. Governments, private individuals and corporations often recognise this. There are many grants, scholarships, sponsorships or investment schemes aimed at helping those with ambition. Do some research, ask some questions and you may get the backing you need. If we are the lucky recipient of grants, investment or loans, we should spend it as if we had to work hard for it. Somebody already did work for that opportunity we now have. Maybe it was the taxpayer, the entrepreneur, the regular saver or a family member. Perhaps we will have to work hard to pay it back. Either way, a healthy respect for the finances we access helps us choose how to spend it consciously.

BUY SMART

If equipment is required to reach a goal, we can take a little time to research reviews from those familiar with such tools. I often google-search equipment I need and read through expert reviews to see which ones consistently rank highest for quality, durability and usability while falling within my budget. The reviewers will often give explanations for their ratings to help us identify the most suitable product. I want the equipment I buy to eventually pay for itself by saving me time or the expense of paying someone else to do the job.

GO FREE

Money doesn't have to be an obstacle to our goals. We can start working on many goals without incurring major, if any, costs. If increased fitness is your goal, you don't necessarily need to buy the best fitness gear on the market, sign up to the best gym or hire the greatest fitness instructors in your area. You could put on an old t-shirt, shorts and shoes and just start walking! While you would need a guitar to learn to play one, a cheap, second-hand guitar will get you going in no time. An old laptop can write a book the same as a new one and any pencil and paper can be used to create art.

MONEY MOTIVATION

If we can afford it, spending money on a subscription, membership or a course can be quite motivational. I've seen this with gym-goers, yoga and exercise class members. When paid in advance, we are more likely to show up to the classes and gym rather than waste the money. I found myself, having purchased a higher-end laptop for some of my online video-editing, feeling compelled to use it more often, to justify its cost. As a result, I completed more work and am happy that the laptop is paying its way.

CHANCE

When investing in our plans and future lives, we must accept that any financial investment made is a gamble of sorts. While I encourage self-belief and "having-a-go", it would be wise to only gamble what we are willing or in a position to lose. Remember that meeting our basic needs for food, shelter and warmth, close relationships etc. is always our first priority. Remarkable success requires a solid, supportive foundation for us to build upon.

IDENTIFY PERSONAL RESOURCES

We are the main workers on the building site of our plans and central to its success. Credited as one of the founders of western philosophy, Socrates said, "To know thyself is the beginning of wisdom". Knowing ourselves has practical benefits when working towards our goals. A non-judgemental but honest self-assessment reveals to us the skills and strengths we bring to our endeavours while showing us the areas where we will need support from others. Yes, we know now that we're all wonderful beings, full of potential, but how exactly has our stardust expressed itself thus far?

We can explore our gifts by asking ourselves some questions. Please don't be shy or modest when answering. List them down as if you were writing an honest, but positive, reference for a friend. If you have difficulty writing or saying them out loud, as if acknowledging your gifts makes you arrogant, I assure you it's not arrogance. It's simple appreciation of your own abilities. It should give you a healthy confidence boost to see how much you've learned and developed already while encouraging you to use them.

Plans will vary greatly from person to person, so rather than questions geared specifically towards one type of goal, these questions can be applied to many. Once you have drawn up a list, you can see how to apply each in practical ways. For example, if you have fitness goals it will help you to identify the exercise forms suited to you, with groups or solo, indoors or out, through competitive sport or as a hobby. If you have a career goal it will help you identify a form of work that inspires you and where you can apply your natural aptitude. It should also aid you in finding the environment that suits your personality.

Personal resource assessment;

- o   What am I naturally good at?
- o   What do others compliment me on?
- o   What do people ask for my help with or advice about?
- o   What can I understand or do more easily than others?
- o   What am I passionate about?
- o   Am I primarily a leader or follower?
- o   Am I self-motivated or more likely to follow another's direction?
- o   Am I happier indoors or outdoors?
- o   Am I an early riser or night-owl?
- o   Am I drawn to physical or mentally challenging work?
- o   Am I more creative and imaginative or practical and logical?
- o   Do I prefer planning and organising or "winging it"?
- o   Do I enjoy the buzz of pressure and deadlines or the calmness of a relaxed environment?
- o   Do I prefer working with others or alone?

Take some time to ponder these questions, looking at your life so far to see where the answers lie. Your gifts could be obvious to all. You may be arty, creative, imaginative, a problem-solver, energetic, charming or motivational. You may have less obvious qualities such as being a good listener, a storyteller, funny, kind, naturally good with children or animals. Acknowledging how we already serve others well can help us to find the best ways to serve in future. By answering the above questions, you will start to get an idea of where and how you can work towards your goals by yourself. If you are creative and imaginative, ask yourself where can these be applied? How can you make you, work best for you? If you have found that you are trying to succeed in an environment unsuited to you, perhaps you can change your environment to suit you, or go elsewhere? Identifying your personal strengths will also show you your limitations. These limitations can be balanced by working with other people with other abilities.

I want to remind you at this point that you do have an abundance of resources already available to you. You will have used them in numerous ways throughout your life. They're waiting to be used again. One of the signature traits of humans over other species is our ability to combine our talents, amounting to something far greater than their sum. You have intellect, energy, vision and drive. You have flexibility, stamina and strength. You possess passion and compassion. You are powerful. You are stardust.

MANY HANDS MAKE LIGHT WORK

We can achieve great feats by ourselves with determination and a strong work-ethic but at some point, we'll want some help. I'm quite self-motivated and will try to upskill myself to do what I can by myself, where possible. Still, everything I've achieved so far has been with the support of others. Some of these people exist in my personal life, and others online though they have never even seen my face. It never ceases to amaze me just how many passionate people are willing to share their in-depth knowledge, wisdom and experience to help those seeking it.

In the last year alone, I have had friends help with, among other things, editing this book, setting up my own DIY recording studio, professional recording of a meditation album, vocal training and recording of my own songs with backing tracks. 30-mins spent watching Youtube videos on how to self-publish, has given me the knowledge others took years to learn. I've learned valuable information about yoga, meditation, nutrition, exercise, rugby coaching, psychology, ancient wisdom and so much more, all from the comfort of my home. These are all essential supports, for me to reach my goals, that I could not have achieved alone, and I am sincerely grateful to them all. You too will find extremely helpful tips, motivation and inspiration if you reach out for it. Tap into these resources and make them part of your plan.

Make a list of the supportive resources available around you. Note the facilities and educational opportunities in your area. Do you have friends or family that have achieved a similar goal to yours, that you could ask for advice? If your goal is less commonplace, is there someone you can look up online, to learn from their successes? Are there online courses and other resources available? Can you avail of paid professional advice? Once you start looking, you will find a wealth of resources that you had never considered.

We can save much time and effort by learning from those who have gone before us. Our mentors can provide motivation, inspiration, advice and guidance to help us on our path. A mentor may be somebody in our life that we can work with personally, or across the globe that we can deal with by phone or email. We may not have direct contact with a mentor, but can still follow their example from a distance, learning all they can teach and putting it into practice. A mentor may no longer even be with us. There are sages and enlightened individuals that left their knowledge behind to help us. Wisdom is often timeless and can be just as beneficial now as it was hundreds or thousands of years ago.

the planning stage

Future Matters

Chapter 24

Smart Planning

"Working hard and working smart can sometimes be two different things", Byron Dorgan

The S.M.A.R.T. goal system has been in use for almost 40 years as a means to plan and achieve goals. Its five main criteria suggest that our plans should be Specific, Measurable, Actionable, Relevant and Timebound. We have spoken about some of these already but will revisit them once more so you can apply them to your Stardust goals. I would suggest referring back to any of the previous chapters that connect to your personal goals when using these to set your smart goals, particularly in relation to making your actions relevant.

SPECIFIC

It's important to be specific about what we really want to achieve. Get detailed about what's most important. Rather than using a broad, general statement such as, "I want to be fit", we must identify exactly what that means to us. Do we see fitness as the ability to comfortably get out of a chair or climb the stairs? Maybe it's completing a 10km walk, a run or climbing a mountain. Do we want more strength, more stamina, more flexibility or all three of these? What does "getting in shape" mean? Do we want to feel good, mentally, emotionally or physically? How do we want to help the environment? Do we want renewable and clean energy sources and materials to become the norm? Do we want to save a specific species that's under threat of extinction?

If we want a new or improved relationship, what will that mean? We must get real about the level of intimacy, activities and time we want to share. How can a partner meet our expectations if we don't even know what they are? If our wish is to be educated, what do we want to learn? What is already interesting to us and therefore easier to absorb? For career related goals, how and where can we shine brightest and make the most use of our talents to serve a greater purpose? How will this career fit in with the rest of our life i.e. work-life balance? What kind of home do we want? How will it look, where will it be and how will it feel when we walk in the door? Where do we want

277

to travel and what do we want to experience? How interesting and exciting do we want life to be? What does living well actually mean to us? A definite destination gives us a real place to aim for.

MEASURABLE

There will be several stages and steps to take before reaching a goal. These must be measured and monitored to ensure progressive results. Running a 10km requires running 1km first, then 2, then 5 and so on. Losing 10kg of bodyfat means losing 1kg, then 2 then 5. Gaining strength involves progressively lifting heavier weights. Cleaning our environment involves monitoring our waste output, the recyclable and non-recyclable, and watching how much harmful chemical cleaning products and cosmetics we buy and then wash down the drain. Saving a species may require donations to those working on such projects. Improving our skills or talents means first developing basic abilities and then progressing to more advanced skills. Goals that require financing may depend on saving more, working more or getting a pay rise. These are all measurable, daily, weekly or monthly, showing the amount of effort we are putting in and how much closer we are getting to our goal.

For work-life balance we can compare our time spent working to our time spent investing in other areas. We may not be in a position to overhaul our entire schedule but adjusting the ratio, even a few minutes a day, is a definite and measurable start. Over time, we can steadily improve this until we have the balance we desire. If improving our working lives, we can use our own rating system, out of 10, to measure how productive, contented and appreciated we feel at work. If this number is low, we can start to look for ways to increase it, point by point, until it is consistently high. We can apply a similar rating system to our home or general life experience and gradually aim to improve these numbers. Writing these down is essential to record our measurements and see if we are making headway. Such a visual record of progress is quite satisfying and motivational. We can use these records to reassess our strategy if we find there is little or no progress.

As the carpenters saying goes, "Measure twice, cut once!" We will need to measure out how much of our resources we want to commit to our goal. We must be realistic about the time we have available each day or week to ensure it is sufficient. We may not require a lot so know when enough is enough to avoid waste. 30 minutes per day can bring life-changing fitness improvements. The same time spent learning a language, musical instrument or practicing an art or craft will surely show meaningful results. Applying just the right amount of any resource, spares the rest for our other plans.

ACTIONABLE

Success is far more likely when we can actually do something to make it so. Even winning the lottery, while largely based on chance, is still only possible if a ticket is bought. As much as I believe in the power of intention, action is required for "ACTual" change to occur. A goal that doesn't involve some action on our part is merely a fanciful wish. When setting a goal, we must be willing to do what is necessary to see it through to fruition. We must live that life, practice that skill and be that person.

We sculpt a healthier physique by actively working our muscles and by sourcing and preparing healthy food to nourish the body. We improve our wellbeing through actively resting, recharging and practicing self-care. Love becomes a greater part of our lives by actively feeling love towards other people. We make new friends by making the effort to be friendly. We develop a positive mind by looking for the bright side and choosing to look at the glass as half-full. We get new experiences by exploring the world and the opportunities it presents. We learn more by seeking out knowledge and opening our minds to it. We feel more joy by spending more time doing whatever makes us joyful. We sometimes forget to do this and expect happiness to find us without going to meet it half-way.

We encourage clean, renewable energies by using and paying for them. We promote animal welfare by taking care of our animals, buying responsibly farmed meat and poultry and donating to charities. We clean our planet by first reducing our waste and then helping to remove our pollution. We get extra money to travel by working more or sacrificing other luxury expenses. Then we can afford to take that trip. We learn to speak languages and play musical instruments by practicing. These happen because we act to make them happen. We build the lives we want by rolling up our sleeves and getting to work on them.

RELEVANT

The actions and measurements we take must be relevant to the goals we wish to achieve. The more efficient and relevant they are, the faster we will reach completion. Of all of the S.M.A.R.T. steps, this is the one that requires us to be most informed. We must educate ourselves on the best means to reach our goals or call on the knowledge of others. Success isn't always easy, but it can be simple. Everything is simple when we know how.

An experienced fitness instructor can ensure our efforts are rewarded with the greatest results. Strength, stamina and flexibility are developed by different training methods and knowing the correct one for our body types can make all the difference. An experienced, published writer can save us years of trial and error with a few top tips. The same holds true for any other skill or talent we wish to develop. A few minutes of research on TripAdvisor, or Googling, "tourist reviews of ___", or "things to do in ___" can make our dream trip even more memorable. Talking to professionals about the career path they took could fast-track our progress.

We need to put quality effort into achieving our dream-life rather than enormous quantities of meaningless time. I could sit and type for hours about anything, measuring as the text clocks up, but the words must be relevant to the subject matter if this book is to be of any use to its readers. The information we study and how we do so can be key factors in passing exams. Some find short study sessions, mind-maps and flashcards to be more effective. A little time spent identifying how we learn best, can vastly increase the benefits of our study time. Making the effort to work to a high standard saves us going back to fix or redo it later.

We also must ensure that we limit our efforts to what is relevant and necessary. If we are producing music, fashion or art, copying a style that was popular in the past may not appeal to our public today. Sure, we might bring it back into fashion but remember that the world may have moved on. Adding extra effort to a goal, beyond what is needed, takes that extra from some other aspect of our lives that could benefit from it. Good-enough is good-enough and finished is better than perfect.

We must assess how effective our effort is likely to be. Buying organic foods that are packaged in plastics and transported by fuel guzzling ships may not be relevant to our goal of protecting our environment. Buying local produce may be more effective. Making online Facebook or insta-friends is less likely to connect us with potential new real-life friends or partners. Real friends are more likely to be found in the real world. The actions we take to bring more contentment into our lives should do so now, or in the near future. We don't need to sacrifice contentment now in the hope we will find it waiting when we retire in years to come.

Learn what is most relevant to your goal to focus your energy on what will give you the greatest return for your investment.

TIMEBOUND

Our time is limited, and it waits for no man. If we wish for it now, we want it to become part of our reality as soon as possible. If we wish for it at a future point in time, we want it to be there, ready and waiting, when that time arrives. A "done-by-date" must be set, or we could keep putting it off indefinitely. When do we want our building completed? When will the foundations be done, then the walls, the roof, windows, plumbing, electrics, plastering, painting etc.? When will we have it, be it or do it?

When will we have a healthy sleeping pattern or dietary habits? When will we enjoy vitality and a sense of wellbeing? When will we look forward to going to work or going home as much as going on holidays? When will we take time to read the book, go for the walk or climb the mountain? When will we run that 10km or lose that extra 10kg that's weighing us down? When will we get that qualification, that job or that partner?

Once we have the completion date set, we must look at the minutes and hours we'll commit each day or week. All goals are reached minute by minute and hour by hour. The days, weeks and months are just the accumulation of these minutes and hours. Mentally, it is far easier to commit to a minute or an hour, staying focused and disciplined, than weeks, months or years. This is where the magic happens. These are the bite-sized chunks that let us get through all the actions required to achieve success. There's no need to bite off more than we can chew! We all get the same number of minutes and hours each day. How we spend them decides what we get in return.

These five elements cover many important points. There is more that we can do to improve our odds of success and increase our enjoyment gained from the process. We can add Exciting and Reach to this S.M.A.R.T. system to create even S.M.A.R.T.E.R. goals.

EXCITING

We are filled with untapped potential in a world of unexplored opportunities. There are exciting prospects waiting. We want to be excited by our goals and the journey we take to reach them. This is what inspires many of mankind's greatest discoveries and adventures. The difference between looking forward to what the day brings compared to a day that you just want to get through, is immense. Excitement energises and motivates us to jump out of bed like a child on Christmas morning, knowing there are gifts waiting. There are gifts waiting. Every single day!

Such inspiration removes much of the need for willpower or strict discipline to complete our tasks. It makes us want to do more, be more and have more. Excitement makes it far easier to "get up and go". So often, we are kept awake at night worrying about what might go wrong. We can trade this worry for a giddy excitement about all that could go right and all that may happen. We want this in our lives. We need it.

REACH

This refers to pushing ourselves a little out of our comfort zone by reaching beyond our current boundaries. We already possess, in a sense, what we hold or what is within our reach. The rest is just outside that range so we must stretch ourselves a little further to get to it. In yoga philosophy, the term "edge" is often used when holding the various asanas or poses. The aim is often to find our edge, i.e. the limit of our flexibility, strength or stamina and work at that until it becomes comfortable. Once it does, we can reach a little further, push a little harder or hold a little longer as our range increases. We ease through our edge and move it beyond to where our potential lies. Our potential is right outside our edge, at our fingertips waiting to be embraced.

I remember working to improve my native Irish language skills when my children began attending the local Gaelscoil (Irish speaking school). Initially, my head would start to ache after ten to fifteen minutes of listening to an audio course. I hadn't used my native tongue in over ten years so fifteen minutes of concentration was the extent of my edge or limit. After a few weeks I could listen for twice as long with no ache as my ear and mind yielded to the language once more. I eventually had several dreams through Irish, which suggests that my mind opened even more to it, over time.

The same applied to the soreness in my fingertips, when playing guitar and the aches in my muscles when exercising. Our edge isn't fixed, and our reach becomes greater by stretching ourselves a little. I see now just how much my reach has extended, particularly in the plans I have now, compared to those I had in my teens. For some, the dreams of their youth were vast until life pulled them back. I find that reaching out in one direction makes it easier to reach out in other ways and so, my reach grows year by year. I only hope I have enough time to get to it all! Reach for the stars!

Future Matters

Chapter 25

Overcoming Challenges

"Difficult roads often lead to beautiful destinations"

There are going to be challenges to overcome in any endeavour. That's part and parcel of almost any great journey. I've found these to make the experience more interesting and the victory even sweeter. For me, the most inspiring stories are of those who triumph through adversity, rising beyond expectation to win against the odds. In sport, the greatest wins are the close or unexpected ones. We can choose to see our challenges as gifts that help us become stronger, wiser and more experienced. All that said, succumbing to pitfalls we could have easily avoided will waste our time and energy. We don't have to fall into every hole to learn how to get around them. We can look ahead to avoid them in time. Plan ahead for obvious challenges, make allowances for some unexpected challenges and leave space within your plans to accommodate them. This will keep you on track towards your goals. For every challenge you encounter, find at least two viable solutions as quickly as possible, to maintain momentum.

SELF-SABOTAGE

We often pose the greatest obstacles to our own happiness and success in life goals. You may have already noted personal challenges that have already held you back in your own life. These might include procrastination, lack of commitment or self-belief, poor-planning or unwillingness to adapt. Sometimes our greatest challenges are our own unrealistic expectations or a tendency to self-sabotage. We can be more afraid of success than failure!

Write your personal obstacles down to start taking ownership of them. In a sense this removes them from you and puts them on paper in front of you, where they belong. When written, you can see them as ineffective habits and actions you have taken, or not taken, rather than viewing them as permanent aspects of who you are. You can then create countermeasures to overcome these and set yourself up for success. It's extremely empowering to take control of unproductive habits. The only constant in the universe is change, remember? We can remove these obstacles from our lives by changing ourselves or working with somebody else that has the motivation, work-ethic, belief, commitment or whatever else we may currently lack.

OTHER SIDE OF THE COIN

We can also look for the positives in these challenging traits to turn them to our advantage. An exhausted people pleaser that struggles with saying no to other's demands, can acknowledge the desire to serve humankind. This is a very noble quality, one that is essential for our species' and society's survival. Such people may just need to balance this with the acceptance that they deserve to have their needs met too. If that sounds like you, say yes to yourself and your needs also.

If we find we're held back from putting ourselves out there by fear of criticism from others, we can use that to raise our standards and the quality of our work. This must be tempered with the understanding that perfection is an opinion and that good-enough is good-enough! If you are happy with it, others may be too.

BE 'SUCCESSFAIL'

If a fear of failure has held us back from even attempting to achieve a goal, we can work on accepting that "failure" plays a vital role in success. There is always a benefit from any attempt, once we learn something from it. Many of the most succesful people on our planet embrace their failures. "It's fine to celebrate success but it is more important to heed the lessons of failure" – Bill Gates, Harvard drop-out and the world's first self-made billionaire at 31 years old. "I've missed more than 9,000 shots in my career. I've lost almost 300 games. 26 times, I've been trusted to take the game-winning shot and missed. I've failed over and over and over in my life. And that is why I succeed." – basketball legend Michael Jordan.

"We don't look backwards for very long. We keep moving forward, opening up new doors, and doing new things, because we're curious... and curiosity keeps leading us down new paths." - Mickey Mouse creator Walt Disney who dropped out of school at a young age, failed in his attempt at joining the army and whose business went bankrupt. He was once fired from a newspaper job for "not being creative enough". If they can turn their percieved failures into resounding success, so can we.

IMAGINED OBSTACLES

Many challenges we face are more perceived than real. We may believe, for example, that to become educated, we must live in a specific area, have significant financial means or do so by a certain age. The truth is that a healthy human brain can learn at any age regardless of financial means or location. With access to libraries filled with books and an ever-expanding internet, knowledge has never been so accessible. Much of this information is free or very inexpensive and there are scholarships for those that earn them. Courses and educational programs come in many forms outside of the mainstream first, second and third levels. Where there's a will, there's often a way!

THE SCENIC ROUTE

There are many ways to reach our destinations that may involve taking "the road less travelled". I have taken an indirect route myself. I finished secondary school at seventeen with very modest results, worked in a factory, returned to education at nineteen, worked in a gym, returned to education again at twenty-four, while working with a builder. I started my clinic practice at age twenty-seven, working from a spare room in a health shop for a few hours per week. Once it had grown enough to justify it, I set up my own clinic at thirty. Fifteen years later, I'm still learning and growing, not so much through formal education but through practice, exploration and self-education. There's rarely a day where I don't learn something new or take a further step towards my own development.

Most importantly, when a challenge or limiting belief presents itself, I focus on what I can do and how I can get where I want to go. If there is a suggestion that I can't do something that I would like to, my first thought is, "Oh really? Watch me!". If I don't try, then the suggestion is guaranteed to be proven correct. If I do try, I'm instantly creating the possibility of success. I have to say I do get a little pleasure from demonstrating how we shouldn't underestimate ourselves or others. After all, we are Stardust!

MAKE MORE TIME

Time can seem like another challenge that we struggle to overcome. We can't, despite the phrase, "make more time" to do what we want to do. We can be more efficient with our time through awareness and mindfulness. We can also use a diary to write down how productively we are using our time. If we were to take one minute, at the end of each hour, to account for how we spent it, we could easily see how much was wasted. Five minutes here, twenty minutes there, sometimes hours. Time spent looking at social media, tv, shopping for things we don't need, and so on.

Even worse than wasting our time, we could be using it to sabotage our health, wellbeing and goal success by engaging in unhealthy, counter-productive behaviour. By reclaiming those precious minutes and the energy spent during them, we could work on our health, wellness, knowledge, skills, relationships and reap the rewards. If we find we have a tendency towards unrealistic expectations in relation to the time in which a plan should bear fruit, we can learn to manage our expectations. We can then allow sufficient time or patience to reach our goals. We can include realistic and achievable "deadlines" to encourage feelings of success in our progress.

ENERGY SAVERS

Energy is another factor that people can cite as their reason for not pursuing a goal, or failing to achieve it i.e. "I just don't have the energy to ____, I'm too tired after work / taking care of the kids to ___, etc.". If this is a challenge for you, look back over the sections on developing fitness, healthy eating and the benefits of a healthy sleep pattern. It may seem to those that haven't yet improved their fitness, that investing some time and energy in our health would deplete our already low energy levels. It is quite the opposite. The time and effort given to exercise improves our physical efficiency so much, that everything we do becomes easier and less draining on our energy levels. We end up with a surplus of energy to direct towards our goals. Improved sleep patterns recharge our batteries more efficiently and eating healthy food adds to our vitality.

INNOCENT TO THE CORE

The past can come back to bite us, if we allow it. Old habits, mindsets or beliefs that we thought were irrelevant can still be obstacles to reaching our potential now. As a tree grows, it adds more layers, a new ring each year. The rings show us that no matter how big or old the tree gets, no matter how much it changes on the outside or adds to itself, at its core is still the sapling. The scarred rings of a young tree that survived fire or the thinned rings of a tree that encountered drought are still present years later. I believe we humans are somewhat similar. At our centre is our youthful self, the innocent part that's full of potential, imagination and wonder. This is the part that hasn't yet been scarred by failures or restricted by other people's expectations. At our core, we are still free to chase dreams. To reconnect with this reopens us to possibility, belief and potential. It can also help us to reclaim the wonder and joy we had as children.

TIED BY OLD LESSONS

I found this to be the case several years ago when, despite doing well in most areas of my life, I found my confidence was still inconsistent. I was quite critical of myself, focusing on the small percentage of patients whose injuries I couldn't resolve, rather than the larger percentage I could. While this had the benefit of pushing me to improve my knowledge, it deprived me of much job-satisfaction. I was tough on myself for the times I was less than a "perfect" parent and forget how much time and effort I put into my kids. I would criticize the parts of my physique that I thought should be more developed and ignore the fact that I had a healthy body that worked well.

As I had already entered the practice of meditation, contemplation and self-awareness, I knew my self-doubt was unnecessary. This made it more frustrating when I felt it. I learned, during a kinesiology session, that the root of this issue came from my teenage years. As a typical teenager trying to figure out my place in this world, I wasn't really sure of myself, my talents and certainly didn't believe I was "good-enough"! I would have traded in most of my attributes for others that were cooler. In fact, I'm not sure I even saw any of my worthwhile traits. I felt that everyone else was better than me. There were the cool musicians, the sporty guys, the popular and funny guys and the good-looking guys that the girls all wanted. I was none of them.

Added to that, I had a teacher that was quite effective at confidence-knocking and regularly honed this skill on me. The days of corporal punishment had passed but the verbal slating can leave a mark on young, impressionable minds. The regular comments about my manner or ability did nothing to aid my developing sense of self. Many of us were on the receiving end of a teacher's sharp tongue at some point, but when an old schoolmate feels compelled to mention the interactions between me and my teacher, 15 years after the fact, you can be sure my situation was exceptional.

During this kinesiology session, I was told, without any prompting from me, that despite my successes in life, my confidence was very low at times. I should clarify that I attended the kinesiology session purely out of interest, having received many positive reviews about the therapist. As such, I offered no health issue to be addressed, but instead asked if we could simply see what he found as the session progressed. He then asked if I ever had a teacher that gave me a tough time in school, one that would stand me out in front of everyone to insult me? I laughed and replied, "Yes and this teacher is attending me for treatment at the moment!". My kinesiologist explained the power and long-lasting effect teachers can have on their students. He felt that some teachers don't understand the responsibility they hold in this regard. He then worked with me to mentally and emotionally let go of these issues, which were never about me to begin with.

15 AGAIN

Two weeks prior to this kinesiology session, in the hours before my first clinic appointment with my teacher, I found myself feeling like a 15-year-old again. I felt a need to prove myself, to show that I was indeed capable of amounting to something. I'll admit that the hurt teenager in me considered, very briefly, taking the opportunity to find some particularly sore points and press them a little harder, for a little longer. He wanted revenge! I was surprised at how strong my reaction was, and how anxious I felt, despite the twenty years that had passed since my schooldays.

I chose to act like the man I wanted to be rather than the vengeful teen. I reminded myself that I had nothing to prove to this teacher, or anybody else for that matter. I accepted that while I would do my best, I would not hang my confidence on a successful result as some injuries are simply beyond my abilities. I approached this session with the same professionalism and friendliness I would any other client. I was a little surprised to find, as we chatted during the sessions, that we had many common interests and very surprised to learn that my teacher had wanted to enter the teaching profession since childhood. I had imagined a forced entry into teaching as the reason for such apparent unhappiness in the role. I also looked at the part I played in the situation, to identify why I was picked out for extra attention. I wondered if somebody that loves to teach would get frustrated by somebody that had little interest in being taught. I have noticed such frustration in myself when coaching rugby to players with obvious ability but without the drive or interest to fully develop it. Such frustration doesn't justify the put-downs I received, but it may explain why they were directed my way.

As it turned out, I couldn't resolve the injury despite my best efforts. Regardless of this, the teacher was very grateful for my treatment and attempt to restore wellbeing. The level of gratitude was above and beyond the norm, in fact. I believe that most of this gratitude came from the fact that my teacher remembered what went on all those years before, and still I tried to help. There was healing for both of us in those sessions and I can honestly say that the anger and contempt that I would have felt previously towards this person, left me completely. I also started to uncouple myself from the negative beliefs I carried since my schooldays. After working on letting go of some other confidence-knocking past experiences, my unrealistic self-doubts left me also. I now have a more realistic sense of what I can do with a belief that I am capable of greater things than I have achieved thus far. Knowing we're made of Stardust helps too!

CHALLENGING PEOPLE

We have discussed the many benefits of working with others to achieve our goals and it is something I would certainly recommend. We must also accept that the opposite may, at times, be the case. As the last paragraphs indicate, sometimes our challenges will come from other people making our life or progress more difficult. Although I believe that people do the best they can with where they're at, others won't always consider our interests along with their own. We must be prepared to encounter this when living, working or dealing with others. It may be unfair, but it doesn't need to stop us from reaching our potential.

It can be helpful to remember that much of what people say and do says far more about them than the person they're saying or doing it to. How they speak or act most definitely expresses their mind-set or emotional state. Understanding this helps us to avoid taking on board another's issues. It can remind us that we deserve better treatment. Listening to another critical voice is difficult but adopting a critical inner voice is far more damaging. A positively minded colleague may well point out some area we can develop or improve but will do so in a constructive way, without knocking confidence. A highly critical individual, in my experience, is almost certain to be critical in general about everything, often in particular towards themselves. Remember that, "We see the world as we are, not as it is". It is almost impossible to satisfy such a person so we shouldn't use their opinion as a measure of our ability. Instead, we can focus our time and energy where it is valued and appreciated.

John Lennon asks us to "Imagine" a world where everybody cares about everybody else. The success of this song suggests that such a world appeals to us, but we're not there yet. We still have those "survival of the fittest" primitive aspects that compel us to do what it takes to come out on top. While our literal survival is rarely threatened by those around us, we may feel like our self-esteem, prospects and goals are at risk. When we don't see our own magnificence, somebody with the qualities we admire can stir jealousy within us. Consciously or subconsciously, we may attempt to "take them down a peg or two" by convincing others that they are not so great after all through twisted truths or downright lies. I'm saying "we" because we can all be that challenging and difficult person at times. Recognising this is empowering and can aid our self-development.

This is common in the political practice of mudslinging, where politicians prove their worth as a candidate by making their rivals look worse. I always find myself thinking, "Give me reasons to vote for you, rather than reasons not to vote for any of you!".

RISE ABOVE THE CHALLENGE

Acknowledging how fear can underlie others' behaviour helps us to deal with such challenging behaviour by allowing us to be compassionate towards them and their fearful state. If we can demonstrate that we pose no threat, there is a greater chance that they will work with us rather than against. If we can show them that we are on the same side and that they stand to gain as much as we do, they are even more likely to become an ally.

If you find yourself on the receiving end of such behaviour, try not to take it personally. Remember that if somebody is trying to pull you down, it's because you're already on top. Stay there, as you are, rather than dropping to their level. If somebody is talking about you behind your back, it's because you're already in front. Stay ahead by carrying on as you were. If they lie about you, it's because they can't find a truth to use against you. Stay true to yourself. It is extremely empowering for us to decide who to be, regardless of others' behaviours. If they're telling truths about you, truths that bother you, take this opportunity to learn to accept the facts and/or change your behaviour in future. If they are engaged in a competition for success, keep your focus on winning through your talent and ability. Of course, we may find ourselves on the other side of the fence, behaving jealously towards others too. If so, we can try to use this as an opportunity to work on self-confidence and perhaps aspire to develop those qualities we are jealous of.

STAND UP FOR YOUR RIGHTS

I have often had clients present with neck and shoulder pain from the stress of bullying. It affects health, concentration, energy levels and mood. These situations occurred at home, in school and in the workplace at the various ages and stages of life. Such behaviour tends to continue until addressed. If not dealt with, it can present itself again in other circumstances, with other people. Bullying is never acceptable, but it can be an opportunity to stand up for our rights and command the respect we deserve. Once we do, we seem to create an invisible boundary of sorts that others won't cross lightly in the future. Should they try, it is easier for us to reassert our rights once more. This assertion of our rights may come through our solo efforts or may require the support of others. Both ways are valuable, so lean on others if and when you need to.

There are more opportunities to be found in the challenges posed by other people. I have personally found that when somebody was "getting in my way" or "holding me back", it turned out to be a blessing in disguise. Challenging people can teach us important lessons on how to work well with others. It's easy to work with easy-going people but connecting with stressed out, judgemental and "negatively" minded people takes compassion and patience. It asks us to look for the good in everyone. These skills, once developed, will be available to us when we need them. A simple technique I have used for connecting more easily to strangers or those that are unfriendly, is to imagine that we are already friends, but they have simply forgotten. I pretend they have lost their memory. To me, they're nice and friendly, but they aren't showing me these qualities because they don't recognise me. Once I treat them with respect, kindness and a little friendly humour, they let down their guard and react accordingly. Often, within minutes, we're getting on as if we're genuinely old friends!

OLD FRIEND

I recall a gruff security guard at a college where I ran some workshops. When I arrived on the first night, his reception was anything but cordial. I imagined him as an old friend, that was tired after a long day and who just wanted to sit at his desk undisturbed and listen to a football game on his radio. I gave him a friendly smile and, using the name on his tag said, "George, sorry for disturbing you, could you please point me in the direction of lecture room 5C" and, "How is the game going?". Twenty minutes later, we were still chatting, and I had heard a good chunk of his life history!

Another way through which I've found challenging people to be beneficial is related to perfect timing. When another's actions have slowed my progress towards a goal, this has often resulted in me reaching it at the perfect time, when other pieces had fallen into place. While I wouldn't have seen this initially, hindsight revealed it later. If I had gotten there sooner, I would have had to wait for other pieces anyway. Now, when I encounter challenging people, I remind myself to trust that they're helping me even if they don't intend or realise it!

Then of course there are the challenging people who actually want to help us despite our willingness to see it that way. There are those who care about us, sometimes more than we care about ourselves. They can see where change is necessary for our benefit when we can't or don't want to see it ourselves. We see them as challenging but they're actually on our side, perhaps more than we are ourselves. I often remind my teenage kids to pick their battles with me. I'm a believer in healthy eating and sleeping patterns. They are not always as keen. When their poor habits result in sickness from a reduced immune system, I tell them that I feel they need more rest and better nutrition, and they resist. I explain that standing up for their rights is great but arguing with me when I'm giving them sound advice for their benefit is not helping them. This applies to us all at some stage so it's worth stepping back to see if these people that we perceive as standing in our way, just might be directing us to a better place.

All challenges can be seen as opportunities for personal growth, to learn a lesson, to practice patience or to trust in the bigger picture. They can show us how we react under pressure.

Take your challenges and turn them into something that makes you grateful they came your way.

overcoming challenges

Future Matters

Chapter 26

The Building Stages

"Whatever good things we build, end up building us", Jim Rohn

We've dreamt the beautiful dream and have a clear picture of how our lives could be. We've gathered up our resources, drawn up the plans and set a timeframe to reach our goals. It takes work to bring all these together and transform them into reality. Now it's time to get to work. In this chapter we'll discuss some practical ways to complete the building of our dream life.

WORK

"Genius is 1% inspiration and 99% perspiration", Thomas Edison. I would happily replace genius with success in this statement too. The design and planning stages are essential to our building process but still only give us a folder full of dreams. It is the construction work done on the site that brings it all to fruition.

I worked as a builder's labourer for about nine months in my younger days. I was teamed up with the most experienced tradesman in the company. He was a man in his sixties with an "old-school" attitude to most things including his work ethic. If it was worth doing, it was worth doing well. A trained carpenter since his teens, he had also picked up the skills of block-laying, plastering, tiling and even a little plumbing. I learned a lot from him as we worked on many of the company's various building projects. I was lucky to be involved in each stage of construction from the foundations to the roof. I found it interesting to see just how much of this work is unseen once finished, but absolutely necessary, nonetheless. I learned about the importance of preparation i.e. having the tools and materials ready, clearing the area so the space was suitable for the job at hand and allowing enough time to get the work done. I learned to measure twice, cut once and to always check that our equipment is working correctly, before use.

I also saw that, as with my fitness and karate training, it took effort to get the job done. I spent much of my time there dirty and sweaty. My muscles ached most days from shovelling cement, carrying bucket loads and hauling materials around. There was also the effort of erecting scaffolding and climb-

293

ing ladders into attics and onto rooves. I got some blisters and splinters, a strained back, a few cuts and scrapes but it was all worth it, especially when we got to stand back and look at a job well done. Jobs we worked on included restoring an unused hospital wing, rebuilding a family home after a fire and adding a wheelchair accessible bathroom and bedroom to a house. There was a real sense of satisfaction from creating something that didn't exist before, that had a purpose and would serve somebody's needs.

We will discuss the importance of preparation in the next section. First and foremost, I would like to remind you to prepare yourself for the fact that you will need to work to reach your goals. I'm going to repeat that. You will need to work to reach your goals! Now I would ask you to repeat it, out loud or in your mind, "I will need to work to reach my goals". I feel that a belief that destiny will come to find us is all too common these days. We must go to it or at least meet it halfway. Wishing for it, praying for it or putting it out there to the universe is not enough, in my experience. It's like sitting on the ground under an apple tree, hungrily wishing that some fruit would fall into your hand, peel and slice itself, then jump into your mouth! No, if you want sweetness and satisfaction, you must reach up and take it. However, when you make an effort by doing your bit, don't be at all surprised when help comes your way.

PREPARATION
"By failing to prepare, you are preparing to fail" – Benjamin Franklin

Every job on a building site starts with preparation of the site and the surfaces to be worked with. We clear sufficient space and give adequate time to get the job done. We check that the area and equipment is safe. We ensure that the materials, tools and skilled individuals required are present and ready. We plan for easy access to the site for any materials that will be needed at a later stage. All of this guarantees that once the work begins, it can continue uninterrupted, so that we can build some momentum and get the job finished quickly. This applies to the construction, the plumbing, the electrics and the painting and decorating.

An artist prepares their canvas, paints or pencils and their muse before their first stroke is made. A student prepares for study by setting aside time in a suitable location, free of distractions and with all relevant material at hand, to make the most of their study session. Those on healthy eating plans prepare by buying the most beneficial foods to stock their cupboards. Much of this preparation starts in the shopping trolley. They then set aside time to prepare meals to eat fresh or to use when they may not have access to quality foods. Those aiming to improve their fitness prepare by committing time to exercise, putting on appropriate clothing and going to a gym, class or heading for the track or hills. Those with the healthiest sleep patterns prepare before bedtime with a wind-down routine. They shut off electronic devices, dim the lights, use calming scents and meditate to relax so they get the best sleep possible. They also ensure that their bed and bedroom is comfortable and calming to create a space conducive to deep, restful sleep.

Successful businesspeople prepare for meetings by organising their presentations into simple, easy-to-follow segments using diagrams, bullet-points and images. By answering questions before they are asked, they can avoid tricky questions and look self-assured and confident. They can also prepare themselves to look competent when unable to answer with some ready-made responses such as, "Great question, I'll get back to you on that when I have more information", or "Interesting outlook, let's talk more about that later". Musicians and singers prepare for performances with practice, practice, practice, making it look effortless when on stage. Sportspeople hone their skills in training for success in competition.

MAKE YOUR OWN LUCK
"Fortune favours the prepared mind!" – Louis Pasteur

Our success in any endeavour is achieved through two primary means i.e. luck or preparation. Sometimes everything just falls into place, the ball bounces our way, or we find ourselves in the right place at the right time. More commonly, we achieve success by preparing for it. The odds of success through luck alone can vary greatly, leaving so much to chance. Relying on luck and wishes makes us little more than gamblers and it's our lives that are at stake. Preparation increases our odds of success and, in some cases, practically guarantees it as we intentionally put ourselves in the right place and within reach of the bouncing ball for that opportunistic score.

Preparation requires effort now if we are to be in a position to take advantage of opportunities that present themselves in future. Ask yourself some important questions and answer honestly. Am I prepared to live my best life? Am I physically healthy, emotionally sound and mentally balanced? Am I giving these areas due attention to offer myself the best chance of success? Am I energetic and motivated? Do I believe in my ability to achieve my goals and my right to expect success? Can I commit to making a concerted effort to achieve such things? For many of us, these are the foundations needed to build our dream lives upon.

SELF DEVELOPMENT
If the personal skills that we've identified as potential resources need more development, we could start to hone them through practice. There are too many human skills to address each one individually but, in general, the approach to improving our skills is the same. We must practice using them regularly in ways that achieve the desired result. If developing creativity, we must take on creative projects. If improving our people skills, we must engage with people. If working on public speaking or communication skills, we must get up in front of crowds. These often mean learning from others with more advanced skills than our own. Sometimes it simply means exploring and using our skills to figure it out for ourselves. Usually it's the combination of both that allows us to master our abilities.

Attending courses is an obvious first choice to learn from others but if that option is unavailable there are other means. Much can be done at home by drawing, painting, writing, singing, building, gardening, reading, or perhaps working with online videos or books. Access to formal education is not necessary for self-improvement. Knowledge and understanding of a subject make it ours to use. This is empowering. As I've said in earlier chapters, there is an abundance of knowledge available for free online thanks to passionate teachers with a love of their subject. There is also a world of opportunities for us to use our skills while we develop them.

To inspire us to practice more and do some good in the process, we could volunteer our time. Clubs are always looking for people to help with coaching, fundraising and organising. A graffiti artist, whose work is considered a public nuisance when uninvited, could make local playgrounds look fantastic for kids through the creation of murals. A naturally gifted counsellor or good listener can be a lifesaver on a Samaritans helpline. A musician could play at a retirement home or at a park to entertain the passers-by, getting practice and encouragement as they do. A self-taught make-up artist could visit a hospital and make someone's day. We don't need to wait until our skill is perfected to use it. It is valuable as it is. Good enough is good enough. As we improve the skill, what we can achieve will improve too.
Preparation is a key element of success.

START

This paragraph is small but its relevance is huge. Why wait until tomorrow, next week, month or year when you could start today? If there is something, anything, that you can do to take you one step closer to the goal or life you want, then take it. This moment is an opportunity filled with choice and possibility. It's a chance to begin again, to turn in another direction or to take another step towards your goal. You can only enter the race if you take your place on the starting line. Sign up, buy a ticket, put your name in a draw, put on your training shoes, take a deep breath and go for it.
Starting is a key element of success.

SHOW UP

Showing-up is as much an attitude as it is a physical act. It means looking for ways to make progress by getting work done, rather than excuses to shy away from it. It gives us the opportunity to find the possibility in each moment and use it for our benefit. I find there is a wonderful sense of satisfaction afterwards on having achieved that little bit extra.

If health improvement is a goal of yours, show up for it. Likewise, for fitness or sporting prowess. If it is important to you, something you want, then give it the time and attention it deserves. Your body deserves this, and you deserve this opportunity to achieve your dreams.

When I practiced karate as a teenager, I showed up to every training session I could possibly make it to. Generally, that meant two weeknight sessions and some extra classes on the weekends. Once a week, I would finish a 12-hour factory shift at 8pm, cycle home to pick up my karate suit, which I ironed the night before, and then on to the training hall. I would miss the first half but take part in the rest. I also showed up to the gym 3 times a week, as I knew fitness would add to my ability. I practiced basic skills at home, in my garden or bedroom, to hone skills I wanted to improve. I never gave much thought beforehand to the effort training would involve. I simply knew that by showing up, I would improve more than if I did nothing at all. Showing up repeatedly rewarded me with a Senior Men's National Karate title along with friends, fitness, discipline and memories.

If you are self-employed, working your way up the career ladder or working for somebody else, show up for the business. Its business is your business. Its success is your success. It pays your bills and it directly impacts on your life experience. While still balancing your work to leave time for other areas of life, a committed approach will be valued and appreciated by customers, colleagues and bosses alike. You will also enjoy the satisfaction of knowing you make a difference every time you go to work.

When I started my Neuromuscular Therapy business, I showed up in a town 40 mins from my home, initially for only one or two clients per day. The commute took twice as long as one appointment. This paid enough to cover my fuel costs and the cost of hiring the treatment room with a little left over. I showed up regardless. Some days, showing up for one client paid off as I received more last-minute bookings while I was there. Once clients became familiar with my routine, some would call by phone or drop in, hoping to get an appointment. Because I showed up for my business, more business showed up for me. I did this consistently until word of mouth spread, my business grew, and my appointments became consistent. My personal training work has remained steady for several years as I show up for my clients, at times that suit them, whenever possible. By showing up for my business, it rewarded me with a livelihood and the flexibility to work around my home life to enjoy the best of both worlds.

As a rugby coach I, and the coaches I worked with, showed up at every training session possible. At times when other teams didn't train due to wet pitch conditions, we could be found training in the carpark. We looked for opportunities to improve our skills rather than excuses to take a break. We have even trained in a dressing room, which turned out to be one of the best training sessions we ever had! The limited space meant we had to focus on some technical aspects of the game that can get missed in general outdoor sessions. The boys were only twelve years old and they loved it. I showed up at every coaching course I could get to. I spent much personal time watching online training games and drills, often professional level videos, to see what I could learn and use.

The boys themselves showed up with strong attendances, positive attitudes and tremendous work-rates throughout those years. They bought into the mindset that all of our practice would help them shine on match-day. That particular group of young men have consistently been one of the most successful teams of their age groups within the club and the region. By showing up for rugby, I was rewarded with the privilege of working with a fantastic group of young men and coaches. I also gained new friendships.

A HABIT OF SHOWING UP

I have also found that showing up is habitual in nature, becoming more normal to us the more we do it. Creating a habit of showing up takes a measure of discipline initially but then takes on a momentum of its own that carries us through the times we may be tempted to cry off work.

I began writing this book over three and a half years ago but initially went through phases where weeks would pass without writing a word. Of course, nothing was achieved during those periods and because I lost momentum, I found it more difficult to get back into my groove each time I would sit to write. Momentum is an extremely powerful force for reaching goals. This applies to fitness training, study and progress in any area of our lives. It's a little like riding a push bike. It takes quite a strenuous push of the pedal to get the bike moving at first but the second push, and the third, require less and less effort. Once we build some momentum, it's easy to keep going. Once in motion, we seem to freewheel along with little or no effort at all.

I have consistently shown up at my laptop every week for the past eighteen months and made far greater progress than in the previous two years. In fact, I have written so much that I decided to leave several chapters for another book. I look for opportunities each day to sit down and write. Sometimes I write for half an hour and there are occasional days where I get nothing done but I'll get back on the "writing bike" the next day. This keeps the wheels turning and, since the last piece I wrote is still fresh in my mind, I don't need to read back over it all before continuing. This makes my writing time decidedly more productive. Best of all, the writing process is more enjoyable as is the reward of completing each chapter. By showing up for this book, I have been gifted with the opportunity to clarify my thoughts, ideas and beliefs, and study health and wellness in more detail. I have also received some healing as I revisited challenging times in my life from a new perspective. Through the book and my Stardust Program, I hope to continue to be rewarded with the opportunity to help others, make connections with like-minded people and develop a truly holistic clinic in the near future.

SHOW UP LONG TERM

All of these achievements took several years of showing up before the desired result was achieved. They were voluntary to begin with, although enjoyable, but it took some time before I could fully appreciate the value of my efforts. Years will pass regardless, and it is now that we choose what those years will bring. In one year, or five, or ten, we can say, "If only we had started then" or, "look at what we've achieved since then!" Whatever your plan or goal is, show up as you would for your dream job interview, your dream first date or a promise you made to somebody you would never let down. Let life know that you are there for it and it will be there for you.

Step up and say, "I'm here to work on my dreams, goals, the life I want and to make my world better than it would be without me and my contribution", then keep that promise. Remember that occasionally, showing up may mean taking a break to rest and recharge your body and mind so you can complete your journey. Sometimes showing up may mean changing direction when you find yourself on a path that is not working for you. This is not giving up, it is showing up for the life and the wellbeing you deserve.

EFFICIENT USE OF TIME AND ENERGY

It may seem like there aren't enough hours in the day or that we simply haven't enough energy to put into our health, relationships, job and other goals. I can assure you that we have an abundance of potential energy, which will increase even more as our health improves. As for time, we all have the same overall amount each day i.e. 24 hours or 1,440 minutes. That's 168 hours or 10,080 minutes each week. It's 8,760 hours or 525,600 minutes each year. Over an 80-year lifespan we would get approximately 700,800 hours or 42,048,000 minutes to spend. If time were currency, we would all be multi-millionaires. How we spend those precious minutes is what counts.

When busy with lots of projects, on top of family commitments and work, it helps to think of responsibilities and goals as plants, in a garden, that need to be cared for. Our time and energy are equivalent to the water in a watering can, which is refilled each night for the following day. There is enough water in that can for all our plants to flourish, but only if we pour it carefully and in the correct amounts for each.

If we rush from one plant to the next, splashing water around aimlessly, we will run out before we get to the last one. Equally if we decide not to attend to them, instead leaving water in the can, the opportunity to use it productively is lost. If we choose to feed the areas of our garden that we don't want to grow, they will thrive, and we will get a garden full of weeds while our flowers, fruit and veg shrivel. However, if we pour our water mindfully and carefully, taking time to pause and steady ourselves between each plant, we can avoid the weeds. Then, what we want will thrive, rewarding us with a colourful and vibrant garden.

Likewise, if we give energy to unhealthy relationships, time-consuming but unproductive habits, jobs that we don't like or mindsets that take away from our wellbeing, they will stay in our lives. But if we put sufficient time, thought and effort into the important aspects, they will flourish. These include our supportive and loving relationships, health, work, education, hobbies, goals and dreams. With regular time, attention and effort, they all will grow stronger and more vibrant. Our lives will become bountiful.

Pace yourself each day. Pay attention to the things you love and want more of in your garden. In time, their growth will reward you with abundance.

THE 80/20 RULE

The 80/20 rule, also known as the Pareto Principle, refers to a theory suggesting that in many cases, 20% of what we do creates 80% of the result we wish to achieve. This rule encourages simplicity and efficiency and is said to apply to many areas of life. Some examples suggest that 20% of employees are responsible for 80% of a company's output i.e., 1 out of 5 employees does 4/5ths of the valuable work, and 20% of customers are responsible for 80% of the revenues i.e., 1 out of 5 customers buys 4/5ths of the products or services. It also suggests that in many countries, 20% of the population own 80% of the wealth. In relation to sport, it states that 20% of the training is responsible for 80% of the skill development and fitness gained.

I have seen similar results in my years as a fitness instructor. The effort put into the first 8 -12 weeks of exercise, and the corresponding gain in fitness within those weeks is normally far greater than the subsequent improvements seen over the rest of the year. For example, I have seen beginners start a running program, barely able to jog for 1km, then run 10 km's after only 8 weeks. That's a ten-fold increase! If that rate of progress was to continue, they would be able to run 100kms after 16 weeks! This has never happened in my experience. Likewise, with strength training, I have seen clients lift double their capacity for lifting weights on various exercises after only 8 weeks. If a client could lift 5kg on a one-armed bicep-curl to start, it was common to see that rise to 10kg within that timeframe. A continuation of such progress would mean lifting 20kg after 16 weeks, 40kg after 32 weeks and 80kgs before the year was out. I have never seen this either. It was far more common to see the weight lifted plateau at 10kg and progress slowly from there until it eventually peaked.

The point here is that a small portion of our effort can give us great gains. If we can identify these portions and focus on them, we will get greater gains for our investment. We can trim the fat by reducing the time and effort we spend on the other areas if they are not absolutely necessary for us to reach goals. If we were to look at our working day, what proportion of our time can be deemed truly productive? Likewise, with our free time, how much of that is spent doing something that will help us reach our goals? Somebody that is meticulous about keeping a tidy house may spend 3-4 hours per day polishing and dusting but most of the necessary work may be done in the first hour. By freeing up the other hours to improve their business or earning potential, they could then pay somebody to clean and enjoy more free time.

Pouring all our efforts into one area, to achieve that extra 20%, may take from all the other important areas of life. If we can identify and apply the essential 20% effort needed to achieve 80% returns in our relationships, health, work, finances, responsibilities, hobbies and goals, we can bring our quality of life to a high standard across the board. We can expect to enjoy success, variety, abundance and fulfilment.

Efficiency is a key element of success.

FOLLOW THE PLAN

At this stage we have our positive and well thought out plan. We started out with great intentions for what we will achieve. We have already put some work into it and may find ourselves getting a little tired or running out of that initial fuel that comes from the excitement of starting a new venture.

the building stages

When I studied fitness instruction back in 1997, I was very surprised to hear that the typical drop-off rate for new gym members was 97%. Only 3% of new members' would become long-term gym-goers! When I began working in a gym, I saw this reflected in our member's commitment to their fitness. On our first session, I would give them a positive speech on how good they would feel and look and how much easier it would get over time, especially after the 8-week-hump. Many still quit within the first 3 weeks. Those who followed the plan to week 8 were far more likely to continue as they had enough work completed to see significant results. During those 8 weeks, I would make slight modifications to their fitness plans to suit their individual needs. I would then prescribe a new plan for weeks 8 – 14 and do this every 6 weeks or so to keep it interesting and effective.

Trusting in a plan that we have developed while in a clear and positive mind-set, perhaps with the aid of those with experience, is essential should we begin to falter. There will be times when we become tired or frustrated and cannot see the progress we've made even when it's obvious to others. Perhaps we get a minor setback, then feel like our efforts are for nothing and want to just drop it. Progress, in some plans, isn't as obvious as building a house where we can see it grow, brick by brick. Sometimes we put lots of work in and have very little to show for it until we receive our qualification, complete the marathon or have a copy of our book in hand. In such situations we must acknowledge the progress made through learning or fitness and also that we are developing commitment and discipline as we continue.

Delayed gratification requires patience and determination in an age when we can have so many of our needs met instantly. And yet, such satisfaction is all the sweeter for the wait, the effort, the build-up, and sometimes the relief of crossing that finish line. Such effort, patience, commitment and trust are worth it. Modify the plan if needed but stick with it till that last roof tile is placed, the book is in your hand or you cross that line.

FOCUS ON WHAT YOU CAN DO

The work that can be done on a building site, at any given time, is sometimes dependent on external factors. We might have great plans and even greater intentions but weather conditions, available materials and other tradesmen getting their bit done will all play a part. Plastering or painting external walls must wait for dry weather. Roofing must wait until the wind and snow subsides. But, aside from the most extreme situations, there is always something that can be done. We can work indoors, clean the site, prepare an area for another day or order what we will need in the near future. These will need to be done sometime anyway so why not now?

It is at those times, when our plans are interfered with by issues outside of our control, that we must show resilience and commitment. If we cannot go to the gym or class, we can exercise at home. If we cannot make it to a course, we can study for ourselves. For every challenge we encounter, there is at least one alternative. For every problem, we should aim to find two solutions and then use the better one.

Look for excuses to get some work done. Search for ways to get over or around any obstacles that you have created for yourself or those that have arisen. Develop an appetite for progress combined with wellbeing. Create possibilities for your dream life to become your real life. Ask yourself, "What can I do today to help me get where I want to go?", then do it.

Focusing on what can be done is a key element of success.

FINISHING POWER
Sometimes finishing can be as difficult as starting. It is at this point that we must end our journey and perhaps show others the results of our labours. I think part of the difficulty is that this is where we must say, "This is the best I can do" and risk the possibility of judgement. While a project is ongoing, if there is criticism, we can say, "It's still a work in progress!". Nobody expects the building site to look pristine while construction continues but when the job is finished, we have greater expectations. It's at that point that people will scrutinise the job and notice any flaws. Up until the last day, we can fix, adjust and change but not once we've said, "I'm finished".

So, how do we overcome that fear of criticism of our work so that we can finish a job and confidently hand over the keys to the house? We can accept that our current level of development and what we have produced is good enough for now. We can still consider ourselves a "work in progress" as we never stop learning and developing but still accept where we are. We can ask for feedback from those with experience to see if there's anything we've missed while accepting that our work doesn't have to be perfect, it simply has to meet what's required of it. We don't have to have the perfect body, but a body that feels good and works well is a gift. If a book we've written is entertaining, educational or enlightening then it's worthwhile. If a piece of music we've performed stirs some emotion, it is valuable.

Focusing on our priorities is necessary to finish projects. I have found that while I have lots of ideas, I've already got more than I can complete in one lifetime. In the past, I started many but finished few. Admittedly, some turned out to be impractical or couldn't hold my interest beyond the initial excitement of a new venture. In recent times I focused on the ones that held my interest and inspired my passion. These have reached completion or will in the near future. This is why it's important to identify what we really want and direct our energies there. Commit to finishing one unfinished project, plan or goal to prove to yourself that you can. This will encourage you to do the same with others that have been shelved or haven't even been started.

Finishing is a key element of success.

REWARD FOR FINISHING
The feelgood factor of completing a project, achieving a goal, reaching a long dreamt of destination, or simply adding healthy and productive habits to our routine is immense. It really feels great. However, we can add

a little extra to give us even more motivation. When teams prove themselves to be the best by winning a league, they get to raise a trophy amidst the fanfare, admired by their supporters. We give awards to those who excel in their achievements at work, in the arts and in the sciences. We make a big deal of them and the efforts they made to produce, to entertain and to discover for our benefit.

I believe that we should make a deal of ourselves when we have imagined, planned, showed up, worked hard and overcome obstacles to reach our goals. We can prepare such rewards, in advance, for when we cross that finish line. These rewards may be connected to the goal itself or something that we simply enjoy but, I would suggest, should not be in opposition to what we have worked for. Binging on junk food as a reward for healthy eating is counterproductive. Planning a drinking session, having given up alcohol to improve health, wellbeing and energy levels defeats the purpose of our goal.

We could book an activity or trip that allows us to use our newfound health and fitness in ways that we could not have, before reaching our goal. We could use the money saved from giving up an unhealthy habit and spend it on something that we wanted but may not have been able to justify the cost previously. We could reward ourselves with a relaxing break to unwind after a period of hard work or study. We could take that certificate and frame it, hanging it where we and others can see as a reminder of what can be achieved. These rewards can be grand or simple, so long as they are meaningful to us and allow us to savour the success.

We can also reward ourselves for mini victories or for reaching stages of completion. Each week of healthy eating and self-care can be celebrated in a way that doesn't undo our fantastic work. We can make a list of beneficial treats to choose from as a little pat on the back to ourselves. These can be applied to any of our goals or behaviours that we wish to encourage. Maybe we managed to keep calm when the kids could have driven us crazy. Perhaps we used understanding and compassion with a friend, colleague or customer that put these to the test. Maybe we exercised when the bed or couch tempted us. We might have worked or studied when social media or TV was calling to us. We could have stopped a negative thinking pattern in its tracks and changed the story in our head. Maybe we were brave and spoke a truth we previously avoided.

These all bring rewards in themselves, but we can acknowledge them with a bonus for our efforts.

Prepare for success, start, show up, be efficient, follow the plan, stay focused and get it finished. Then you will have created what you set out to build.

Future Matters

Chapter 27

Keep a Diary

"I never travel without my diary. One should always have something sensational to read on the train", Oscar Wilde

Keeping ourselves on track to reach our goals takes discipline and consistency. A diary is a fantastic tool to help us do this. It gives us something solid on which to write our dreams and plans. As the pages fill with notes of our efforts, a diary shows us the progress we make towards their completion. There is a real sense of satisfaction from writing down our achievements each night. Each morning, we can use it to make a deal with our day so that we will have another list of positives to note before we sign it off and go to sleep.

SUPER 17 DIARY

In 2016, I received a beautifully bound diary as a Christmas present from my mother. As I had already purchased a work diary for 2017, I decided that this gift would become my "Super 17 Diary". Cheesy, I know! I thought, "This is going to be put to the best use possible". I already knew that when I make a promise to somebody else, I would do everything in my power to fulfil it so I decided to apply that principle to myself and the life-improving goals I had.

I wrote in the front pages of my diary, a list of the areas of my life that I wanted to improve or at least maintain over the year. They included plans to work on opening my heart more, to maintain health and fitness, to make progress with my books, to produce music and meditation CD's, to travel to new destinations, to gain new experiences and to develop an underage rugby coaching syllabus.

Under this list I wrote, "Every day, I will spend time and energy on at least 4 of the above. Each of these is to be developed at least 3 times per week. I commit to these". I signed and dated it "Neil Dennehy 26.12.2016" as I would for any official and binding contract, knowing I would honour the agreement as best I could.

On the following page I clarified each of my goals with specific notes and details of what they meant to me. I then abbreviated them, to make it easier to record what I had done each day as the year progressed. Rather than writing out long lines of information into my diary each day, short notes that I understood would be enough.

Here is my list of abbreviations and what they meant for me;

H.O.	Heart Opening;	Understanding, compassion, soft, kindness, patience, unconditional (love).
H.F.	Health and fitness;	D – drink 2ltrs water minimum, S – sleep 10.30pm – 6.30am ish.
E	Eat;	Natural / balanced, varied, learn new recipies,
F	Flexibility;	Stretch, foam-roll, massage.
St	Strength;	Strength training was part of my routine, so I didn't add specifics.
End	Endurance;	As above
M	Meditation;	Affirmations, letting go, grounding, trust, faith, acceptance, mindful,
P	Positivity;	Find the good reason or benefit
T	Travel;	Visit at least 2 new places each year, learn about local customs, ramble, eat local foods, make it (travel) part of my work, visit friends abroad.
N.E.	New experiences;	Anything new, Skiing, rock-climbing.
B	Books;	What to do with Stardust? Structure / framework, case-study(ies), publishing, typing, get feedback, Rugby 101 - illustrations,
Mu	Music;	L – Listen to music, G – Guitar play, S – Sing, V – Voice exercises / lessons, W – Write new songs, R – Record,
GM	Guided Meditations	Affirmations, Guided Meditations, Relaxation, Write Scripts, Record Music, Binaural Beats. I wrote these twice. I obviously needed it!
R - Rugby;		Syllabus, proposal, draw up fundamentals plan, support from committee + players, coach coaches, record footage, develop app.
Mel		(a mascot / character I developed for the minis section of our rugby club), redraw character, use as mascot, logo, fundraise for costume.

Looking at it now, I can see that it was a lengthy list, but I had an entire year to work on it and 365 days is a lot of time if it's used well. I found that each day, there was no, "Will I work on my plans?" just "What will I work on today, and for how long?". I also noticed as I recorded my effort each day that there was a real sense of achievement. It was so rewarding to look at the pages filling up with my notes of the work I had done. It also helped me massively towards creating productive habits. As the year continued, I found I was less consistent at writing my progress into the diary, but I was still disciplined at doing the actual work. I didn't finish everything on my list. Some were out of my control and I let them go. But, as a result of my discipline, most of what I had aimed for was achieved. Overall it was a very productive year.

I went skiing for the first time and loved it. I started taking singing lessons to improve my singing voice and grow confidence in performing. This also encouraged me to write more songs. I joined another choir, 'Uproar Rock Chorus' for more singing practice and met a great bunch of people. We recently travelled to Budapest to an international choral festival and performed at a new 80's festival at home in Ireland. I worked consistently on my fitness and felt the benefit of that in my daily life and my physical therapy work. I also started playing tag rugby, which was fun and introduced me to new people. I added more written content to this book and began to research self-publishing and printing on demand, to plan ahead for when it was completed.

I wrote and recorded guided meditation scripts, which I feel were of a better quality due to the voice coaching I received. I changed my sleeping pattern to rise earlier and make use of that very productive time of day. The heart opening practices helped me to balance all the thinking and doing with more feeling. I felt the benefit of that through the year also. Simply put, I made a lot of personal progress in 2017. These good habits carried on since. All of these positives came about because I made some simple decisions and stuck with them. The contract I agreed with myself turned out to be a very rewarding deal indeed!

FILLING YOUR DIARY

If you have a copy of the "What to do with Stardust daily diary", use it to mindfully plan your day, week and year in ways that are productive and beneficial to you and your Stardust plans. Write your own contract at the start, including the best terms and conditions you can imagine, sign it (maybe even have someone witness it) and then start working on it. If you don't have the diary, make one of your own to fill in each day. Take note of areas such as time spent sleeping or at rest, the time and quality of meals, time given to healthy activities and any compassionate gestures you made during the day. Also include new experiences, fun and joy, steps taken towards achieving a life goal, your use of creativity and any effort put towards development of your skills.

Write in any other noteworthy information in the notes section. This may relate to challenges you encountered and how you overcame them. It may include thoughts, insights and realisations that came to you during the day or future goals you would like to work towards. The aim, of course, of all of these is to increase your overall sense of wellbeing, so be sure to write in the feel-good-factor associated with each activity. This will let you see, in black and white (or multicolour if you want to get arty with your diary), that these do indeed make a positive difference to your life and are as such worthwhile.

STARDUST TABLE OF ELEMENTS

As you may remember from chemistry class in school, there is a periodic table of elements which lists all the atoms that make up our physical universe. This Stardust table of essential elements works on a similar principle but is a list of many elements that combine to form a great life experience. The abbreviations will allow you to make quicker notes in your diary to save you some time when writing. They'll also allow you to fit in more information. Remember that one activity may include several elements i.e. dancing can involve A, Cn, Ex, Fr, Fu, H/F, I, Mu, Sc and more. Seeing all these written down, serves to remind us just how much benefit something as simple as dancing can bring, for which we can feel Gt...

A	Action	L	Love
Af	Affection	Me	Meditation
Bv	Believe	Mu	Music
Co	Compassion	Na	Nature
Cn	Connection	Ne	New experiences
Cr	Creativity	O	Open mind
D	Discipline	P	Peaceful
Ex	Exercise	Q	Quality
Fe	Feeling	R	Rest
Fr	Friends	S	Social Contact
Fu	Fun	Sv	Service
Gl	Goals	Tr	Truth
Gt	Gratitude	U	Understanding
Hf	Health/Fitness	V	Variety
I	Interests	W	Water
J	Joy	X	X-Factor
Kn	Knowledge	Y	You
Lg	Let go	Z	Zest

Fitting absolutely everything into each day may seem impossible but you'd be surprised what you can get from one activity. A nature walk with a friend could tick half those boxes in one go. If you miss out on some of these one day, make them a priority the next. Over the course of a week we should easily be able to fit in all our essential elements.

Create a weekly routine that suits your needs and fits in with your schedule. Generally, doing some exercise early in the morning works well as it means that we start our day on a healthy and positive note. This often carries through in our food choices, posture and mind-set for the remainder of the day. I find it sets us up for more productivity and wellbeing, and, no matter what challenges may come as the day progresses, it's already done.

Waiting until later to exercise can leave an opening for tiredness, delays or a lack of enthusiasm to interfere with our plan. Aim for about 40 minutes most days of the week with lots of variety in your exercise of choice. Choose activities that will develop flexibility, strength, stamina, balance and coordination. Try to get out in nature for some if not all of these for the added benefit of fresh air and sunlight.

Note – all activities should be performed at an intensity level that reflects your current fitness levels i.e., an effort level that pushes you a little beyond your comfort zone but that feels good during and afterwards. This is worth repeating. We want to feel good both during and after exercise! Trust that your fitness will develop, at its own rate. Your body is designed to adapt to exercise and improve itself, once nourished with the nutrients contained in healthy foods. Be sensible in your exercise choices. Get a guide or instructor if trying something new and ensure you have the correct equipment. Use good sense and stay safe. The purpose is to get you feeling good after all.

Since the ideal sleep pattern for most people is roughly 10pm to 6am and typical working hours begin from 8 to 9 am, many of us can find forty minutes to an hour before work, school etc., to use for our own benefit. Even if your sleep pattern doesn't fit with this, you can still find a way to fit some exercise into your day. This may seem like a lot, if unused to exercise, but you will find very quickly that not only is it manageable but very enjoyable and that you will want to do even more! You'll also see that you will get far more out of your exercise than what you put in, as your energy, well-being, confidence and quality of life improve.

I would recommend daily meditation for 5 – 20 minutes. More if you have time and are getting what you want from it. When practicing, be patient with yourself. At times your mind will get distracted, negative, judgemental and uncomfortable. Acknowledge these thoughts without allowing them to stop your practice. Keep returning your attention to your original intention for each practice. In time, you will become less distracted, less judgemental and find deeper states of relaxation, contentment and peace. Trust in your mind's ability to be reprogrammed by your practice and continue to nourish it with positivity each day.

Apply the S.M.A.R.T.E.R. plan to your personal goals to improve your likelihood of success in reaching them. Get the most from your time and effort by learning from others' experience. Remember that we don't need to figure everything out for ourselves or reinvent the wheel.

Cultivating a loving approach to life, ourselves and others will automatically lead to more affection, compassion, joy, peace and prosperity. Feel love, show love and be love whenever and wherever possible. You will draw such people to you and together you will do remarkable things, making a real difference to our world.

Writing your goals down sets a real intention to transform them from possibility to reality. Just by putting the words on paper, you have brought them from your imagination and into the physical world.

Start writing your future story today.

Future Matters

Chapter 28

Ownership

"Freeing yourself was one thing. Claiming ownership of that freed self was another", Toni Morrison

The greatest and possibly most memorable part of building our dream house is the handing over of the keys. It is at that point that we take ownership of our home and begin a new and exciting chapter of our lives. With ownership, we can set roots and make long-term plans. We can invite whomever we choose into our home and refuse entry to those that are not welcome. We can decorate it to suit our own personal taste. We can act as we wish within our own space. We can make rules to suit our needs or wants.

Each room or corner of our home can have purpose and significance. One can be dedicated to rest and recuperation. One where we nourish our bodies with tasty food. One for entertainment through music, books, or television. One for creativity through art or writing. One for wellness through meditation or exercise. One for contemplation or study. One can be devoted to planning and organising. One for entertaining others to enjoy the buzz of social contact. Our dream home and life can include all these and more.

The point at which we take ownership of our lives is even more powerful. It is then that we become truly independent individuals, ready to embrace our power to choose life. When we accept our lives as truly ours to do with as we please, we can assign space for self-care, rest, nourishment, entertainment, creativity, solitude, contemplation, planning, social contact, exercise, hygiene, earning, relationships and so much more. We can also see our lives as something worth investing in. We will want to maintain our lives in good condition so we may relish living them. We can make our lives inviting to others so they will want to visit us and spend time in our company. We can inspire others with the quality of our lives to make alterations to their own that will bring them the same benefits we enjoy. The abundance we create will afford us opportunities to share our surplus with those in need.

Own your Stardust. Own your place in this universe. Own your feelings. Own your actions. Own your voice. Own your thoughts. Own your right to choose. Own your past, your present and your future. Own your life.

Summary

What to Do with Stardust?

"Shine for you are light and wonder, for their are galaxies within you and stardust dances in your soul. Stars live in your eyes and glory and grace live in your bones. You are beautiful. You are light and wonder. You shine", G.C.

As we come to the end of this book, I would like to refer back to the suggestions I made at the start on how to use it.

I asked you to;

- Read it all
- Accept the wonder that is you
- Understand your value and importance
- Embrace your potential to be and do more
- Take care of your valuable body and mind
- Give yourself permission to feel good
- Commit to living the life you want
- Make a plan that serves you and our world
- Build that life
- Shine!

Having read through all the previous chapters, you now get a greater understanding of your magnificence and that of the human species. You now have a sense of the individual and collective power we possess to shape our Stardust to create the world we want. I say "sense" because, for all that I have included in this book to remind you of how incredible we are, even that is only the tip of the iceberg. Still, that much is sufficient for you to be empowered with knowledge that can liberate your mind from the ego's limiting fears and doubts, so your indomitable spirit may shine through. You can see that our power of creation is expressed through the actions we take in each moment. You recognise that we exist only in the present moment so you can focus more of your energy and attention on the here and now. You understand that we are an integral part of creation.

Summary

This is indeed an age of enlightenment, a time when light is shone on the darker areas of our past so that they can be accepted or avoided in future. This is a time when knowledge can be shared instantly across the world so that humankind can work together for the benefit of all. This is a time when scientists use their valuable time and resources to study the power of hugs and of breath on the chemical balance of the brain and body. Our greatest minds study the effect of human intention on the laws of physics and the interconnections between humans, bacteria and nature in general.

It is a time when technology allows us to bring our wildest imaginations to the silver screen, and in many cases, to reality. This is a time when self-love is seen as "self-ful" not selfish, and when caring for others, rather than controlling them is seen as the greatest sign of strength. We now openly discuss as a species, our footprint on our world and our role as caretakers. We speak of mental and emotional wellbeing, not with judgement but with concern and an intent to help make things better. This is a time when billions of bright and beautiful human beings can bring more light to this world than ever before. Now that you recognise how important you are, I ask you to allow your light to shine.

I have intentionally used "we" for the vast majority of this book because I am speaking to you about us. Accepting our potential to improve our own health, wellbeing and quality of life empowers us to individually make the necessary changes. Understanding that we are all in this together empowers us to work collectively with others, focusing our time, energy and resources on what we really want. There is no "I" there is only "We".

We have searched for answers and we have found many. We know what to do, how to do it and we are ready to make it happen. We will use our gifts, our talents, our intellect, our strength, our determination and our compassion. We will be the change we wish to see in our lives and in our world.

We will get where we want to because now we know what to do with Stardust...

what to do with stardust

Summary

Acknowledgements

I'll begin my acknowledgements with Roma and Luca, of whom I am so very proud. It's fair to say that you have taught me many important life lessons. What it means to love someone unconditionally, the power of hugs, the magic of looking at the world through innocent eyes and the importance of play. As you grow through your teens, I've learned the importance of giving space to grow, granting trust, keeping the lines of communication open and still, when I'm lucky, the power of hugs. You also ensure that I never take myself too seriously. I'm very grateful to have you both in my life and I look forward to all our future moments and lessons.

To my parents, Michael and Helen, among others, you gave me one of the most important gifts there is - the freedom to find my own path, always welcoming me home warmly, no matter how long it had been since my last visit. To my older brother Brian, our good old-fashioned sibling rivalry, when we were younger, taught me to fight my corner and your sporty nature helped inspire me to get fit at 13. That led to a career in wellness. To my sister Lisa, our shared interest in the spiritual side of healing and your ever-present encouragement and belief in what I do has been priceless to me. Thank you all.

To my friends, you are a wide and varied bunch and all important to me. From those of you that remind me where I come from and who will always be there, no matter how much time passes, to those that show we can make new and valuable friends at any stage of life. From those with whom I can discuss my wildest ideas without fear of judgement, those that make me question what I'm doing or thinking, those with whom I can be totally unfiltered and laugh till my face hurts, to those I can lean on for support and advice. You are my friends and I am yours. Thank you for your friendship.

To all who walked with me, crossed my path, taught me or touched my life in any way, thank you for the memories, the moments and the lessons learned.

Acknowledgements

To John McCarthy, my editor, friend and rugby mentor (except for that one time when I was right), your help has been crucial to me. Your honesty, humour and editorial skills have made this book better than it could have been otherwise. I hope this acknowledgement is printed a million times. Thank you!!

To Gerry Mitchell, MA Psychotherapy, Advanced P.Q. Dip. Adolescent Psychotherapy, Cert. Reality Therapy, the time and professional experience you gave to review my material was invaluable. Your encouragement and constructive feedback were priceless.

To Aine Roche, BA Strength and Conditioning, NCEF, dip Sports coaching and Pilates instructor, thank you for taking the time to review my "Body Matters" section and for your very positive feedback.

To Brian O'hÁonghusa BSc Nutritionist, the "Food and nutrition" chapter is all the better for your comprehensive feedback, extensive knowledge and your input. Thank you.

To Marian Gleeson M. Health Psych, Soultreat Holistic Center owner, our discussions on spiritual matters and the Chakra System and your encouragement were so helpful. I am most grateful.

To Aoife O'Brien, BA in International Business and Languages, Diploma in Executive & Life Coaching, MSc in Organisational Behaviour, thank you for the time and effort you gave to review my entire "Future Matters" section. It was of great benefit.

To all the Youtubers, internet site owners and writers that share your knowledge and experience freely and graciously, thank you for mentoring and guiding me in so many ways.

To you the reader, I am grateful for your decision to shine brightly as it makes this world a nicer place for all of us. By purchasing this book, you are also supporting "The Stardust Program" which, I believe, will help many more people on their path to finding wellbeing and purpose.

Lightning Source UK Ltd.
Milton Keynes UK
UKHW011250120521
383590UK00001B/14